Analog Digital ASIC Design

Dragemu prijatelju Zoranu
Igor in Janez

Analog Digital ASIC Design

Janez Trontelj

Professor of Microelectronics and Electrical Measurements
University Edvard Kardelj, Ljubljana

Lojze Trontelj

Professor of Microwave Theory and Microelectronics
University Edvard Kardelj, Ljubljana

Graham Shenton

ASIC Management Consultant
Graham Shenton Associates

McGRAW-HILL BOOK COMPANY

London • New York • St Louis • San Francisco • Auckland • Bogotá
Guatemala • Hamburg • Lisbon • Madrid • Mexico • Montreal
New Delhi • Panama • Paris • San Juan • São Paulo • Singapore
Sydney • Tokyo • Toronto

Published by
McGraw-Hill Book Company (UK) Limited
Shoppenhangers Road
Maidenhead, Berkshire, England SL6 2QL
Telephone Maidenhead (0628) 23432
Cables MCGRAWHILL MAIDENHEAD Telex 848484
Fax 0628 35895

British Library Cataloguing in Publication Data
Trontelj, Janez, *1941 –*
    Analog digital ASIC design.
    1. Electronic equipment: Integrated circuits. Design and construction
    I. Title II. Trontelj, Lojze, *1934 –*   III. Shenton, Graham, *1939 –*
    621.381'73

    ISBN 0-07-707300-2

Library of Congress Cataloging-in-Publication Data
Trontelj, Janez, *1941 –*
    Analog digital ASIC design / Janez Trontelj, Lojze Trontelj,
Graham Shenton.
        p.   cm.
    Includes bibliographical references.
    ISBN 0-07-707300-2
    1. Application specific integrated circuits--Design and construction.
2. Linear integrated circuits--Design and construction.   3.Digital integrated
circuits--Design and construction. I. Trontelj, Lojze, *1934 –*   .
II. Shenton, Graham, *1939 –*   . III. Title.
    TK7874.T76   1989
    621.39'5--dc20   89-36768

12345 RC89109

Typeset in Ljubljana and printed and bound in Great Britain
by Richard Clay Ltd, Bungay, Suffolk

Contents

List of Plates

Foreword

Recent studies of biological systems show their mixed analog digital nature. Such systems are very efficient for solving problems that involve the processing and selection of relevant information from a large mass of data. The structures of these biological systems provide a rich source of ideas for future electronic ones.

The promise of early analog and hybrid computers was not fulfilled because of technological and economic issues. Modern microelectronic technology has overcome these problems to such an extent that there now exists an application gap between what can be economically integrated and the innovative system designs available for integration.

In order to enable mixed analog digital designs to be implemented by a wide variety of engineers, a structured design methodology is required to ensure that innovative hybrid systems can be systematically and predictably designed.

The present book describes such a methodology: the authors have focused on the personalized standard cell, allowing effective cell synthesis and layout compilation. It gives a very broad description of the activities involved in implementing a mixed analog digital system design in silicon.

The book is written with a practical bias and should be easily comprehended by graduate engineer or practising system designer.

The text is comprehensive and liberally illustrated. It covers CMOS, technology, design, CAD and testing, design management, foundry interface, and cost issues. It is a useful contribution to the subject at the present time when a practical implementation scheme is needed for a wide variety of mixed signal applications.

Carver Mead
Gordon and Betty Moore
Professor of Computer Science
California Institute of Technology

Chairman's preface

Readers of this book need no reminding of how microelectronics has impacted and continues to impact on modern society. Microelectronics technology is the largest single force driving improvements in human productivity. This fact, along with the continuing need to respond to the technical challenges imposed by a large competitive and demanding market, sets the stage for an exciting and rewarding career to the microelectronics professional for whom the book has been written.

The benefits of a microelectronics resource to the community, as evidenced by the rapid growth of Silicon Valley companies and their customers in this field, has not escaped the notice of other regions, countries and their governments. Today, microelectronic technology is international, with centres of research and development spreading in growing numbers globally. With modern communications, such centres not only monitor international competition closely, they also collaborate effectively. This book is a case in point.

It was written to help fill the gap between system designers and chip designers. VLSI technology is allowing more and more systems functions to be integrated into a single chip. The chip becoming the system and where there has been a segregation of chip design from system design it is becoming clear that the two functions must begin to merge.

The same VLSI technology accommodates nearly all the digital functions of the many systems into a single chip. The next level of integration must make it possible to incorporate the interfaces between the outside analog world and the digital electronics embedded in chips. This book assists the professionals involved in microelectronics in this process.

The CAD challenge of automating digital chips has been difficult during the eighties. While the effort to automate design technology continues, the fact that the manufacturing capability now exists to produce both analog and digital devices in a single chip provides a new, major challenge to the CAD industry and the information contained herein helps define the methodology.

That CMOS technology has been a major process technology milestone is no longer disputed. CMOS devices today equal the speed performance of NMOS and indeed it is also approaching the performance of bipolar devices. CMOS is primarily recognized for having lowered the power consumption of devices, but its ability to accommodate high performance analog devices and dense digital circuits on the same chip may prove to be an even more significant advantage in the future.

In summary, this book is evidence of the international pervasiveness of microelectronics. It helps fill the gap between available technology and its applications in system solutions, and does so by providing the system designer with a reference text on structured microelectronics design. Its focus is on the leading edge of mixed analog and digital integration, on the methodology required to automate the design of such chips, and on the CMOS and BiCMOS process technologies serving as a vehicle to implement the design.

I would like to thank the authors for their work and for achieving a good balance between theory, data and practical examples of solutions. They have succeeded in describing the state-of-the-art in mixed analog and digital design methodology while also providing a framework for future development.

George W. Gray
Chairman of the Board
IMP

Authors' preface

It is becoming increasingly common in many countries to find important research work being done in collaboration between Universities and Industry. Unfortunately it is not as common that the collaborators are given the opportunity to publish the results of their work for a wider audience.

The work described in this book was largely carried out as research projects at the University of Ljubljana and as collaborative projects between the University and International Micro-electronic Products (IMP), both in California and in Europe, during the period from 1984 till 1988. Highlights of the work have been presented at conferences and published in journals but because of the importance of mixed analog digital design techniques to the present ASIC market the authors believe that an opportunity exists for the publication of a more detailed treatment of the complete design methodology.

The technology chosen for the work is CMOS. While a basic digital CMOS process can be used for mixed designs, for the highest performance circuits a CMOS process with analog enhancements is desirable. The results presented here are based on such enhanced processes in use at IMP.

The authors would like to acknowledge their thanks to IMP's management for permission to publish detailed material concerning the CMOS processes, circuit components and cell libraries and design procedures. Also for their encouragement for the publication of the complete work.

The authors would like to state contributions made to the text by their colleagues: in particular, at IMP Europe for the contributions to Chapter 3 on methodology from Ioan Jones, on digital place and route in Chapter 6 by David Lucas and in Chapter 8 on testing by Geoff Rickard and Steve Morris; at IMP California, Moiz Khambaty for his contributions to Chapter 2 and for processing the circuit described in Chapter 9. At the University the following colleagues deserve specific mention: Andrej Belič for contributions in preparing the CMOS process flow diagram and SEM photos in Chapter 2, Drago Hercog for contributions to design methodology in Chapter 3, Tomaž Slivnik jr. for contributions in layout synthesis and switched-capacitor filter design in Chapters 4 and 5, Drago Strle for contributions on switched-capacitor filter synthesis principles in Chapter 5 and Tone Pleteršek for preparation of the operational amplifier synthesis and compilation results in Chapter 5.

In addition to those mentioned by name many others helped in the task of producing the book. They include our secretaries, draftsmen and design and test engineering staff who made helpful suggestions and undertook many careful reviews.

Janez Trontelj
Lojze Trontelj
Graham Shenton

1. Analog digital ASIC design

1.1 Introduction

Recent conferences on integrated circuit design and design automation have produced an increasing number of papers on the subject of mixed analog digital designs. * This growing interest in the subject is also seen from the number of semiconductor companies who are specializing in this area and the CAE/CAD vendors who are beginning to offer a range of new tools to serve mixed designs.

It is interesting to consider why this is happening, and why particularly now? In the past most designers considered the integration of analog functions problematic and hence something to be avoided. This was a logical conclusion if we consider the benefits of digital systems and the fact that the evolution of integrated circuit technology has been in the direction of continually reduced dimensions. This evolution has enabled the integration of several orders of magnitude more digital functions, but has not always helped with the integration of analog functions. In fact the reduction of dimensions has increased electrical field strengths and introduced many undesirable phenomena such as lower break-down voltages and higher substrate currents. These in turn have reduced the available analog dynamic range and signal to noise ratios.

Such issues, together with the problems of testability and reproduceability, have led to the belief that every system being considered for integration on a chip should be converted to a digital solution, or at least the analog signals should be digitized as soon as possible. This widespread belief is not correct for many applications. In fact superior solutions, from the point of view of performance, cost and reliability, can often be achieved with mixed analog and digital circuits on the same chip.

A number of factors have contributed to this apparent change of position.

The first factor is that modern semiconductor fabrication equipment and processing technology allows better dimensional and parametric control. This tighter control can be exploited by

---

*   The 1988 IEEE Custom Integrated Circuit Conference (CICC) in Rochester NY had 49 papers on analog and analog digital design out of a total of about 150 papers. The previous year's conference had only 22 similar papers out of a total of 169. Similar increases were seen at the European Solid State Circuits Conference (ESSCIRC), Manchester 1988, and the 8th International Custom Microelectronics Conference, London 1988.

analog circuitry to give greater accuracy and repeatability than was previously possible. In addition, a number of processing modules have been introduced to add new and improved analog components such as high quality inter-layer polysilicon capacitors and SiCr resistors.

The second factor is that discrete time circuit techniques such as switched-capacitor filters have now been developed to the extent that competitive high performance solutions can be realized.

The third major factor is reliability. It may not be apparent at first why mixing analog and digital circuits on the same chip can have a significant impact on system reliability. A short anecdote can help. A major European company producing electronic equipment recently decided to instruct its product managers to improve field reliability. After studying causes of failures the equipment designers identified system interconnections as being the major area causing reliability problems. On investigating the points of the system where the majority of interconnections occurred it was discovered to be at the interface between the analog and the digital sections of the system. As a consequence of this discovery the company has undertaken a major initiative to introduce mixed analog digital ASIC design to its products.

A generalized interface between the analog and digital sections of an electronic system is shown in Fig.1.1.[1] This shows analog and digital inputs and outputs to and from the chip as well as digital control signals as feedback to the analog sections. From this diagram it can be seen that, in general, the analog digital interface is a point of high interconnectivity. There are thus major gains to be obtained in both package pin count reduction and system reliability by integrating this interface.

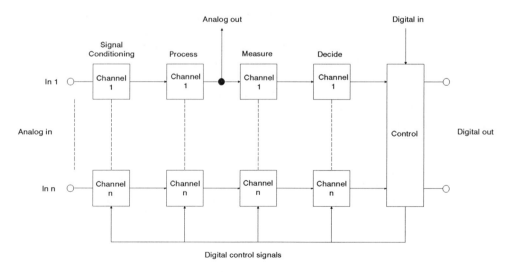

Fig. 1.1 Generalized analog digital system

There are other advantages which are not immediately obvious but can be seen by reference to Fig.1.1. For banks of analog circuits (signal processing is a typical example) the individual channels can be better matched to each other when integrated than they could be if built from individually packaged chips. In addition, for analog systems where there is a stringent low power requirement, it is possible to design for just the power that is needed. It is also possible to power-down all the unused analog sections. In a design where the analog circuit is separately packaged, integrated power-down features are not normally available.

1.2 Examples

The widespread commercial use of a mixed analog digital design was first seen in the integration of the conversion of speech into digital form within a PCM codec. This was required to facilitate the economic transition from analog to digital transmission and switching.[2] The design techniques that had to be developed for this integrated codec paved the way for the application of mixed analog and digital circuits to many other systems.

Plate 1.1 shows a photomicrograph of a single chip PCM codec device. The device contains an 8-pole receiving switched-capacitor filter, an A- or μ-law compression A/D converter, a dual channel expanding D/A converter with smoothing filters and sinx/x compensation, and 128-time slot assignment circuitry for digital switching. The exacting requirements of the codec specification taught the industry a great deal about the design and layout of complex mixed analog digital circuits. In particular, the problems that had to be solved concerned crosstalk, noise, accumulating offset-voltages, accuracy and long term stability. The majority of studies on basic high quality analog building blocks were carried out on early codec designs.

A more recent telecommunication subsystem that has been successfully integrated as a mixed analog digital design is the subscriber line interface circuit (SLIC). Plate 1.2 shows a photomicrograph of a SLIC design using a personalized analog cell library.

Another mixed analog digital application which combines demanding measurement accuracy with long term stability requirements is a system for electrical energy measurement and management.[3] Plate 1.3 shows a photomicrograph of an integrated solution which contains a Hall effect device as the integrated electrical power sensor. The mixed analog digital system on the chip performs the power integration over time, makes correction for sensor non-linearities, provides temperature compensation and by autocalibration ensures the long term accuracies to meet a class 2 meter specification.

These few examples illustrate that the design techniques now exist for the successful implementation of complex mixed analog digital designs. The task remaining is to organize the design methodology into a form in which it can be used by a wider design community.

1.3   To whom is this book addressed?

This book is addressed to electronic equipment designers who are currently designing electronic systems using discrete analog components and a variety of digital techniques including gate arrays, other ASICs or microprocessors. In addition this book should prove useful to technical managers and strategic planners who are concerned with the future directions of electronic hardware design. Graduate students who have not yet started design work should find instructive material on modern design principles and techniques.

The book is primarily intended for those who are not currently involved in the design of mixed analog and digital chips, but who see a future need to be so. In a widening variety of applications the economic and strategic advantages that can now be gained by a successful integration of mixed analog and digital circuits are significant. Companies and electronic engineers who ignore mixed designs could be at a significant disadvantage in the future.

1.4   Purpose of the book

The book is not intended to teach basic analog design. Many texts are available that do this adequately.[4] It is also assumed that the reader has specific knowledge of the systems he wants to integrate, and a basic electronic engineering education.

The intention is, however, to illustrate the "personalized standard cell" approach to mixed analog digital design. This approach has been chosen for a number of reasons:

Firstly every electronic engineer cannot afford the time and effort required to become a specialist in analog IC design. The experience gained through the development of a wide variety of analog and digital functions can be made available to electronic designers through the use of personalized analog and digital cells. This is possible because the related specialist design knowledge is built into the library and its personalization algorithms. This in effect masks many of the complex design problems which must be solved for successful on-chip analog digital design.

In addition it is the intention of the book to illustrate the types of analog functions that should be in a personalized library and to show the performances that can be expected from such elements. The book is not intended to be an exhaustive catalogue of the functions; this information can be obtained from silicon vendors. The book does, however, show the performances that have been achieved by one particular optimization of certain key cells. The book further illustrates how amplifier cells may be differently optimized to meet different sets of target specifications. The reader can thus gain an insight into the trade-offs that are involved in library element personalization.

A description of many of the steps required to implement a complete chip design using the personalized cell approach is given so that the reader can see what is involved in applying the techniques described to a practical problem. The described libraries and associated design tools are restricted to CMOS technology, which is widely recognized together with its BICMOS derivative as being the current and future mainstream technology for mixed analog digital designs. Throughout the book the analog issues are given the more detailed treatment as numerous texts exist that deal with the issues for digital design.[5]

1.5   New skills to be acquired

Particular care is taken to highlight the additional skills which must be acquired by electronics designers to successfully complete mixed analog digital chip designs.

The first new skill is acquiring knowledge of the system performance and performance limitations of integrated analog digital designs. This is a knowledge base which will be unique for each particular system. The starting point for the assembly of this knowledge is a study in turn of the process technology, the integrated components available to the designer and the higher level macrofunctions that can be generated. This will give the designer the ability to predict possible dynamic ranges, signal to noise ratios, matching accuracies, frequency limits, minimum operating currents, etc.

The next new skill is a clear understanding of where conventional methods of design do not contain sufficient discipline to manage the complexity of analog digital ASIC designs. The structured approach that has been developed for full digital ASIC designs must be adapted to a mixed analog digital design environment. In practice this means starting with a clear specification of the overall system requirement. The system must then be broken down into modules which can be specified in more detail. This procedure continues breaking the complexity of the design down until a known performance is reached; in our case, the performance of the personalized cells.

A further new skill which must be acquired is the ability to design with complete chip testability in mind. This is essential because it is possible (and probably inevitable) that if testability is not deliberately designed in, an untestable chip will result.

The next new set of skills that must be acquired is the ability to use design automation or computer aided design (CAD) tools to predict and verify the chip performance and design validity. It is essential that the designer learns to use a range of CAD tools as the design complexities are such that it is no longer possible to accomplish mixed designs by hand.

Having completed the design it is then necessary for the designer to understand the interface to the silicon vendor. This is different from, and more complex than, an interface to a printed circuit manufacturer.

Finally it is important for the designer to know something about the topology of the final chip. This is useful in the case where the design verification process involves an internal diagnosis of the chip.

1.6   Summary of the key messages of chapters

Chapter Two familiarizes the reader with state-of-the-art CMOS technology, highlighting those features which are important in converting an electronic design into silicon. The chapter shows that although the designer has control over only two physical dimensions, i.e. geometries on a set of masks, the silicon structures are in fact three dimensional. This is intended to give the reader a better understanding of the design media and to provide the necessary topographical insight to guide him in potential future microprobing and on-chip diagnosis.

Chapter Three introduces the need for design discipline and a structured and hierarchical approach to manage the design complexity. It provides a theoretical basis for design methodology as well as a practical review of current simulation techniques.

Chapter Four describes the components available in an integrated mixed analog digital CMOS process. The properties of the integrated components are compared with the properties of discrete components. This chapter highlights the techniques that are available to optimize the performances that can be obtained with these integrated components. It subsequently shows the influence of the components on analog design techniques.

Chapter Five describes the techniques for the design of functional blocks and macrocells. The use of synthesis and layout compilation techniques are described and examples are given for operational amplifier and switched-capacitor filter design automation. The chapter provides some measured results of characterized library cells which were personalized to specific requirements. Three new important concepts of cell personalization techniques are introduced. The first is the restriction of cell design variables to maintain constant the key characterization data which cannot be adequately simulated. The second maintains critical layout areas constant to preserve the embedded layout expertise of the cell's original designer. The final innovation is the derivation of the new cell specifications from the real system requirements, whereby the cell is designed together with its on-chip environment. This deterministic method of design has significant advantages over the widely used "cut and try" approach.

Chapter Six introduces the importance of the layout on final performance. It highlights the fact that certain critical layout-related information should be introduced into the design process in an organized way. The method suggested is through an extended schematic capture program which can handle data such as cell placement, power supply and grounding buses and sensitive analog signals. The chapter also introduces a solution for a mixed analog digital chip floorplan and gives an example of automatic placement and routing. It also includes a survey of digital standard cell and block place and route techniques.

Chapter Seven describes the complete design procedure and the interface with a silicon foundry and mask-making facility. The different possible levels of interface, i.e. specifications, simulated schematic and data base are reviewed. Finally design acceptance and cost issues are discussed.

Chapter Eight first describes the different types of testing, design verification, device characterization, production testing, etc. It highlights the differences between analog and digital testing and points out the types of problems to be considered in design-for-test. It describes the different types of testers available to enable the designer to consider the appropriate testing options. *Ad-hoc* and formal testing methods are discussed as are a variety of techniques for on-chip diagnosis.

Chapter Nine provides a case study which illustrates the top–down design approach using personalized standard cells. It starts with the description of the overall chip requirement, partitions the chip into modules and then describes the design of one module in detail. The approach described includes a design-for-test strategy.

1.7   Conclusions

Despite the widespread and growing interest in mixed analog digital design, the development of a design methodology that can be used by a wide number of designers is still in an early phase of evolution. The authors believe that the personalized cell approach described in this book can be used as the basis for future design automation in this field. There are many areas requiring improvements. These include the methods of system performance definition, complete system simulation and testing. A great deal of time in the design process is currently taken up making comparisons between simulated and desired performance. Techniques and tools are needed to facilitate these comparisons. Some synthesis and silicon layout compilation has been successfully applied to a number of analog functions. Further work is needed to extend the types of analog functions available from these synthesis and layout compilation techniques.

In order for designers to take advantage of these new techniques, silicon manufacturers must become aware of the additional parameters and the higher level of control of these parameters required by mixed analog digital designs. In addition the silicon manufacturers have to appreciate the exacting modelling requirements and the need for distribution of this information. The trends in new production equipment and modelling tools show that such controls and modelling accuracy will be possible. Indeed some vertically integrated companies are already practising the very advanced concept of allowing the designer to control certain process parameters to optimize his integrated design.

References

1.   Shenton, G., Mixed analogue/digital integration – the modern need, *Proceedings of Seminar on ASICs*, International Society for Hybrid Microelectronics (UK), London, June 1988.

2. Haque, Y.A., Gregorian, R., Blasco, R.W., Mao, R.A., Nicholson, W. Jr, A two chip PCM voice CODEC with filters, *IEEE Journal of Solid State Circuits*, **SC–14**, (6), Dec. 1979.

3. Shenton, G., Trontelj, J., Trontelj, L., Levovnik, F., Standard analog cell design for electrical energy management IC, *Proceedings of Custom Integrated Circuits Conference*, Rochester, NY, pp.386–90, 1986.

4. Allen, P., Holberg, D., *CMOS Analog Circuit Design*, Holt, Rinehart and Winston, Inc., 1987.

5. Weste, N.H.E., Eshraghian, K., *Principles of CMOS VLSI Design*, Addison Wesley, 1985.

2. CMOS processes for mixed analog digital design

2.1 Introduction

Silicon BICMOS technology is positioned to become the leading technology for the realization of monolithic integrated circuits in the 1990s. It combines the advantages of CMOS and bipolar technologies and can benefit from the continually reducing dimensions of its basic structures. Despite some added processing complexity, it is the technology in which the majority of analog and digital system functions will probably be most economically realized.

The fundamental technological steps are briefly described, which transform a slice of silicon monocrystal into a monolithic integrated circuit. It is instructive to do this by considering the dialogue between the designer of the electronic circuitry on one side and the process technologist on the other. Finally the influences of the individual process parameters on the reliability and the expected life span of the integrated circuit produced with this technology is considered.

2.2 The processing steps

The starting material for the BICMOS process is a monocrystaline P-type silicon wafer with crystal orientation ⟨100⟩ and resistivity 7–8.5 Ω cm. Its diameter is 125 or 150 mm and it is coated by a thin P-type epitaxial layer.

The processing of the silicon wafer can be divided into three basic operations:

1. diffusion with oxidation and ion implantation
2. deposition
3. photolithography and etching

Diffusion, oxidation and ion implantation change the physical properties of silicon wafers. Deposition adds, on top of the wafer surface, conducting and insulating layers. Photolithography and etching form and shape the desired layers either below or above the surface of the wafer on selected locations.

The individual processing steps of the three operations must follow each other in a strictly predetermined order. The main steps are interlaced with procedures of cleaning and "preparing" the surface as well as testing of electrical and material geometric parameters. Table 2.1 shows a simplified process flow chart of the individual processing steps for the BICMOS process with a polysilicon gate electrode.

Table 2.1 Simplified 1.2 μm BICMOS process flow chart

1. Initial oxidation
2. N-well masking
3. N-well ion implantation-phosphorous
4. Oxide etch
5. N-well drive in
6. Oxide stripping
7. Base oxidation
8. Punch through channel stop, ion implantation–boron (blanket)
9. Nitride deposition
10. Nitride masking and nitride etching
11. N-channel field ion implantation masking
12. N-channel field implantation–boron
13. Field oxidation
14. Nitrox stripping
15. Pregate oxidation, oxide etching
16. Gate oxidation
17. Back side oxide etching
18. Bottom polysilicon deposition
19. Bottom polysilicon doping
20. Bottom polysilicon masking, poly etching
21. Oxide etching
22. Gate/poly (interpoly) oxidation–gate oxidation
23. Boron base ion implantation masking
24. Base ion implantation–boron
25. Threshold voltage adjustment ion implantation (blanket)–boron
26. Backside oxide etching
27. Polysilicon deposition
28. Polysilicon doping
29. Polysilicon masking and etching
30. Polysilicon oxidation
31. Lightly doped drain (LDD) masking
32. Phosphorous LDD ion implantation
33. Spacer LTO deposition
34. Spacer etching
35. Arsenic source-drain (S/D) masking
36. Arsenic ion implantation
37. Boron S/D masking
38. Boron S/D ion implantation
39. S/D reoxidation

40. Low temperature oxide (LTO) deposition
41. Backside oxide etching
42. POCl$_3$ densification
43. Contact masking
44. Metal I sputtering (Al/Si/Cu) and masking
45. Intermetal oxide deposition (plasma oxide) I
46. Spin on glass (SOG) planarization
47. Planarization etching
48. Intermetal oxide deposition II
49. Planarization annealing
50. Via masking
51. Metal II sputternig Al/Si/Cu and masking
52. Planarization annealing and alloying
53. Plasma passivation
54. Pad masking
55. Stabilization annealing
56. Mapping

Figs.2.1(a) to 2.1(p) show the sequence of processing steps. These cross sections through a silicon slice show the generation of an integrated NMOS and PMOS transistor pair as well as a bipolar transistor, interpoly capacitor and a precision SiCr resistor.

The sequence illustrates the complexity of a modern BICMOS process. This process is in fact one of the simpler versions that does not require a buried epitaxial layer and therefore fits directly into a CMOS fabrication facility. The isolated npn bipolar transistor produced in this process can be used to improve circuit performance with respect to input offset-voltage, sensitivity and noise.

The cross sections in Fig.2.1 show intermediate steps in the process flow. The processing activities that have been completed at each step are shown in the individual diagrams. An important aspect of the process architecture is the reduction of high electric field strength and the resulting hot electron problems. This is accomplished by the use of lightly doped drain (LDD) structures. These structures are produced by two different drain implantation steps. The implants are separated by the use of oxide spacers. This is illustrated in step 5.

1. After   Initial oxidation
            N-well masking and ion implantation
            Oxide etching
            N-well drive in
            Base oxidation
            Punch through ion implantation

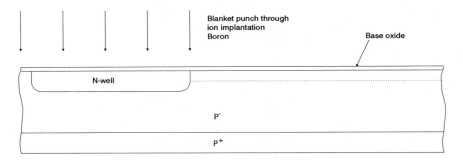

Fig. 2.1(a) Process and mask sequence — CMOS transistor pair cross section

2. After   Nitride deposition
            Nitride masking and etching
            N-channel field implant masking and ion implantation
            Field oxidation

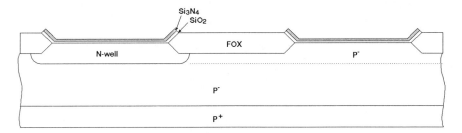

Fig. 2.1(b) Process and mask sequence — CMOS transistor pair cross section

3. After   Nitrox stripping
                Pregate oxidation, oxide etching
                Back side oxide etching
                Bottom poly deposition and doping
                Bottom poly masking and etching
                Oxide etching

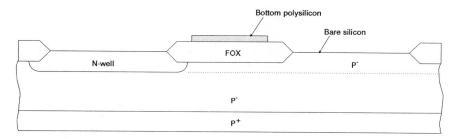

Fig. 2.1(c) Process and mask sequence — CMOS transistor pair cross section

4. After   Gate polysilicon oxidation
                Boron base ion implantation masking and implantation
                Threshold voltage adjusting ion implantation
                Back side oxide etching
                Polysilicon deposition and doping
                Polysilicon masking and etching
                Polysilicon oxidation

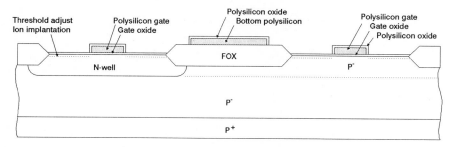

Fig. 2.1(d) Process and mask sequence — CMOS transistor pair cross section

5. After   LDD masking and ion implantation (phosphorus)
              Spacer LTO deposition
              Spacer etching
              Arsenic masking (S/D) and ion implantation

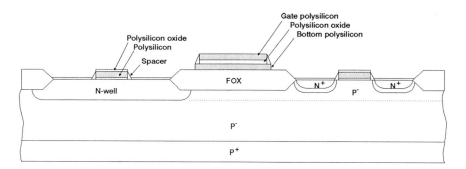

Fig. 2.1(e) Process and mask sequence — CMOS transistor pair cross section

6. After   Boron S/D masking and ion implantation
              S/D reoxidation
              LTO deposition
              Back side oxide etching
              POCl₃ densification
              Contact masking

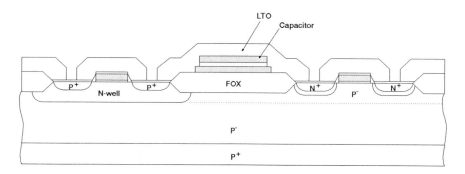

Fig. 2.1(f) Process and mask sequence — CMOS transistor pair cross section

7. After   Metal I deposition
             Metal I masking and etching
             Intermetal oxide deposition
             SOG planarization and etching
             Intermetal oxide deposition
             Planarization annealing
             Via masking
             Metal II deposition, masking and etching
             Planarization annealing/alloying
             Plasma passivation

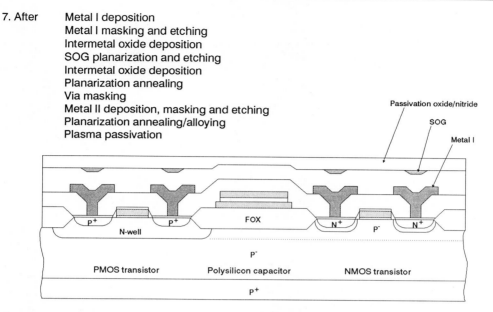

Fig. 2.1(g) Process and mask sequence — CMOS transistor pair cross section

1. After   Initial oxidation
             N-well masking and ion implantation
             Oxide etching
             N-well drive in
             Base oxidation
             Punch through ion implantation

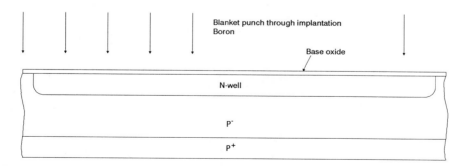

Fig. 2.1(h) Process and mask sequence — bipolar transistor cross section

2. After   Nitride deposition
                Nitride masking and etching
                N-channel field implant masking and ion implantation
                Field oxidation

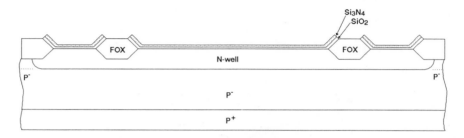

Fig. 2.1(i) Process and mask sequence — bipolar transistor cross section

3. After   Nitrox stripping
                Pregate oxidation, oxide etching
                Back side oxide etching
                Bottom poly deposition and doping
                Bottom poly masking and etching
                Oxide etching

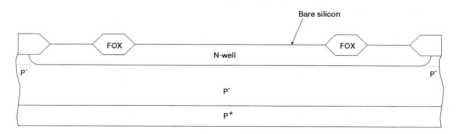

Fig. 2.1(j) Process and mask sequence — bipolar transistor cross section

4. After   Gate polysilicon oxidation
              Boron base ion implantation masking and implantation
              Threshold voltage adjusting ion implantation
              Back side oxide etching
              Polysilicon deposition and doping
              Polysilicon masking and etching
              Polysilicon oxidation

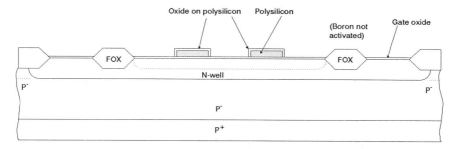

Fig. 2.1(k) Process and mask sequence — bipolar transistor cross section

5. After   LDD masking and ion implantation (phosphorus)
              Spacer LTO deposition
              Spacer etching
              Arsenic masking (S/D) and ion implantation

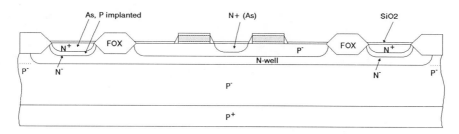

Fig. 2.1(l) Process and mask sequence — bipolar transistor cross section

6. After   Boron S/D masking and ion Implantation
            S/D reoxidation
            LTO deposition
            Back side oxide etching
            POCl₃ densification
            Contact masking

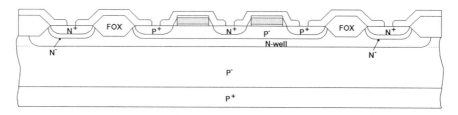

Fig. 2.1(m) Process and mask sequence — bipolar transistor cross section

7. After   Metal I deposition, masking and etching
            Intermetal oxide deposition
            SOG planarization and etching
            Intermetal oxide deposition
            Planarization annealing
            Via masking
            Metal II deposition, masking and etching
            Planarization annealing/alloying
            Plasma passivation
            Pad masking and etching
            Stabilization annealing

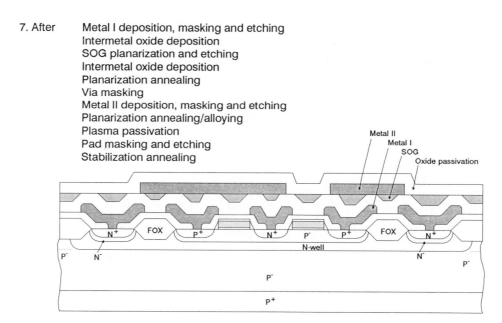

Fig. 2.1(n) Process and mask sequence — bipolar transistor cross section

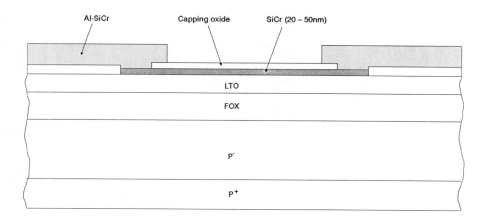

Fig. 2.1(o) SiCr resistor

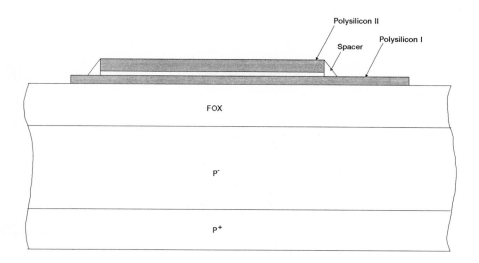

Fig. 2.1(p) Interpoly capacitor

It is important to be aware of the major relationships that govern the basic operations of silicon processing.

2.2.1 Diffusion and oxidation, ion implantation

In a silicon substrate diffusion "current" J_x of impurities is determined from the gradient of concentration of the impurity c and with the diffusion coefficient D in the following way:

$$J_x = -D \frac{\partial c}{\partial x} \tag{2.1}$$

This expression, known as Fick's first law, is built up in a similar way to Ohm's law for current flow. Here the diffusion current corresponds to current flow, similarly the concentration gradient to the voltage and finally the diffusion coefficient to the conductivity. One can make use of this duality between Fick's and Ohm's law in establishing the continuity relation for a space without any chemical reactions (or additional current sources):

$$-\frac{\partial J}{\partial x} = \frac{\partial c}{\partial t} \tag{2.2}$$

Combining expressions (2.1) and (2.2) yields the diffusion expression (Fick's second law) for the distribution of the impurity concentration:

$$D \frac{\partial^2 c}{\partial x^2} = \frac{\partial c}{\partial t} \tag{2.3}$$

The diffusion coefficient generally depends on the composition and temperature of the phase under observation. The solution of the partial differential equation governing the local distribution of the impurity concentration can be approximated for simplicity by a complementary error function:

$$c(x,t) = c_0 \left(1 - \text{erf} \frac{x}{2\sqrt{Dt}}\right) \tag{2.4}$$

where c_0 represents the layer impurity concentration. The boundary conditions are the following: $c(0, t) = c_0$, $c(\infty, t) = 0$ and $c(x, 0) = 0$. Here the x coordinate axis is normal to the wafer surface.

The solution of the above equation describes fairly well the first step in the diffusion process, usually named deposition. This is a procedure in which molecules from an inert gaseous vector saturated with impurities of the p and n type (the molecules of boron, phosphorous or arsenic) are deposited on the surface of adequately preheated silicon wafers.

The second step of diffusion follows after interruption of the flow of new impurities. The previously deposited impurities now travel into the interior of the chip along the x axis. The solution of the diffusion equation can now be described with a Gaussian type probability:

$$c(x,t) = \frac{Q}{\sqrt{\pi Dt}} \exp\left[-x^2/4Dt \right]$$
(2.5)

In equation (2.5) Q represents the total number of impurity atoms from the deposition phase.

The properties of the diffused layer can be generally described with three parameters:

1.   the surface layer of impurity concentration c_0, by which the type of the layer and its resistivity are determined,
2.   the substrate concentration of the opposite impurity type c_B and
3.   the junction depth x_j.

"Pure" silicon wafers (with an intrinsic concentration v or π) are never used. The wafer usually has a normal electric conductivity, hence the designation c_B.

As already mentioned, use is made of these very simplified considerations about the diffusion process, only for a rough determination of parameters of impurity distribution along the x axis towards the depth of the junction.

In reality the complicated diffusion process occurs in an oxidizing atmosphere, which results in a growth of the oxide layer on the surface during this process. In the presence of oxygen the silicon is oxidized and thus the border between the newly formed oxide layer and silicon moves into the surface of the wafer along the x axis.

The growth of the oxide layer can be seen in the Fig.2.2, while Fig.2.3 shows the schematics of oxidation system.

The velocity with which the impurity concentration is changing due to the movement of the oxide–silicon border is given by the relation:

$$c(x,t) = c(x - bw, 0)$$
(2.6)

and

$$\frac{\partial c}{\partial t} = \frac{d(bw)}{dt}\frac{\partial c}{\partial x} + D\frac{\partial^2 c}{\partial x^2}$$
(2.7)

where w is the thickness of the oxide layer and b is 0.44.

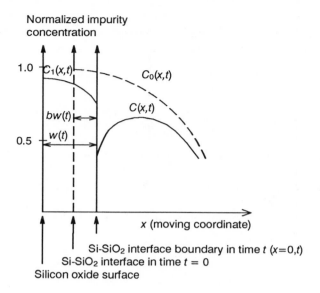

Fig. 2.2 Growth of silicon oxide layer

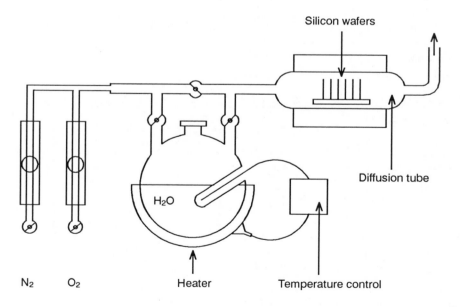

Fig. 2.3 Wet oxidation system

The impurity concentration is reducing in accordance with the diffusion equation (2.3). The oxidation process usually takes place at a temperature of about 1000 °C.

The model of the one dimensional growth of the oxide layer can be described with:

1. the flow of the oxidizing medium towards the surface of the wafer
2. the flow of the oxidizing medium through the newly formed oxide layer (for a layer of oxide thickness x_0 we use $0.44\,x_{Si}$ silicon) and
3. the reaction on the silicon surface

The thickness x_0 is given from the solution of the following equation:

$$x_0{}^2 + Ax_0 + B(t + \tau) = 0 \tag{2.8}$$

The expression (2.8) means:

$$A = 2\,D_{ef}\left(\frac{1}{k} + \frac{1}{h}\right) \quad \text{and} \quad B = \frac{2\,D_{ef}\,c^+}{c_1}$$

where c^+ is the equilibrium concentration of the oxidizing gas, and c_1 is the number of oxidizing molecules per unit volume, which take part in the growth of the oxide layer, h is the gas-phase mass transfer coefficient in terms of concentration in the solid, and k is the rate constant of chemical surface reaction for silicon oxidation.

Furthermore a shift in the time constant τ is

$$\tau = \frac{x_i{}^2 + x_i\,A}{B}$$

with x_i the initial oxide thickness.

The quantity B is called the parabolic constant of the oxide growth and is of primary importance at high temperatures and prolonged oxidation periods. The linear growth constant B/A is of primary importance in the case of thin oxide layers. In the case that $t + \tau << A^2/4B$, the thickness x_0 can be approximated by $(B/A)(t + \tau)$. In the case that $t >> A^2/4B$, x_0 is simply $x_0 = \sqrt{B(t + \tau)}$.

Ion implantation permits at room temperature a controlled, clean and comparatively well defined process for transporting the impurities onto and into the silicon wafer. Using a linear accelerator an ion beam is produced with ions of only one kind (B^{11}, P^{31}, As^{75}) using energies from some ten up to several hundred keV and currents of some μA up to several mA.

The mechanics of implanting the impurities into the target is governed by the laws of Gaussian statistics. The distribution of impurities along the x axis is given by:

$$c(x) = c_p \exp \left[-1/2((x - R_p)/\Delta R_p)^2 \right] \qquad (2.9\,a)$$

and

$$c_p \approx \frac{0.4\, C_s}{\Delta R_p} \qquad (2.9\,b)$$

In the expression (2.9) ΔR_p means the standard deviation, R_p is the projected range, c_p is the peak concentration of the impurities and C_s the number of implanted ions.

The projected range can be evaluated from the expression:

$$R_p = \frac{R}{1 + (M_2/3M_1)} \qquad (2.10)$$

where

$$R = 0.7 \frac{(Z_1^{2/3} + Z_2^{2/3})^{1/2}}{Z_1 Z_2} \frac{M_1 + M_2}{M_1} E_0 \quad (\text{Å}) \qquad (2.11)$$

The suffix 1 in the expressions (2.10) and (2.11) is valid for the entering ion while the suffix 2 refers to the target. M and Z represent the mass and atom number of the ion, while E_0 is the energy of the incoming ion in eV.

The advantage of ion implantation over diffusion is in the purity of the procedure, which can be easily monitored and controlled. It is possible to inspect, continuously during the process, the implanted doses, which determine the layer resistivity.

Modern ion implantation machines are very adaptable. They enable the production of junction depths of submicron order thus partially or totally replacing the classic diffusion process. On the other hand there is a drawback in damaging the crystal structure of the substrate, which at higher currents or ion energies can cause the crystal to become even amorphous. With adequate annealing processes, however, it is possible to control the damage.

2.2.2 Deposition

The epitaxial growth process enables the production of a layer growth with steep gradients of impurity concentrations among layers. The mono- and polycrystaline layers can be made of various thicknesses from 0.5 to 20 μm and with different impurity levels. Thus the layer resistivity can be varied from 0.005 to 10 Ω cm. The crucial parameters met in this process are:

1. Thickness and resistivity of the individual layers
2. The problem of self doping and diffusivity and
3. The crystallographic defects

These parameters can be influenced by:

1. The geometry and vapour pressure inside the reactor
2. The rate of heating of the substrates
3. The degree of the growth and temperature
4   The purity of gases

Epitaxial growth is governed by the following steps:

1. The diffusion mass transport of the reagent molecules (e.g. SiH_4) in the epitaxial reactor from a turbulent layer through a stagnant layer on the silicon wafer
2. Absorption of the reagent atoms on the wafer surface
3. One or more chemical reactions on the surface
4. Desorption of the product molecules (for example H_2)
5. The diffusion mass transport of product molecules through the stagnant layer back into the turbulent layer
6. The crystallographic arrangement of the adsorbed silicon atoms. This process can take place simultaneously with the process in item 3

The overall layer growth is determined with the slowest of the steps 1 through 6 mentioned above.

The silicon growth is usually achieved from gaseous molecules (SiH_4, $SiCl_4$) containing silicon. The growth mechanism is governed by previously mentioned growth rules from the gaseous phase (mass transport, nucleation). The newly deposited solid phase grows in a hydrogen atmosphere on a heated substrate. Another condition is also a clean active surface (produced by etching with HCl prior to the process in the reactor). The newly developed layer has to be adequately doped. This can be achieved by the addition of doping gases (PH_3, B_2H_6...) along with the reagent molecules.

The most frequently used chemical reactions met in the epitaxial process (at atmospheric pressure) can be found in Table 2.2.

Table 2.2 The chemical reactions in epitaxial process

Layer	Vector gases	Reaction	T_{dep} (°C)
Si	H_2	$SiCl_4 + H_2 \Rightarrow Si + HCl$	1125–1200
Si	H_2	$SiH_4 + heat \Rightarrow Si + H_2$	1000–1075
Poly Si	$H_2(N_2)$	$SiH_4 + heat \Rightarrow Si + H_2$	850–1100
Si_3N_4	H_2	$SiH_4 + NH_3 \Rightarrow Si_3N_4 + H$	900–1100
Si_3N_4	N_2	$SiH_4 + NH_3 \Rightarrow Si_3N_4 + H$	600–700

A very efficient method of depositing polysilicon, silicon, nitride, oxide and certain metal layers is to use the deposition techniques described above at reduced pressure. Special low pressure chemical vapour deposition (LPCVD) reactors are designed for this purpose. Fig.2.4 shows the LPCVD reactor cross section.

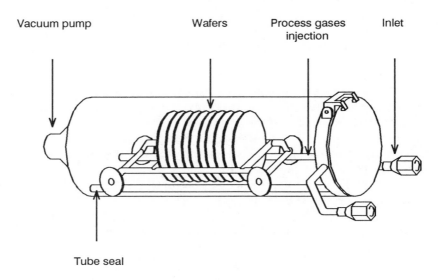

Fig. 2.4 LPCVD cross section with process gases injection

Table 2.3 shows data concerning the uniformity of the layers as well as the uniformity among the wafer lots.

Table 2.3 The growth and uniformity of deposited layers

Layer	Growth (μm/min)	Along wafer	Uniformity (%) Among wafers	Among lots
Poly Si	9–10	2	3	3
Si_3N_4	4.5–5.5	2	3	3
SiO_2	7–8	3	3	3
LTO	12.5–35	3	3	3

The low temperature growth of silicon dioxide (at 400–420°C and 25–55 Pa pressure) from silane using doped gas (PH_3) and oxygen is typically used for insulating layers. It is used between polysilicon and aluminium layers and between two adjacent layers of polysilicon. This process is known for producing exceptionally uniform layers with few defects and with excellent covering properties for steps with sharp edges in the fundamental structure.

A system which feeds in doping gases along the reactor tube, as in the one shown in Fig.2.4, is suitable for doping of polysilicon layers *in situ*. It thus replaces the later deposition of dopants with ion implantation and diffusion.

Such equipment enables the deposition of layers of 500 nm thickness and 10–15 Ω/square sheet resistivity. This equipment also permits the deposition of other metallic layers (refractory metals) with lower sheet resistivity than polysilicon, which diminishes the parasitic influences of the electrical interfaces among the building elements of a monolithic circuit in the very dense structures formed in micrometer technologies.

The silicon nitride and oxide layers are usually deposited on the substrate in plasma at low pressure chemical vapour deposition (LP CVD). This method also offers, in contrast to the two previously described, looser tolerances in the setting of substrate temperatures. The nucleation of atoms and molecules from the gaseous into solid phase is a very sensitive function of the substrate temperature. The chemical reactions in the gaseous plasma are no longer thermally controlled thus permitting substantially lower temperatures in comparison with other deposition methods of achieving similar layer properties. This method also represents an industrial standard for the primary surface protection of integrated circuits by a layer of silicon nitride. A typical growth is in the order of 30 μm/min at a pressure of some hundred Pa. The reagents are usually silane and ammonia. The layer thickness and the index of refraction are typically inside the limits of ±5 per cent among individual wafers and major lots. The silicon nitride layer obtained this way is distinguished by excellent coverage properties, e.g. over metal steps having a step height of about 1 μm. This layer is also well protected against cracking during later heating and cooling in the final stages of wafer fabrication.

2.2.3 Photolithography and etching

In the formation of the thin layers necessary for the development of basic elements for microelectronic circuits there is a series of processing steps. These steps and the properties of individual layers determine the electrical parameters of the basic elements.

Recently the patterning capabilities have enabled the production of structures whose horizontal or planar dimensions are of a similar size to their vertical dimensions.

The production of various shapes in microelectronics is made possible by the formation of layers of light-sensitive organic resins called photoresists. These photosensitive layers must have specially developed properties which will enable them to give a true depiction of the masking pattern when used with a good system of alignment and exposure. In addition photoresists should have excellent mechanical and chemical properties for adhesion to the basic material as well as chemical resistance against etching substances used in the process of removing the uncovered portions.

Today positive photoresist is normally used consisting of lighter polymers in a base of formaldehide resins. The illumination destroys the bonds among the light-sensitive substances and the polymer. The exposed material is soluble in alkaline developer.

In spite of the continuing development in electronic and X-ray photolithography, deep UV light still has the dominant role in the illumination of photoresist covered wafers. In order to achieve accurate designs with minimal problems at successive alignments of the individual levels of photomasks in the micrometer range, wafer step alignment with wide aperture lenses is used.

For smaller structures an alternative system is needed. A step alignment and exposition system can be used with 5:1 reduction lenses. In this way the errors caused by the geometrical optics are partially eliminated. With such an appliance of course only a part of the wafer can be illuminated. The number of exposure steps is usually related to the dimensions of the chip.

In using a wafer stepper the time necessary for the exposure of the whole wafer is somewhat longer, making the process more expensive.

In still smaller structures, i.e. denser circuits, the exposure procedures are switching to light of shorter wavelength (electron beam, X-rays) and increasing attention is paid to the precise transfer of the pattern from the photomask to the wafer.

Fig.2.5 shows in a somewhat exaggerated way how the information of the photomask is mutilated because of the wave nature of the light and the errors in the optical system. The profile of the developed photoresist layer is the result of successive reflections and thus of standing waves of light in the semi transparent layers on the wafer. As a consequence of this phenomenon a variable energy distribution is formed along the incoming direction.

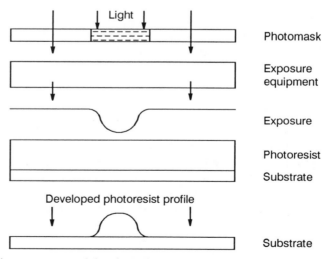

Fig. 2.5 Photoresist exposure and development errors

Because of this non-uniform energy distribution of light waves along the depth of the photoresist layer, the primary information built into the light and dark fields on the photomask is degraded. This loss of information is more pronounced in photomasks used for forming the final layers on the wafer. These are more demanding because of the increasingly "hilly" surface of the wafer and consequently thicker layer of photoresist. The solution lies in combined photoresist layers and planarization procedures (spin on glass technique — SOG).

The next step in forming the individual layers on the wafer is etching, i.e. removal of the unwanted parts of these layers in the areas not covered by the developed photoresist. The possible techniques of etching are given in Table 2.4.

Table 2.4 Methods for etching of thin layers

Process	Mechanical etching	Plasma etching (RIBE, RIE)[*]	Wet etching
Mechanism	Linear momentum	Stimulated chemical reaction	Chemical reaction
Selectivity	Low (2 to 3:1)	Fair (5:1) to excellent (30:1)	Excellent
Directivity	Anisotropic	Anisotropic/isotropic	Isotropic

[*] Note:
RIBE stands for reactive ion beam etching
RIE stands for reactive ion etching

The meaning of directivity is explained in Fig.2.6.

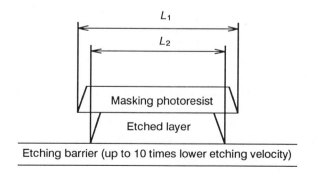

Anisotropic model: $L_1 = L_2$
Isotropic model: $L_1 \neq L_2$

Fig. 2.6 Etching profile model

In scaling down the geometrical dimensions of the integrated building elements for circuits the anisotropic process for removing the unwanted parts becomes increasingly important.

Table 2.5 shows an overview of the gases and reagents used in connection with some layers on silicon.

Table 2.5 Plasma etching and burnout of some typical layers

Layer	Gas	Reagent	Product
Photoresist	O_2	O	O_2, H_2O, CO_2
Si	$CF_4 + O_2$	F	SiF_4
SiO_2	$C_2F_6 + He$	CF_3, F	SiF_4, CO, CO_2
Si_3N_4	$CF_4 + O_2$	F	SiF_4, N_2
Al	$CCl_4 + He$	Cl	$AlCl_3$

The advantage of plasma etching, beside being anisotropic, is that the product of etching is in a gaseous phase, which is usually not absorbed into the surface of the wafer or into the covering layer. This process more accurately reproduces the information from the photoresist and hence from the photomask. It is also a very clean process.

The producers of the equipment have developed for this process an effective control of the depth of the etched out layer using a method of optical and mass spectroscopy. By this control method the etching process is automatically interrupted when the layer is etched out.

2.3   Final operations on silicon wafer

After performing the parametric and somewhat simplified functional tests the processed silicon wafers are sawn into individual chips. They now undergo a series of full functional and climomechanical tests after being assembled into packages. The type of these packages depends on the circuit application. Some categories of circuits are subjected to an accelerated ageing process at higher temperatures with a prescribed static and dynamic load.

The application and test procedures for circuits, together with the properties of incoming materials, the application environments and also the production machines are described in technical regulations and standards published by pertinent offices and other services. The trend towards a world-wide unification of these regulations and an ever increasing discipline of producers in their strict application represents a strong effort towards a higher quality of circuits.

The factors having a decisive influence on the life span of the circuits are temperature (whether constant or varying), voltage and humidity. Among the important breakdown factors are: the electric charge formed on the silicon and silicon dioxide interface, poisoning through moving ions (sodium), various polarizing effects, faults in the oxide (non-uniformity, break through due to increased voltage) and last but not least electromigration.

Bonding defects (ground short circuits), cracked chips and pollution with foreign objects are also factors, the presence of which significantly diminishes the reliability of the circuit and may also render it useless.

The technology is of course able to guarantee a proper operation of the circuit in extreme conditions for a prolonged period (many decades). A vital condition for a long life is, however, a strict adherence to the design rules. The monitors provided by the industry in the process procedures are, beside optical inspection, adequate temperature shocks and cycling, leak inspection of packages as well as the quality of leads, and finally the testing of the bond strength and the X-ray inspection of the finished circuit.

The prediction of the life time of the circuit can be extrapolated by the use of accelerated life tests at elevated temperature and other working conditions of the circuit.

2.4   Process evaluation device (PED)

After all process steps are carefully executed the wafers are subjected to parametric testing. In order to perform such tests every silicon foundry has designed specific test structures, e.g. process evaluation device (PED) which appears two, three or five times on every processed silicon wafer (Fig.2.7). The PED allows the monitoring of several key electrical, physical and

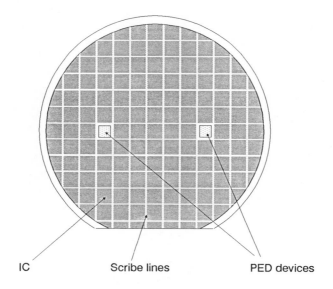

IC   Scribe lines   PED devices

Fig. 2.7 Placement of process evaluation devices (PED) on silicon wafer

technological properties of the integrated structures of interest. Table 2.6 lists parameters, which are usually checked. A computer print-out of the parametric measurements for every wafer should prove the compliance with the predicted ranges for every particular parameter before functional testing of the IC is started.

Table 2.6 List of parameters tested on PED

1.	VTOSN (P)	Threshold voltage of N (P) channel transistor (short channel)
2.	VTOLN (P)	Threshold voltage of N (P) channel transistor (long channel)
3.	IDS	Subthreshold transistor current
4.	GAMMA S	Body factor (short channel)
5.	GAMMA L	Body factor (long channel)
6.	L-eff S	Effective channel length (short channel)
7.	BVDSS S	Source drain breakdown voltage
8.	BVNPG	Junction breakdown voltage under gate
9.	BVDSS	Source drain breakdown voltage at 10 mA
10.	BETA L	Conduction factor
11.	P^+ (N^+)POLY RSH	Sheet resistance P (N) type poly 1 (2)
12.	P (N)POLY CD	Critical dimension P (N) poly 1 (2)
13.	P^+ (N^+)RSH	Diffusion sheet resistance P^+ (N^+) type
14.	N^-FLD RSH	Sheet resistance N^- field
15.	N^-ACT RSH	Sheet resistance N^- active
16.	MPL CNTACT	Metal poly contact resistance
17.	MCNTACT	Metal diffusion contact resistance
18.	BV N^+P^-	Breakdown voltage N^+P^- junction
19.	BV P^+N^-	Breakdown voltage P^+N^- junction
20.	BV P^-N^-	Breakdown voltage P^-N^- junction
21.	VTFP (N)	Field threshold P (N) type poly
22.	VTFMETALP (N)	Field threshold P (N) type channel parasitic transistor
23.	P^+ (N^+)BRDG	Leakage current test of junction P (N) diffusion
24.	P^+ (N^+)WIDTH	Effective P^+ (N^+) diffusion width
25.	DELTA-W	Poly gate P (N) width variation
26.	BV G-OX P (N)	Breakdown voltage of P (N) type channel gate
27.	BV EDGE	Breakdown voltage of P (N) type channel gate oxide (edge)
28.	TOX GATE P	Gate oxide thickness
29.	LAMBDA P (N)	P (N) channel length modulation
30.	HFE LAT.PNP (NPN)	Current amplification factor of lateral PNP (NPN) bipolar transistor
31.	HFE VERT.PNP	Current amplification factor of vertical NPN bipolar transistor
32.	VERT PUNCH NPN	Punch through vertical NPN transistors
33.	IDSAT P (N)	Saturation P(N) type transistor current
34.	P1-P2 CAP	Poly 1 poly 2 capacitance

2.5   Design rules

The successful design of an integrated circuit depends very much on an established definition of the selected technology. The dialogue among the process engineers and the designers is successfully accomplished by obeying the so-called design rules. These rules convert the electronic properties of integrated building blocks into geometrical dimensions. The design of any selected circuit is accomplished only when all circuit elements are properly expressed in geometrical shapes and a corresponding database tape is created. This in turn allows a mask-making facility to produce the set of photomasks. There are several process instabilities which do not allow the exact printing of the designed photomask pattern on the silicon wafer, as discussed in paragraph 2.2.4. The drawn dimensions differ from final ones due to the limited accuracy in the particular mask geometry fabrication and its alignment to other layers in the set. They differ also because of exposure and development mechanism of photoresist and because of etching profiles, lateral diffusion and because of masking oxide growth known as "bird's beak" formation.

Topological design rules call for minimum allowed line widths and spacing of particular shapes, their stackings and interconnections. The example in Fig.2.8 explains the set of rules for the formation of intermetal contacts in a 1.2 μm process. The design must comply with the topological design rules to ensure that a circuit of high yield will result.

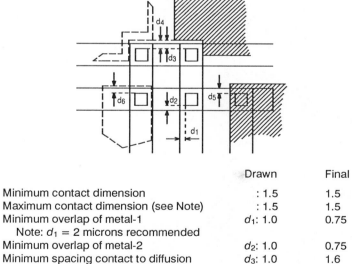

	Drawn	Final
Minimum contact dimension	: 1.5	1.5
Maximum contact dimension (see Note)	: 1.5	1.5
Minimum overlap of metal-1	d_1: 1.0	0.75
Note: d_1 = 2 microns recommended		
Minimum overlap of metal-2	d_2: 1.0	0.75
Minimum spacing contact to diffusion	d_3: 1.0	1.6
Minimum spacing contact to poly	d_4: 1.0	1.15
Minimum space contact to diffusion edge	d_5: 1.0	0.4
Minimum space contact to poly edge	d_6: 1.0	0.85

Fig. 2.8 Example of 1.2 μm process design rules, metal-1 to metal-2 contacts

2.6   Surface views of the finished silicon

After completion of the design a separate layer for each level of masking in the process is generated. Normally a composite plot consisting of all layers at a scale of typically several hundred times to one is produced for visual checking purposes. Gross placement and continuity errors can be detected using the composite plot. However, complete checking software, as described in Chapter 6 and 7, is used before the design is released to mask making. The example of such a plot drawn on several scales is shown in Plates 2.1, 2.2 and 2.3. The final silicon surface when viewed with incident light will appear two dimensional. The pattern of silicon seen in the plates will correspond to the layers of the composite plot. Most corners are rounded because of the photolithographic process.

High magnification views of the silicon surface can be obtained with the use of a scanning electron microscope (SEM). Fig.2.9 shows SEM photomicrographs of the MOS and bipolar transistors. The higher resolution of the SEM enables the physical shapes to be seen more clearly.

2.7   Cross sectional views of the finished silicon

It is possible to examine the structure of a modern BICMOS process by sectioning and staining techniques. The die is cut vertically through the section to be examined. The resulting cut is

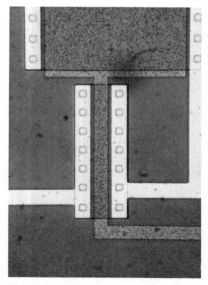

Fig. 2.9(a) Photomicrograph of MOS transistor

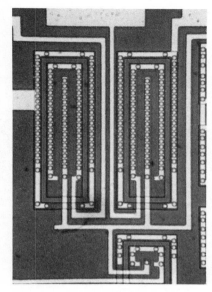

Fig. 2.9(b) Photomicrograph of bipolar transistor

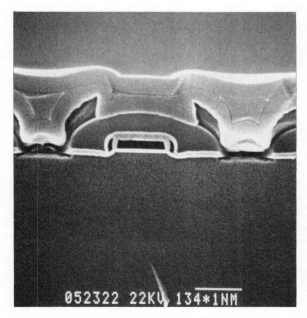

Fig. 2.10 SEM photomicrograph of MOS transistor with spacers

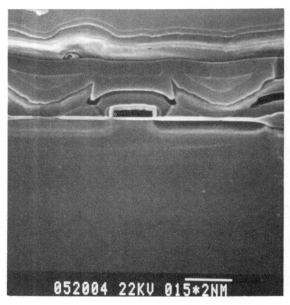

Fig. 2.11 SEM photomicrograph of MOS transistors with recognizable source and drain areas

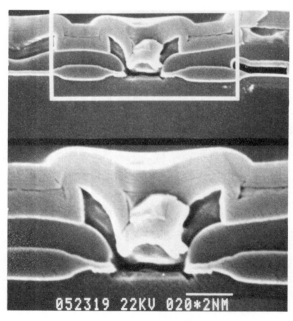

Fig. 2.12 SEM photomicrograph of aluminum contact to the source area

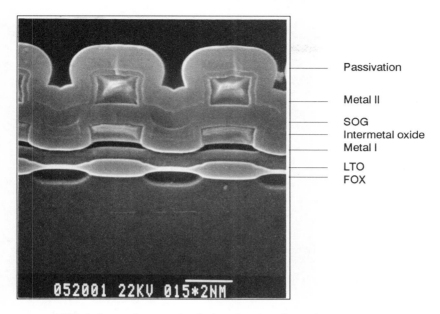

Passivation

Metal II

SOG
Intermetal oxide
Metal I

LTO
FOX

Fig. 2.13 SEM photomicrograph of planarized surface with metal II deposition

polished and etched. Contrast is achieved with the appropriate stain. Fig.2.10 shows an MOS transistor with oxide spacers clearly visible. In Fig.2.11 a similar transistor cross section is seen in which the source and drain areas are recognizable. Fig.2.12 shows the aluminum contact to the source area. Fig.2.13 shows the planarized surface with metal II deposition.

The three previously described groups of process steps are specified to produce a desired set of integrated device parameters. Particular variables of the process are optimized to match these parameters. Computer programs and process statistics data are utilized to accommodate process variables to the specific demands.

References

1. Maly, W., *Atlas of IC Technologies*, The Benjamin/Cummings Publishing Co. Inc., Menlo Park, CA, 1987.
2. Scot Ruska, W., *Microelectronic Processing*, McGraw-Hill Book Co., New York, 1987.
3. Sze, S.M., *VLSI Technology*, Second Ed., McGraw-Hill Book Co., Singapore, 1988.
4. Wolf, S., Tauber, R.N., *Silicon Processing for the VLSI Era*, Lattice Press, Sunset Beach, CA, 1986.

3. Design methodologies for VLSI systems

3.1 Review of VLSI design methodologies

3.1.1 Introduction

Before examining in detail particular design methodologies suitable for mixed analog digital designs, it is interesting to review some of the major design methodologies that have been used for VLSI. Rather than look at the great variety of historical methods, it is instructive to focus on the driving factors (and the limiting ones) that have given rise to the widely differing approaches to VLSI design. Such an analysis will be useful to the systems designer attempting to make choices of methodologies for digital circuits and should also give some indication of future directions in mixed analog digital methodologies. A more formal description of the wider design problems and the importance of methodology is given in Section 3.2 on "Theory of Design".

A prime driving factor in most design methodologies is cost, either design cost (D) or unit cost (U), or both. The volume of units (V) to be produced over the production life of the design is a key linking factor, i.e. the total cost (C) of design plus production for the design can be expressed as:

$$C = D + V \cdot U \tag{3.1}$$

It can be seen that for designs that will be produced in large volume (V),

$$V \cdot U \; > \; D \tag{3.2}$$

and hence the total cost (C) is dominated by the unit cost (U). Here there is a strong driving force to minimize total cost by reducing U even if necessary at the expense of increasing D.

For small V, $D > V \cdot U$ and C is dominated by D. In this case there is a strong drive to reduce design costs, even, if necessary, at the expense of increasing U.

These two extreme cases have led, not surprisingly, to the extremes of IC design methodologies which are often termed full custom ($V \cdot U > D$) and semi-custom ($D > V \cdot U$).

3.1.2 Full custom

In the full custom case the unit costs are normally dominated by the silicon chip costs, which in turn are dominated by silicon die size and process yield. The design methodology focus thus becomes the minimization of die size, or more accurately the maximization of good die per wafer. Historically the enabling factors here have been device, circuit and layout innovation.[1] Consequently the design skills have been very closely linked to the silicon technology.

The full custom design methodology evolved as a bottom–up procedure. This occurred because it was necessary to develop the circuit techniques, the layout structures and the functional elements that were efficient in the particular process technology. As illustrated in Fig.3.1, an IC based system design using the full custom methodology actually involved a complex top–down procedure with a great deal of iteration from low level to high level. Some of the reasons for this were:

1. All functional blocks were customized to optimize silicon area and performance (e.g. speed and power). They could be chosen from recommended structures but were customized for the specific design in hand, e.g. number of bits.
2. All circuits within the functional blocks were designed to optimize area for specific speed/power requirements, hence device sizes and in some cases circuit techniques were optimized or completely redesigned.
3. Until the functional blocks were designed, no general method of interconnect could be established, hence the floorplan had to wait for, and iterate with, the individual block designs.
4. Circuit design was an interactive process with typical transistor circuits being a complex network of new quasi-analog elements, the actual values of which depended on the voltage conditions on neighbouring devices. The design procedure had thus evolved as a primitive "cut and try" approach where the speed and quality of the design solution was very dependent on the ability and past experience of the IC designer.

In the 1970s and early 1980s this full custom methodology was widely practised by skilled IC design specialists for the minimization of unit cost, and the maximization of performance and function per unit cost for a given technology. Plate 3.1 shows a microphoto of a mixed analog digital custom chip designed in this way in 1982. Note the dense coverage of the surface with circuitry and interconnect.

The full custom design methodology has suffered from severely increasing design costs as IC chip complexity has continued to approximately double annually. As pressures increased to reduce design cycle times to bring products to market faster, advances to the full custom methodology were sought.

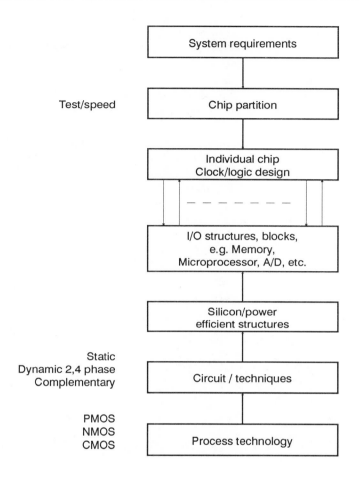

Fig. 3.1 Full custom methodology

3.1.3 Advances in full custom methodology

As a result of these pressures to reduce design cost and cycle time with increasing design complexity a number of key issues was addressed.

3.1.3.1. Design Accuracy

Full custom designs, even those containing no analog elements, were usually characterized until the early 1980s by requiring more than one prototyping iteration to obtain a design that met the original chip specification. Techniques that had to be improved were:

(a) Design verification. This included design rule checking, electrical continuity testing and extraction of schematics from the layout with a comparison to the original input.

(b) Accuracy and completeness of simulation. This was often limited by allowable computer run times and the accuracy of the simulation models. Techniques were needed to check that the chip design fully met the specification. Computer models have been improved and multilevel simulations developed to replace "bread-boarding" for chip design validation.

(c) Completeness of chip specification and testing methods. Fig.3.2 shows a complete electronic system with an IC as a part of that system. The chip specification must be adequate to ensure that if the chip design meets the chip specification, then the system will function as intended. Unless the chip and its environment have both been simulated or some form of hardware emulation of the system has been performed, this is difficult to ensure. In addition, it was realized that methods to test the chip must be part of the design methodology or untestable devices would result.

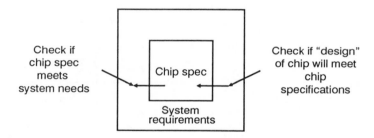

Fig. 3.2 Simulation of chip in system environment, internal and external views

The development of more structured design methodologies and the supporting CAD tools, coupled with decreasing computing costs, have done much to solve the design accuracy problem. Despite this, for the most complex chips the CAD tools are constantly struggling to keep pace and other techniques of design methodology must be used if further improvements in design automation are desired.[2]

3.1.3.2. Reduction of design variables

The restriction of the degrees of freedom available to a designer is a well known, if not always popular, technique to reduce the time and hence cost of design. To make these restrictions and still achieve a final result that is a good trade-off between performance and cost requires a careful choice of the variables to be restricted. Many different schemes have been used, starting at the device level and working up the design abstraction levels through circuit techniques, logic structures to completely pre-defined chip architectures. A few well known examples are:

1. Standardized transistor sizes or ratios
2. Synchronous systems with standard 2-phase or 4-phase clocked elements[3]
3. Standard cells employing standard blocks of functional elements and fixed height rows of interconnect[4]

The standard cell system has the advantage of providing a simple and automatable method of interconnection. This method is interesting because it allows a top–down and a bottom–up design methodology which can generate a "meet in the middle" approach.[5] The elements needed can be optimized for the particular technology, but can also be available at the beginning of the design as the intermediate form to which the top–down process is directed. This methodology has been used widely and successfully by major companies in the USA, Japan and Europe for custom and standard parts as a good compromise between design cost and unit cost. Plate 3.2 shows a microphoto of an early digital standard cell chip design containing approximately 2 000 logic gates. Note the fixed height rows of cells and the "unused" silicon in the wiring channels.

3.1.4 Semi-custom

As was defined earlier, the objective in semi-custom design is to minimize design cost when it is the dominant factor in the equation $C = D + V \cdot U$. The approaches adopted are aimed at reducing design errors and design variables as major contributors to design cost as was described for the full custom approach. The process is taken further by reducing masking costs and associated production time. An added goal is to simplify the design process so that semi-custom designers do not need to be aware, as a full-custom designer must be, of all of the niceties of silicon IC circuit design techniques, and their impact on the final design. The objective in fact is to utilize the available design knowledge of digital system designers with a minimal of retraining for designing ICs.

3.1.5 Gate arrays

Perhaps the most widely used form of semi-custom design over the past 10 years has been the gate array, which consists of rows or arrays of "uncommitted" transistors which are connected into circuits and logical elements by an interconnect pattern.[6] Design cost is reduced by the provision of libraries of elements, and the reduction of mask layers to only those required for the interconnect patterns. The libraries can be stored as "soft macros" which are the interconnect patterns to form particular functions from the available uncommitted transistors. Plate 3.3 shows a microphoto of a gate array using fixed height rows of transistors.

Apart from the mask cost reduction, the design process is not inherently faster or cheaper than a standard cell design with similar sets of library functions and CAD tools. In fact several vendors offer both methodologies and a choice for the customer at a late stage of the design process. Gate arrays for digital circuits continue to be used in far more designs and it is interesting to analyse the reasons.

(a) Mask cost difference.   While gate arrays use two to four masks (two contacts and two layers of metal) typically, standard cells use 10 to 14—say a mask cost difference of eight masks (ΔM) or \$8K − \$12K depending on geometries. As processes line widths shrink, mask costs rise and this difference increases. For the same technology standard cell designs occupy less silicon area than gate arrays and so should have lower unit costs. If the difference in unit cost (U) is \$1 − \$10 then, the cross over point of volume (V_c), above which the standard cell will have lower overall project cost, is given by the relationship

$$V_c = \frac{\Delta M}{\Delta U} \frac{8 \text{ to } 12 \text{ K}}{1 \text{ to } 10} \tag{3.3}$$

i.e. range of volumes 800 units to 12 000 depending on technology gate count, etc. In practice even though today the tools are adequate normally to ensure that in a semi-custom design, the silicon will meet the chip specifications first time, the chip specification is often not right for the system. Consequently two or more sets of mask costs need to be considered to determine the break-even volume. This can prove a strong incentive for the design engineer to choose the gate array solution and minimize the risk of overspending his development budget.

Two other factors are worth considering.

(b) Availability of libraries.   The generation of soft macros is much less time consuming than the generation of "hard macros" or all-layer representations of library elements and so a greater number of complex functions can be made available by a vendor for the same level of expenditure on gate arrays. These complex functions can significantly reduce the time to design a large digital system, particularly if they are in the form of commonly used catalogue parts—familiar to the designer. Thus an important element of learning time can be reduced for a system designer.

(c) Number of vendors and vendor tool investment.   These factors are not always complementary but it is possible for the CAD tools and, indeed, the technology being offered for gate arrays to be in advance of that being offered for other design methodologies.[7] This can distort the picture and give a significant weighting in favour of one particular methodology and indeed may enable it to attract even more development capital. This was the case with gate arrays in the early and mid 1980s and has resulted in a range of denser structures and indeed mixed technology of large "mega functions" as hard wired blocks on the same chip as gate array blocks.[8] These overcome some of the gate array's disadvantages in handling large memory integration efficiently. However, in having to pre-define the memory sizes they lose some of the gate array's flexibility and simplicity.

3.1.6 Analog arrays and tiles

A number of semiconductor companies have offered analog arrays of different levels of components which can be connected together in a user defined pattern by final layers of metalization.[9] The predominant technology used has been bipolar and many vendors have offered soft or hard macros usually called "tiles" of well known analog standard components. This makes the transition to "IC design" as simple as possible. These arrays have primarily served the purpose of providing low complexity analog custom ICs to be used with digital chips, but do not offer a route to VLSI in a mixed analog digital integration because of the limitations of the variety and mix available on any one array and the lack of a dense digital technology on the same chip. BICMOS array solutions should start to address this problem.

3.1.7 Programmable logic

The latest methodology to gain a significant position in IC design is that which employs some form of field programmable element. This enables a particular logical function to be programmed into a device after the manufacturing process.[10] The obvious advantage here is the elimination of mask charges from the design cost and the reduction in design prototyping times. Most of the techniques available involve additional circuitry and suffer in density and performance. They are nevertheless providing a low cost method to designers using semi-custom for parts of their systems—particularly those that need to be finalized at the last minute. They also provide a low cost method of bringing a new product to market quickly.

The catalogue of programmable devices includes:

FPLAs—field programmable logic arrays
PALs—programmable array logics
EPLDs—electrically programmable logic devices
LCAs, PGAs—logic cell arrays, programmable gate arrays

The last two categories encompass a wide spectrum of architectures, process technologies, storage technologies and applications. The earlier PLA architectures have been enhanced with more flexible I/O cells and gate array-like architectures are now available. Both CMOS and bipolar technology is used and programming technologies include EPROM, EEPROM, static memory and various fuses. Electrically programmable logic devices are finding increasing use in systems and are replacing standard logic and gate arrays for the lower end of the gate complexity market.[11] Logic cell arrrays are becoming increasingly popular because of the on-chip static memory, containing the configuration data, which can be loaded or changed on-the-fly.

3.2   Theory of design

3.2.1   Introduction

The number of elements which fit on a single chip and therefore compose an integrated circuit has been rapidly growing in recent years making the task of a chip design more and more difficult. In the present VLSI era, *ad-hoc* methods no longer suffice for chip (or even more, system) design. The development and use of design methodologies has thus become both a necessity and a practice. There are many different aspects of design difficulties, and at least as many opinions how to overcome them. Hence there are many different design methodologies.[12] The following section will present a theoretical background of one of them, although a great deal is applicable to design methodologies in general.

It is possible to identify three basic problems of system design: its complexity, its correctness, and its optimality. The first problem makes a design task harder and causes it to consume more time and money. The second problem involves the risk that the designed product will not be usable because of design errors, and the last raises the issue that some other solution for the requirements could be better in terms of effectiveness, resource consumption, yield, cost or some other parameter. Therefore the main goals of any methodology are to reduce design complexity, guarantee (at least to a certain degree) its correctness, and at least facilitate, if not guarantee, an optimum design.

Complexity is usually defined as the amount of information one encounters when solving a problem.[12] It can be said that this amount depends on the number of objects the problem is composed of, and relations between them. Complexity can be looked upon as either an integral or a difference quantity. In the first case the information involved in the overall design process is considered, and in the second case the information involved in just one portion of the design process (including interface with other portions) is important. Of course, both aspects of complexity must be considered when developing a design methodology, but one of them may have more emphasis placed upon it.

The correctness problem is partly intrinsic to any human endeavour and partly a consequence of complexity. It can be defined as the problem of the conformity of a design with its specification. Of course, this conformity can be unambiguously verified only if both specification and design are formally expressed. Therefore some kind of formalism is necessary, which with its syntax and semantics makes specification and design description unambiguous. As these formalisms are often read by computers, they are usually referred to as design or hardware description languages.[13] Development of these languages often goes hand in hand with the development of design methodologies.

The optimality problem is perhaps the most difficult of the three. It has been satisfactorily solved for smaller classes of problems, but remains unsolved for very broad problem classes. The reason for this is the difficulty in defining the optimality itself. The optimality is formally defined as an objective function which can then be minimized. However, this function depends on many weighted factors which are of a subjective nature and some of which are difficult to formalize. On the other hand, the minimization problem itself can be quite difficult to solve. In addition to classical optimization methods, heuristic and knowledge-based methods have become available in recent time for such tasks.[14]

The large quantities of information which must be handled during a design process and the large numbers of operations which must be carried out necessitate the use of computer tools. These also require the formalism of design descriptions. The development of computerized design tools also closely follows the development of design methodologies. It is possible to divide these tools into two classes. The first class includes those tools which help a human designer solve particular time and memory consuming problems; however, it is still a human designer who governs the main flow of the design process. The second class includes those tools which accept specification of a global problem and yield its solution; their development leads towards so-called "silicon compilers".

The following section is devoted to the description of a methodology which helps a human designer conduct his design process from quite high levels of abstraction down to some basic level which can then be mastered by automatic design tools. The whole design process is divided into design steps and the complexity of any such step is minimized. Also, the correctness of any design step is separately verified such that the correctness of the overall design process can be guaranteed. However, as the methodology does not bound itself to some small class of design problems, the optimality of the design is not addressed; rather this issue is left for the designer's intuition and good sense.

3.2.2 Abstraction and hierarchy

Here, two basic concepts will be described which play important roles in the majority of present-day design methodologies: abstraction and hierarchy.

It has been recognized for a long time that "the most powerful tool available to the human intellect is abstraction".[15] The abstraction principle means that only a limited set of properties of an object are being considered while others are being rejected or neglected (at least for the time being). Abstraction simplifies the object, but it also loses some detail. If some information is added to the object it possesses more detail and becomes less abstract or more concrete; it is said to be at a lower level of abstraction than the original object. So adding information lowers the level of abstraction and vice versa. As a certain object can be considered from different viewpoints it can possess different abstractions.

An abstract object is an abstraction of a set of less abstract objects which are called its implementations or realizations. All these realizations can be said to be equivalent with respect to some abstract property if all of them can be interpreted as the same abstract object. So it can be seen that interpretation is a transformation from a lower to a higher level of abstraction and can be used to establish equivalence of different objects with reference to a more abstract object.

In contrast, hierarchy is a mere structure which, due to its simplicity, is very suitable for solving complex problems. It is a recursive, tree-like structure. The main virtues of such a structure are the following:

1. Relations between components (which are also called nodes in hierarchical terminology) are well defined.
2. Communication between components is limited. As was stated already, the problem of complexity depends on relations between components. In a hierarchical structure complexity is reduced.[12] Limited communication also makes the interface of a component to the rest of system much simpler, which also means that the "divide and conquer" method is much easier to apply.
3. If a component in a hierarchical structure is equipped with the necessary abstractions its descendants need not be considered further and hence the component can be viewed as a leaf in the structure. That is why both hierarchy and abstraction go hand by hand in reducing design complexity. While hierarchy is the syntax of a system, abstraction provides for the semantics of its nodes.

It should, however, be noted that abstraction and hierarchy must be viewed as two distinct concepts. The only kind of abstraction which a node in a hierarchical structure could be said to intrinsically possess is its identity; however, this is a rather philosophical property. Therefore, other abstract views of components will also be needed in system design.

In accordance with the concepts of abstraction and hierarchy, one can treat the levels of abstraction and hierarchy separately. However, they usually coincide and that will be the case in the present text too. Often they will simply be referred to as design levels.

3.3   A design methodology

In this section, a particular methodology will be presented which is based on the above concepts. The important roles of abstraction, implementation and interpretation in a hierarchical design process are especially emphasized.

3.3.1   General principles

The methodological principles which are followed by the presented methodology are:

1. Methodology is hierarchical.
2. Abstraction is widely and intensively used. In conjunction with hierarchy, abstraction is capable of isolating one design level from another.

3. Abstraction of a component is complemented with its implementation. It is required that the abstraction of a component holds no information about the implementation of the component.

4. Design views which are used in design of integrated circuits include structural, functional and geometric views.[16] According to that, any system component may have structural abstraction (which defines how this component can be included in the system), functional abstraction (which determines its behaviour within the system), and, finally, geometric abstraction (which describes its external physical appearance or shape).

5. Components which are used to design an integrated circuit are modules and signals. While the purpose of the former is to receive, store, transform, and generate information, the latter transfer information from one place to another. Structurally speaking, modules are subcircuits, and signals are connections or nodes (in the sense which is used in circuit topology).

6. Modules and signals are designed and structured concurrently and in a similar way; as will be seen soon, the structures of their respective descriptions are very similar, too.

7. Components are defined as types which can be instantiated in implementations. In order to enhance the flexibility and allow for non-essential differences between instances, a type can be parametrized.

3.3.2 Signal description

The description of the signal v is the triple

$$D^v = (A^v, R^v, I^v) \tag{3.4}$$

where A^v, R^v, and I^v are signal abstraction, implementation, and interpretation, respectively.

The abstraction of signal v consists of structural abstraction A_x^v, functional abstraction A_f^v, and geometric abstraction A_g^v. The structural abstraction defines sources and drains of information which can be transferred by the signal. The functional abstraction defines the information model which is the set of values which can be transferred by the signal. When defining the properties of a system or its component, these values are usually of interest as functions of some independent variable, say ξ, which in most cases is time or frequency. The value of signal v as a function of ξ will be called behaviour on that signal and denoted by $v(\xi)$; thus for any value of ξ, $v(\xi) \in A_f^v$ holds.

The set of all possible functions $v(\xi)$ will be denoted as $\{v(\xi)\}$.

And finally, geometric abstraction of a signal determines the external shape of the signal as a connection.

The implementation of the signal v consists of a set of subcomponents R_s^v and the geometric implementation of the signal R_g^v. Subcomponents R_s^v are subsignals, information on which implements the abstract information on the signal. These subsignals cannot communicate among them. Geometric implementation defines implementation in terms of geometric abstractions of subsignals and their relative positions.

Because the subcomponents of the signal cannot communicate among them a designer must explicitly specify how independent information on subsignals is to be interpreted at the abstract level of the signal. Hence the interpretation of the signal is defined as a function which transforms behaviours on subsignals into the abstract behaviour on the signal:

$$I^v : \{R_s^v(\xi)\} \rightarrow \{v(\xi)\} \tag{3.5}$$

3.3.3 Module description

Much like a signal, the description of the module m is the triple

$$D^m = (A^m, R^m, I^m) \tag{3.6}$$

where A^m, R^m, and I^m are module abstraction, implementation and interpretation, respectively.

The abstraction of the module m consists of structural abstraction A_x^m, functional abstraction A_f^m, and geometric abstraction A_g^m. The structural abstraction of a module is the set of its external signals by which it communicates with other modules and which can be input and output signals:

$$A_x^m = V_{ext}^m = V_{in}^m \cup V_{out}^m \tag{3.7}$$

The functional abstraction of the module determines the behaviour of the module on its external signals; hence it is a transformation of behaviour on input signals into behaviour on output signals:

$$A_f^m : \{V_{in}^m(\xi)\} \rightarrow \{V_{out}^m(\xi)\} \tag{3.8}$$

Geometric abstraction defines the external geometrical shape of the module and relative positions of its external signals (including layers where they appear).

The implementation of a module consists of a set of subcomponents R_s^m, module topology R_t^m and its geometric implementation R_g^m. Subcomponents of a module are both submodules and subsignals; topology defines internal interconnection of the module, and geometric implementation defines implementation in terms of geometric abstractions of subcomponents and their relative positions. If the module is a leaf in a hierarchical structure, its geometric implementation will be defined in terms of polygons. It should be emphasized here that module implementation sees implementations of external signals of the module rather than their abstractions.

Let us define the behaviour of the module implementation on subcomponents of its external signals as the function

$$\Phi^m : \{ R_s{}^{V_{in}{}^m}(\xi) \} \rightarrow \{ R_s{}^{V_{out}{}^m}(\xi) \} \tag{3.9}$$

This behaviour can be determined out of subcomponents abstractions and their interconnection by means of analysis or simulation; this transformation is called interpretation of the module:

$$I^m : \{ R_s{}^{V_{ext}{}^m} \} \times \{ R_s{}^m \} \times \{ R_t{}^m \} \rightarrow \{ \Phi \} \tag{3.10}$$

Let us emphasize that, in opposition to interpretation of a signal, interpretation of a module is not defined, but evaluated.

3.3.4 A design step and its correctness

Let us now consider abstractions of a module and its external signals as specification of a local design problem. A solution of this problem will be called a design step which will be carried out in the following way:

1. Implementations and interpretations of external signals are determined and abstractions of their subcomponents are defined.
2. Implementation of the module is determined and abstractions of its subcomponents are defined.
3. The structural, functional and geometric correctness of the design step is verified.

Structural correctness means that external signals of submodules agree in type and direction (input may be connected to drain, output to source, and bidirectional to bidirectional) with internal and external signals of the module.

Functional correctness means that the behaviour of the implemented module is equivalent to its functional abstraction. Of course, both must be compared at the same level of abstraction and that is the level of the specification. Therefore the behaviour of the implemented module must be interpreted at the abstract level before the comparison can be made. Hence, the functional correctness of a design step is defined by the following predicate:

$$A_f{}^m (I{}^{V_{in}{}^m}(R_s{}^{V_{in}{}^m}(\xi))) = I{}^{V_{out}{}^m}(\Phi^m (R_s{}^{V_{in}{}^m}(\xi))) \tag{3.11}$$

where

$$\Phi^m = I^m (R_s{}^{V_{ext}{}^m}, R_s{}^m, R_t{}^m) \tag{3.12}$$

This must be true for any excitation of implemented structure

$$R{}^{V_{in}{}^m}(\xi).$$

Finally, geometrical correctness means that the geometrical implementation fits into geometrical abstraction and that connections of subcomponents are geometrically compatible.

In a design step the following properties can be identified:

1. A component is implemented with a structure of subcomponents, hence a step is made from a higher to a lower level of hierarchy.
2. A step is specified by abstractions of some components and determines abstractions of their subcomponents which are less abstract; hence it is a step from a higher to a lower level of abstraction.
3. From the previous two items one can easily see that such a step is an element of a top–down design process.
4. Interpretation of behaviour on external signals is a transformation from a lower to a higher level of abstraction and enables correctness verification.
5. Because a design step is formally and hence unambiguously specified a designer does not need any knowledge about the higher design levels.
6. Because a design step is carried out exclusively in terms of subcomponents abstractions, and never (including correctness verification) needs their implementations, knowledge of the following design steps is not necessary. The implementation bias of specifications is even deemed harmful.
7. The two preceding facts ensure that a design step can be solved as a stand-alone problem with its complexity being bound to two levels of abstraction.
8. Because all specifications at both levels of abstraction are formal, correctness verification is unambiguously defined.

In this subsection, a very general form of a design step was described. In practice, a lot of flexibility is offered to a designer. So he is free to implement some components in a certain design step and leave others unchanged. For example, he may choose to implement only a few external signals in a design step and to defer implementation of others until later design steps. Also, he is not obliged to conduct geometrical design concurrently with the functional and structural design. Top–down geometrical design is very difficult if area requirements are stringent because it requires accurate area predictions. Structural views are of course central to the design process because they define the design hierarchy, and it is strongly recommended that functional abstractions are also strictly specified as they allow for functional correctness verification.

3.3.5 Design process

The design process is a top–down one and consists of a sequence of design steps which are recursively repeated from the root of the hierarchical design tree down to its leaves. Recursiveness can be seen in the fact that any design step proceeds from specifications at one design level to specifications at a lower level; the latter in turn serve as specifications of the next design step.

A design process begins with the specification of the whole system which means abstractions of the top-level module and its externals signals. These specifications are important for the designer as well as for the customer. However, implementation hierarchies of external signals are usually also meaningful to the customer if not even required by him. Hence it can be seen that the specification of the global design problem may be given in a hierarchical form and at different levels of abstraction. Because these specifications are formal there can be no misunderstanding between the two parties. However, the specifications may not always be easily readable by the customer, so tools must be provided to transform them into a more understandable form; these include analysis and simulation tools, graphic displays, etc. Tools may also be available to transform design data from any design level to the top level, which enables the customer to monitor and possibly cooperate in the design process.

At the other end of the line, the design process ends at the level where further structuring of the system is no longer necessary, and where all components can easily and reliably be implemented in terms of primitive layout data. Usually this is the level where specifications are accepted by automatic design tools such as a silicon compiler.

Between the two limits the design process is a sequence of design decisions taken by the designer which leads him through a space of design abstractions. The design trajectory in this space must not only fulfil the local design goals of particular design steps (i.e. their correctness) but must also achieve as closely as possible the global design goals which are, in addition to the basic correctness requirement, effectiveness, reliability, testability and a low cost of the system.

It is very important that modules and signals can be concurrently designed. This fact allows specifications at all design levels to be simple, readable, and easily understandable. Design complexity can thus be maintained at an approximately constant and reasonably low level throughout the design process. Correctness verification which is carried out concurrently with the design decisions minimizes the risk of bad decisions leading to non-optimum solutions, and therefore reduces loops in the design process.

3.4   The impact of simulators on design methodology

3.4.1   Introduction

As described in Section 3.1, design methodology is driven by prevailing market forces, and the available technology. In this context, technology is a combination of manufacturing and design capabilities. In terms of manufacturing, the fabrication processes with their associated structures, e.g. MOS, BIPOLAR, BICMOS, etc. are characterized by the specialized steps which define process geometries. These in turn define the available devices and interconnection possibilities, which then define the complexities and performances of VLSI designs that can be accomplished. In order to exploit this manufacturing technology there must be a corresponding "design technology" which can predict the performance of a completed design and provide a method to verify that the design meets its specification.

Predicting design performance has been enhanced by the use of CAD tools, as described in "Design accuracy", Section 3.1.3. Simulators have become the major CAD tool used in this area. Once a preliminary design has been completed, the next step is to simulate the design before any physical implementation takes place. If the simulation results conform to the desired performance, a physical implementation (layout) will then be attempted. Parasitics added during the physical implementation will be extracted and fed back to the simulator to verify that the design performance was not impaired by the physical realization. The design verification is the conformance of the simulation results to the system requirements.

Obviously the accuracy and the completeness of simulation and the results comparison is of paramount importance for design prediction and verification. As a designer must view the circuit differently to satisfy the different aspects of the specification, different simulation models are needed. Those models have led to different classes of simulators which can be broadly classified as digital, analog and mixed analog digital. A single simulator which handles each specific simulation task equally well does not appear to be commercially available today. There are good analog simulators, good digital simulators and several good mixed A/D simulators, but compromises must be made if one simulator is to be used outside of its main functional area. This unfortunately increases the modelling problem and the risk of incorrect interpretation of simulation results.

3.4.2 Digital simulation

Traditionally, the task of logic verification was carried out by building a "bread-board". This in itself was often difficult to design, build and verify. Further, it was not a guarantee that the IC implementation would function because assumptions had to be made in converting the bread-board logic. With the introduction of computing power to the IC design environment, techniques for modelling logic design in software were developed, and designers began to substitute logic simulation for bread-board building.

The early logic simulators were able to model only a limited number of structures, mainly logic gate functions. Frequently they had difficulties in modelling some of the widely used MOS circuit structures. Typically, the MOS "transmission gate" caused difficulties. This structure, illustrated in Fig.3.3, is a simple MOS device. When turned "ON" it acts as a low resistor, and when "OFF" as a high resistor. As a low resistor, it can pass signals in both directions. This complication was not easy to solve in a logic level model. A new type of simulator called a "switch level" was used which considered each transistor as a switch having finite properties.[17] It introduced the meaning of "strength" into logic simulation. Newer simulators began to have more "states". Thus a three level simulator had "HI", "LO" and "UNKNOWN" states. At least these enhancements allowed the designer to see a potential problem. The disadvantage was that if something was wrong, then the entire network would end up in an unknown state. This made the debug process very difficult.

More levels of strength were introduced, and today we have simulators handling 12 levels and more. Fig.3.4 shows the 12 states of the digital simulator *Silos* supplied by DAISY-CADNETICS. Using these tools, the designer can see the difference between a floating node and a node driven into an indeterminate state by two conflicting signals.

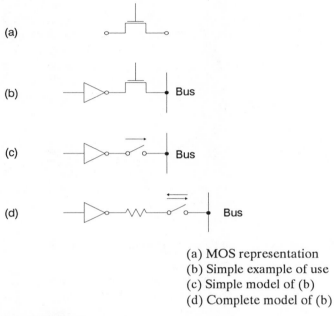

(a)

(b)   Bus

(c)   Bus

(d)   Bus

(a) MOS representation
(b) Simple example of use
(c) Simple model of (b)
(d) Complete model of (b)

Fig. 3.3 MOS transmission gate

	Supply	Driving	Resistive	High-Z
High	S1	D1	R1	Z1
Unknown	S*	D*	R*	Z*
Low	S0	D0	R0	Z0

Fig. 3.4 Typical 12-state logic simulator

About the same time as these enhancements were developed, designers wanted to include some time model of the electrical performance. The early simulators were "unit delay" simulations where all the signals appeared one "time clock" after the stimulus which caused the change. Within the IC design, the engineer is free to design logic elements to give the required performance (within the bounds of the technology). Simulators which could account for the time delay associated with logic elements were introduced. At first, these simulators required integer units of time delay attributed to each logic element. Fig.3.5 shows an example. Load-dependent delays were then introduced. These calculate the fan out of a logic element and derive the delay according to a predefined formula—as shown in Fig.3.6.

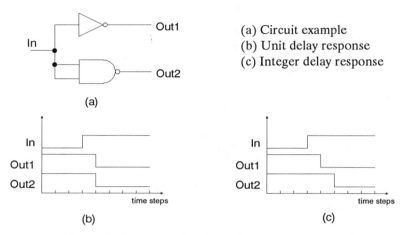

(a) Circuit example
(b) Unit delay response
(c) Integer delay response

(a)

(b)

(c)

Fig. 3.5 Difference between unit delay and integer delay simulation

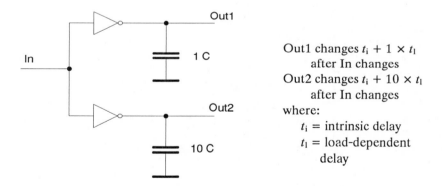

Out1 changes $t_i + 1 \times t_l$
after In changes
Out2 changes $t_i + 10 \times t_l$
after In changes
where:
   t_i = intrinsic delay
   t_l = load-dependent
      delay

Fig. 3.6 Load-dependent delays

All these features make the modern logic simulator a complex program and execution times can be long. Speed improvement techniques have been used to improve simulator performance. One such technique is to use an event-driven algorithm for network simulation. The principle here is to calculate the new output of a logic element only if one of its inputs has changed, rather than to recalculate the outputs of all logic elements in the network at each time step.

The digital simulator has done a great deal to ensure that digital VLSI circuits can be designed with predictable performance. Many products are commercially available. A recent survey of logic simulators is given in Ref.18.

To address the problem of long run times, several companies have developed "accelerators", which are pieces of specialized hardware designed to implement the logic simulation algorithm very efficiently. The performance increase achieved using accelerators ranges from about 10 times faster comparing a 3–4 MIP dedicated mainframe to a minimum configuration accelerator, to about 300 times faster comparing a 1 MIP shared mainframe to a medium powered accelerator.

A high powered accelerator can process more than 10 million events per second, giving a 1000 clock simulation of a 100 000 gate system in less than 10 seconds.

Because of the parallel nature of this processing, the hardware costs are high. A hardware accelerator is generally only suitable for the purpose of logic simulation. The financial justification for a simulation accelerator thus requires a large number of simulation events. With the use of fault simulation (see Chapter 8) the number of events which need to be simulated increases dramatically, thus bringing the justification to a lower level.

As circuit densities have increased, the number of logic elements possible within a given silicon area has also increased. This has compounded the problem of logic verification. To address this, techniques developed in specialist system applications have been added to the tools used for IC design. These are the use of higher level models and simulators known as functional and behavioural simulators. Examples of behavioural simulators are *ELLA* from Praxis and *HELIX* from Silvar Lisco. Such simulators return to a less detailed or more abstracted model of the final solution, but are capable of handling larger functions of the system. Hence a simple logic circuit will simulate very quickly, or a complex circuit will simulate in a reasonable time without having to resort to very high computer power or simulation accelerators.

Behavioural simulators are very useful for developing concepts of logical structures. Many different design solutions can be tried and compared before investing in the detailed logic design.

The disadvantage of behavioural simulators is that any detail added into the behaviour, e.g. logic levels, delay times, signal strength, etc. complicate the model. This adds time to developing the model and adds time to simulating the performance.

In summary, there are a number of different options open to the designer to assist in the task of proving the logic design. It must be emphasized that each method has strengths and weaknesses. It is the skill of the designer that is needed to choose the correct simulation techniques to match the problem being addressed. Frequently more than one form of simulation will be required for the digital part of a design. This is before one considers the circuit aspects, mixed analog digital sections or switched-capacitor simulations.

3.4.3 Analog simulation

In the bottom–up design methodology described in Section 3.1.2, the individual cells (whether analog or digital) must be designed in terms of transistor sizes and resistor and capacitor values. Normally, the design engineer uses some method to arrive at an initial solution. These methods vary from "hand" calculations, graphs or charts or even a simple CAD program which uses a simple model to calculate the important parameters. Having obtained an approximate design, the engineer uses his intuition and experience to verify the design. At this point, the use of a circuit analysis program is required to check all aspects of the design, and to allow for parasitic effects ignored by the simpler analysis.

By far the most commonly used circuit analysis program for IC design is SPICE (Simulation Program with Integrated Circuit Emphasis—developed by the University of California at Berkeley) or one of its derivatives. This type of simulator generates simulated waveforms and applies them to transistor level models of the circuit. The simulator analyses the analog characteristics of the circuit, such as voltage-over-time, frequency, noise and temperature. The simulator works by solving differential equations for individual circuit nodes using matrix inversion techniques. It makes successive approximations until it converges on a solution. Such simulations are accurate but slow. Consequently, in practice runs are limited to circuits of less than 100 transistors. Ref.19 gives a current survey of circuit analysis programs and their relative performance.

The use of SPICE can be an art in itself. On the surface, the circuit is captured (either with a keyboard and netlist or through a schematic capture program) and then analysed. For circuits consisting of MOS or BIPOLAR transistors acting as switches, and circuits not containing feedback, this is indeed true. However, as circuit designers are required to meet higher performance, and in circuits where the MOS transistor is not primarily acting as a switch the task of analysing the circuit becomes much more difficult. A great deal of skill and experience can then be needed in order to converge on a solution in a reasonable period of time. Indeed, there has been a book published recently solely on the use of SPICE.[20] In addition an excellent section on the use of SPICE for simulating analog circuits is contained in Ref.21.

3.4.4 Mixed A/D simulation

Having designed the system "top–down" and the individual cells "bottom–up", the remaining task is to see that the circuit will function properly in the mixed analog digital mode.

The problem for mixed analog digital simulations is either to extend the level of complexity of digital simulators to have enough accuracy to model analog circuits, or alternatively to speed up analog simulation to model complex digital circuits in a reasonable time. Currently there are three approaches to solving this problem:

The first is to use two separate simulators—one digital and one analog and to control the interaction between the two. This is referred to as "glue-simulation".[22] Generally the simulators are loosely coupled so that the output of one can drive the input of the other.

Any mixed-mode simulation that models feedback between analog and digital sections, must synchronize the time steps of the analog simulation with the event queue that drives the digital simulation. This is normally accomplished with a handshaking protocol that coordinates the two separate simulators.

It is in the control of this interaction that problems can arise with this technique, e.g. if both simulators are running at the same time an important event in one may not be observed from it while attention is focused on an event in the other. To help overcome this problem some vendors now provide the ability to step back in simulation time to observe particular nodes. Vendors currently offering tools based on the "glue-simulation" approach include Viewlogic, Daisy Systems and Mentor Graphics.

The second approach extends either a digital simulator to handle analog models, usually at a behavioural level or extends an analog simulator to handle gate-level digital models. This can be done with any digital simulator that provides a behavioural modelling language. Examples of this type of simulator are "MIXsim" from Sierra Semiconductor which supports its company's libraries of cells and "Salt" from the CAD Group of Santa Cruz California, which is more general purpose and supports a broad analog modelling capability. It must be remembered in using this class of simulator that the behavioural analog models cannot give the accuracy of SPICE. Consequently, SPICE level simulations must be performed where appropriate, e.g. especially to evaluate transients at the analog digital interface—which, of course, can be a significant problem in mixed designs.

The third approach is to write a new simulator specifically to handle the problem. This has been called the "unified approach" and is based on a tightly coupled set of algorithms that can handle both analog and digital circuitry.[22] "Andi" from Silvar-Lisco is the most mature of these products. It provides a functional time domain simulation for mixed analog digital designs. It is not as accurate as SPICE for analog but better than a switch level logic simulator. It has been successfully used by IMP for several years to give a good verification of the analog digital interface. Andi is currently limited in that it provides only one level of modelling of analog and digital elements. An example of a unified approach that supports a range of modelling is LSIM from Silicon Compiler Systems. LSIM is a collection of algorithms synchronized with one event-driven timing queue. It includes gate and behavioural level logic simulation, circuit simulation and probabilistic fault grading. A SPICE-based simulator "LSPICE" has been added to this collection of algorithms, as has "HSPICE", a very accurate commercial derivative of SPICE supplied by Metasoftware.

Another simulator offering a range of modelling options is "Saber" from Analogy. It can model most electrical and even some mechanical phenomena up to a behavioural level and runs an order of magnitude faster than SPICE. Saber is not yet a mixed-mode simulator, but can represent time and state information explicitly in models. This is useful in A/D and D/A converters and transmission lines. It also facilitates the transfer of analog information to a digital simulator.

It will be seen from the foregoing discussion that a wide variety of mixed analog digital simulators are becoming commercially available with very different capabilities. The choice depends on the types of problems which need investigation, the modelling available or ease of modelling new components and the links to the rest of the tools being used in the design methodology.

3.4.5 How to design with accuracy in mind

In order to produce an IC design that works first time the design methodology must be able, as was mentioned earlier, to predict the performance and verify that it meets the specification. In complex VLSI designs the prediction and verification are not single steps, but multiple repetitions of a very disciplined set of comparisons. Fig.3.7 shows a complex design flow in which a design is developed from an overall system specification by a number of design steps. After each step the design is simulated or evaluated and results are compared with the specification.

Several issues arise from an analysis of this process:

1. For VLSI designs the design process is complex and the number of comparisons and iterations around one comparison loop is large. Some procedures or tools are needed to keep track of or manage the design process, e.g. for revision control, especially if more than one designer is involved. Such "design managers" are becoming available as DA tools and can provide invaluable audit trails. Ref.23 describes a design file tracking system developed by AT&T.
2. Each simulation step gives a particular window or view into the performance of the final device, the accuracy of which is dependent on the models used. It is obviously important that there should be consistency between the models used at different levels of simulation. Also when "entering" or "capturing" the complete circuit special care must be taken to avoid ambiguous or incomplete representations.
3. The development of input patterns and waveforms is an important and time consuming task in the performance prediction and verification phase. In many cases these must also be "models" of the actual signals. This must be done carefully to simulate the actual system. These patterns can later be used as the test patterns for testing prototypes and production devices. This is discussed further in Chapter 8.
4. The design complexity problem is contained by the use of library elements that are well characterized and modelled or by the use of module generators that enable new

functions to be generated, but limit the detailed design skills needed. These are described in Chapters 4 and 5.

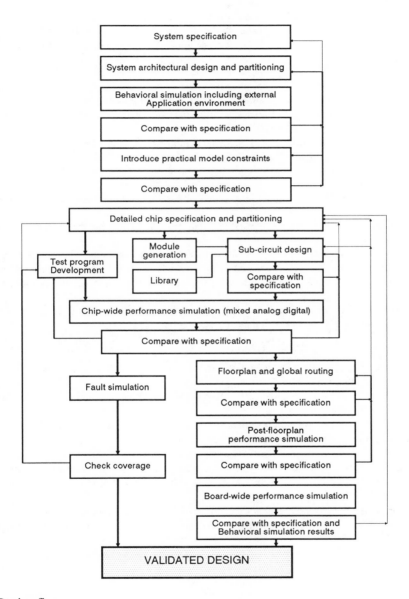

Fig. 3.7 Design flow

References

1. Mead, C.A., VLSI and technological innovations, *VLSI'81*, ed. Gray, J., Academic Press, London, 1981.
2. *Design Methodologies*, ed. Goto, S., North-Holland, Amsterdam, 1986.
3. *MOS Integrated Circuits*, ed. Penney, W.M., L. Lau Van Nostrand Reinhold Co., 1972.
4. Donze, R. and Sporzynski, G., Masterimage approach to VLSI design, *Computer*, pp.18–25, Dec. 1983.
5. Man, H. de, Rabaey, J., Six, P., Claesen, L., Cathedral II — a silicon compiler for DSP, IMEC, *IEEE Design and Test*, pp.13–25, December 1986.
6. Hicks, P.J., *Semi-Custom IC Design and VLSI*, Peter Peregrinus Ltd, London, 1983.
7. Anderson, F., Ford, J., A 0.5 micron 150K channel-less gate array, *Proceedings of the IEEE 1987 CICC*, Portland, Oregon, 1987
8. Chan, T. *et al.*, Advanced structured arrays combine high density memories with channel free logic array, *Proceedings of the IEEE 1987 CICC*, Portland, Oregon, 1987.
9. Analog arrays and circuit techniques — Session, *Proceedings of the IEEE 1987 CICC*, Portland, Oregon, 1987.
10. User programmable logic devices — Session, *Proceedings of the IEEE 1988 CICC*, Rochester, New York, 1988.
11. Most systems don't need many gated semi-custom, *The Technology Research Group letter*, February 1986.
12. Niessen, C., Abstraction requirements in hierarchical design methods, in Ref. 3.2, pp.151–82.
13. *Hardware Description Languages*, ed. Hartenstein, R.W., North-Holland, Amsterdam, 1987.
14. *Proceedings of International Workshop on AI-Applications to CAD-Systems for Electronics*, Munich, 1987.
15. Hoare, C.A.R., Notes on data structuring, In Dahl, O.J., Dijkstra, E.W., Hoare, C.A.R., *Structured Programming*, pp. 83–174, Academic Press, London, 1972.
16. Gajski, D.D., Kuhn, R.H., Guest editors' introduction: New VLSI tools, *IEEE Computer*, **Vol. 16**, (12), pp. 11–14, Dec. 1983.
17. Bryant, R.E., A switch-level model of MOS logic circuits, *VLSI '81*, ed. Gray, J., p.329, Academic Press, London, 1981.
18. 1988 Survey of logic simulators, *VLSI System Design*, p.50, CMP Publications Inc., Manhasset, New York, Feb. 1988.
19. Barros, G., A survey of circuit simulation programs, *VLSI Systems Design*, p.32, CMP Publications Inc., Manhasset, New York, July 1986.
20. *Semiconductor Device Modelling with* Spice, ed. Antognetti, P., McGraw-Hill, 1988.
21. Allen, P. and Holberg, D., *CMOS Analog Circuit Design*, Holt, Rinehart and Winston Inc., 1987.
22. Coering, R., A full range of solutions emerge to handle mixed-mode simulation, *Computer Design*, p.57, 1 Feb. 1988.
23. Mahmood, Z., Singer, D., Singhel, A., Wu, K., A design data management system for CAD, *Proceedings of International Conference on CAD*, p.220, IEEE Computer Society, Santa Clara, CA, 1987.

4. Design and layout techniques for high performance analog subcircuits

4.1 Introduction

An analog circuit's performance is often strongly dependent on its physical layout, much more so than a typical digital circuit. A mixed analog digital circuit can pose serious difficulties because of this layout dependence and because of potentially undesirable interactions between the digital and the analog parts.

The design and layout automation of high performance and layout-sensitive functional blocks has not yet reached a mature state. Because of this the experienced analog designer and the skilled analog layout expert both play key roles in a successful analog or mixed analog digital design project.

Unfortunately there are too few experienced analog designers and their expertise is not well documented, nor is it supported by appropriate design tools. This situation is changing slowly towards a more systematic design approach with the use of expert system design tools which allow the designer to spend more time on the creative system design and circuit development.

This chapter is devoted to a description of some of the more important analog design and layout techniques. The emphasis is on a systematic design approach which can be automated to some extent, while still allowing the designer to guide the design to the final goal. This is a design and layout methodology which will allow the less experienced IC designer, in most cases the system engineer, to create his own complex analog and mixed analog digital integrated circuits.

The most common analog integrated circuit building elements are resistors, capacitors and transistors. In the present design methodology these elements are compiled into physical layout composites called "primitive cells". When designing such primitive integrated circuit components it is important to bear in mind their actual characteristics compared with discrete devices.

The design procedure is in both cases a compromise between cost and performance where usually neither cost nor performance is simply or well defined. With some simplification the performance of a primitive cell can be characterized by its:

1. Accuracy
2. Stability (long and short term)
3. Sensitivity to power supply variations, temperature and other environmental changes
4. Power consumption
5. Presence of parasitics

to name just a few of the most important parameters. The cost of an integrated primitive cell is a function of its size, i.e. occupied silicon area. However, fabrication yield is the dominant parameter, which is itself a function of chip size and design quality. This last factor is particularly important for high performance analog functional blocks.

A very significant portion of the cost of a particular integrated function is determined by its testability and related test time. These issues are discussed in greater detail in Chapter 7 and Chapter 8.

4.2   Properties of integrated circuit components

4.2.1   Disadvantages of integrated circuit components

Primitive elements of integrated circuits have many disadvantages compared to discrete electronic components. The most serious disadvantage is the poor absolute tolerance of their electrical characteristics, as is shown in Tables 4.1, 4.2 and 4.3 where some of the characteristics are summarized for integrated resistors, capacitors and transistors. As can be seen from these tables, the integrated components suffer not only from poor absolute tolerances but also from large temperature coefficients.

Another disadvantage of integrated components is the small range of useful electrical values. This is true for both large integrated capacitors and large integrated resistors.

Table 4.1 Integrated capacitors available in analog CMOS process

Capacitor type	Typical capacitance per $1\,\mu m^2$	Absolute tolerance	Relative tolerance	Voltage coefficient	Cost: silicon circa per 1 pF	Usable range
Metal - SiO_2 – diffusion	0.6 $fF/\mu m^2$	± 15 %	0.1 % – 1 %	–20 ppm/V	1660 μm^2	0.5 pF – 1000 pF
Poly silicon – SiO_2 – poly silicon	0.6 $fF/\mu m^2$	± 15 %	0.1 % – 1 %	–10 ppm/V	1660 μm^2	0.5 pF – 1000 pF
Poly silicon – (SiO_2 – nitride) – poly silicon	0.7 $fF/\mu m^2$	± 15 %	0.1 % – 1 %	–3 ppm/V	1420 μm^2	0.5 pF – 1000 pF

Table 4.2 Integrated resistors available in analog CMOS process

Resistor type	Typical resistance per square	Minimal square	Absolute tolerance	Relative tolerance	Absolute temperature coefficient	Voltage coefficient	Cost: silicon area per 1 kΩ	Usable range
Poly silicon (not in boron area)	15 – 25 Ω	3 x 3 μm	± 30 %	0.1 – 1 %	0.0173 Ω/sq./°C 800 ppm/°C	very small	800 μm²	10 Ω – 100 kΩ ***
Diffusion	20 – 80 Ω	3 x 3 μm	± 30 %	0.5 – 5 %	0,0322 - 0.0770 Ω/sq./°C 2000 ppm/°C	large	500 – 800 μm²	10 Ω – 100 kΩ ***
P-well (field)	2 – 10 kΩ	8 x 8 μm	± 50 %	1 – 10 %	0.0616 Ω/sq./°C 12 000 ppm/°C	2 %/V *	32 μm²	2 k – 5 MΩ
Transistor as resistor	---	---	± 80 %	1 – 10 %	--- 4000 – 7000 ppm/°C **	very large	100 μm²	---
SiCr	0.5 – 1 kΩ	2 x 2 μm	± 10 %	0.1 – 0.5 %	0.5 Ω/sq./°C 50 ppm/°C	very small	8 μm²	0.5 k – 2 MΩ

* voltage dependent
** temperature dependent
*** contact resistivity dependence limit

Table 4.3 Integrated transistors available in analog CMOS process

Transistor type	Transconductance g_m (saturation) at $I_d = 10\,\mu A$	k' (β) $k' = \gamma \cdot C_{ox}$	f_T	Absolute tolerance at 20 °C k' (β)	Absolute tolerance V_T (V_{BE}) I = const.
3 μm p-well analog process					
N-MOS $W = 4\,\mu m, L = 3\,\mu m$	24 μS	43 μA/V²		± 20 %	± 100 mV
P-MOS $W = 4\,\mu m, L = 3\,\mu m$	15 μS	16 μA/V²		± 20 %	± 200 mV
NPN Common collector	400 μS at 25 °C	500	1 GHz	± 100 %	± 50 mV
1.2 μm n-well analog process					
N-MOS $W = 4\,\mu m, L = 1.5\,\mu m$	45 μS	70 μA/V²		± 20 %	± 200 mV
P-MOS $W = 4\,\mu m, L = 1.5\,\mu m$	26 μS	25 μA/V²		± 20 %	± 200 mV
NPN	400 μS	100	1.1 GHz	± 100 %	± 50 mV

4.2.2 Advantages of integrated circuit components

Apart from their smaller size the most important advantage of integrated circuit components is the better relative or matching accuracy of their electrical parameters. A matching accuracy between 0.05 per cent and 0.1 per cent can be achieved by observing some simple design and layout rules as will be explained later.

The next significant advantage of integration is the smaller influence of parasitic effects, which can be controlled by design and layout techniques. This fact allows the realization of circuits which are not in practice possible with discrete components. A good example of this is switched-capacitor circuits. These circuits cover broad applications ranging from S–C filters, to A/D and D/A converters and closed loop amplifiers.[1]

Another advantage of integrated components is the possibility of designing for almost any electrical value of component (in its useful range). The only restriction upon the component value is imposed by the grid of the layout which can be very fine. On the other hand the designer has two degrees of freedom by varying the x and y dimensions of the device.

4.3   Matching of integrated circuit components

The most important design and layout techniques are based on the close matching of the circuit components. In practice this means that a circuit has to be designed so that its performance depends on the component ratios rather than on their absolute electrical values.

The first and most important rule for the layout of matched circuit elements is the composition of the network from a number of equal elements with unity value called unity cells. If the ratio of circuit elements is created with equal unity cells in each element, the designer can neglect any inaccuracies of the three dimensional physical device structures resulting from the computed two dimensional device layout. During the fabrication process involving photolithography and silicon processing, the actual device dimensions can vary several tenths of a micrometer from the calculated value of device geometry in the layout database. If the device ratios were based on non-equal structures, these errors could easily contribute as much as 10 per cent of the total mismatch.

The other possible cause of a large mismatch error in a layout which does not use the unity cell approach is the use of inaccurate and simple device models which neglect the three dimensional effects of the integrated devices. This is true also for such simple elements as resistors and capacitors. Non-uniform behaviour of these devices caused by the discontinuity at the edges of the structures is usually not fully characterized nor adequately modelled.

The influence of parasitic capacitances and parasitic resistances of the interconnections and contacts among different levels of interconnections can be the source of gross matching errors if the layout is not based on unity cells. On the other hand if the unity cell approach is correctly utilized, the results can be very insensitive to this type of parasitic.

The following rules should be observed when the unity cell approach is used:

1. Use the same cell orientation. Mask making and photolithography can be sensitive to the cell orientation. In addition the device characteristics may vary with the cell orientation relative to the substrate crystal structure. The transistor pair shown in Plate 4.1(a) using the same unity transistor cells, but placed in different orientations, can exhibit larger mismatches than the same structures oriented in the same direction as shown in Plate 4.1(b).

2. Use the centroid or interleaved cell placement wherever possible. Usually there exists an average gradient of electrical characteristics of the devices across a silicon die. Centroid cell placement helps to minimize this effect. Plate 4.2 is an example of centroid placement of a transistor pair. This placement is normally used to minimize the input offset-voltage of operational amplifier differential stages and for close capacitor and resistor matching. Plate 4.3 shows an interleaved structure of polysilicon resistors which observes this rule.

3. Provide consistent cell borders to avoid the "neighbour effect". The etching rate in photolithography depends among other things also on the pattern being etched. The cells at the border will etch differently from the cells in the middle. Plate 4.4 shows a precision switched-capacitor structure used for S–C filters. Automatic generation of this macrocell introduced both dummy capacitor cells (not connected capacitors) and the border structures to provide the same neighbour pattern for all unity cells.

4. Create correct non-unity cells. When the required ratio is not a whole number, the non-unity cell should be scaled to the required relative value (dimensions) between 1 and 2. It is important also that the parasitics are scaled accordingly. Plate 4.5 shows an example of a computer generated non-unity capacitor cell with a value of 1.432 units.

In this case the area-to-periphery ratio is kept the same as in a unity capacitor cell. (Because of the three dimensional nature of the capacitor structure the total capacitance is the sum of the perimeter capacitance and the area capacitance.) The interconnecting metal is scaled according to the capacitor's relative value. This approach guarantees that both parasitics are scaled proportionally to the non-unity value.

4.4 Automation of matched primitive cell layout generation

In this section the generalized algorithms for automatic matched cell generation are presented. The automatic matched cell generation module can be used as a stand-alone program for the generation of macrocells composed of matched primitive cells, i.e. resistors, capacitors, transistors, etc. Such primitive cells are used as building blocks in the synthesis of complex analog functions. In this case the matched primitive cell layout compilation program module is incorporated into the synthesis program. The following are the basic steps which form the algorithms for the matched cell generation:

1. Primitive cell topology generation
2. Identification of cell descriptors
3. Selection of unity cell type
4. Unity cell value calculation and layout compilation
5. Non-unity cell value calculation and layout compilation
6. Placement of the cells
7. Internal interconnecting within the primitive cell

Primitive cell topology generation can be performed either automatically using a circuit synthesis program or it can be entered manually using a schematic capture program or a simulation file. Cell descriptors are electrical or topological values determining the cell performances. They can in some cases be deterministically calculated from the input data provided by the designer, while in other cases their values are estimated on the basis of process statistics or the designer's experience.

The deterministic descriptors are W/L values for transistors if their operating point is given, the number of squares for resistors if the resistor value is known and capacitor area for capacitors if the absolute capacitance value is known. The descriptors are also the requested ratio accuracy, voltage and temperature coefficients, predicted offset-voltage for transistors, current density, leakage current, parasitics, etc. They determine the unity cell type on the basis of the closest matching between the requested descriptors and available cell structures in the library.

When the cell type is selected the required unity value is calculated and the requested cell is automatically sized and entered into the user's database. The same procedure is followed for the non-unity cells. Various algorithms are used for cell placement, normally using an interleaved or centroid placement method. The final step is to interconnect the cells. It is required that the interconnecting parasitics are equal for all unity cells while the interconnecting parasitics of the non-unity cells must be scaled according to the non-unity values for the best matching results.

4.5   Design and layout of integrated resistor networks

Integrated resistors in analog circuits are considered to be very expensive elements. The reason for this is that in most processes developed mainly for digital applications the resistors are side products and are not specifically designed to be used as resistors. They do not have favourable ratios of resistor value to area. Depending on type they can exhibit large voltage and temperature coefficients and their absolute accuracy is usually very poor (see Table 4.2).

The selection of a resistor type is always a trade off between cost and performance. It is evident that wherever possible the designer should replace resistors by some other circuit element or technique (in most cases switched-capacitors). Nevertheless there are situations where the use of resistors results in a superior circuit performance or a more elegant design. Integrated resistors are mandatory for applications such as continuous time analog circuits. They have much better performance regarding noise and bandwidth characteristics when compared with discrete time solutions.

Another area in which integrated resistors are often utilized is D/A and A/D converters. Designing with integrated resistors is basically similar to traditional analog design using discrete resistors. The difference is that the facts presented in Table 4.2 and a knowledge of resistors layouts must also be born in mind. An algorithm for an expert system assisting the designer to synthesize and compile integrated resistor networks is shown in Fig.4.1.

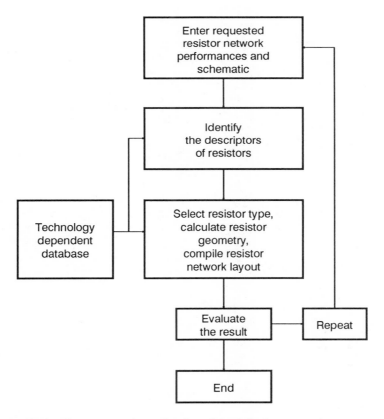

Fig. 4.1 Integrated resistor network synthesis and compilation procedure

As illustrated in Fig.4.1 the system assists the designer in the following:

1.   It summarizes and formalizes the resistor network characteristics.
2.   In the second step it provides a general technology independent description
     of the requested characteristic, i.e. it generates the descriptors table.
3.   In the third step the optimal resistor type is selected. Resistor geometry is calculated and
     the resistor layout is compiled.

To illustrate the procedure consider an example of using the program module to create a resistor network cell in a $3\,\mu$m analog CMOS process.

The first step, i.e. the schematic entry of the resistor network is shown in Fig.4.2.

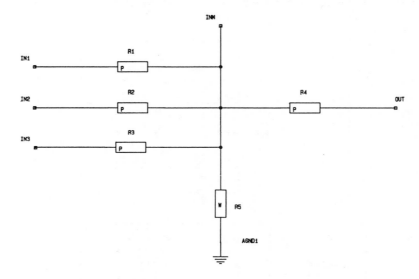

Fig. 4.2 Resistor network cell

The following resistor ratios are required:

$R_1 = 0.741\, R_4$
$R_2 = 3.185\, R_4$
$R_3 = 1.729\, R_4$
$R_5 = 10\, R_4$
Ratio tolerance $R_1, R_2, R_3, R_4 = 0.5$ per cent
Absolute value $R_4 = 10\,k\Omega$
Absolute tolerance $R_4 = \pm 30$ per cent
Absolute value $R_5 = 100\,k\Omega$
Absolute tolerance $R_5 = \pm 50$ per cent

Maximum voltage swing: 1 V
Substrate potential: +5 V
Temperature range: −30 °C to +90 °C

In the second step the following descriptors were identified for the network:

Resistor R_1: clustered ratio
$I_{max} = 19 \cdot 10^{-6}$ A
Temperature range: −30 °C to + 90 °C
Parasitic capacitance: don't care
Tolerance: 0.5 per cent
Resistor nominal value: 7 410 Ω
Resistor leakage current: 10^{-10} A
Shielding: yes, AGND1

Resistor R_2: clustered ratio
$I_{max} = 19 \cdot 10^{-6}$ A
Temperature range: −30 °C to +90 °C
Parasitic capacitance: don't care
Tolerance: 0.5 per cent
Resistor nominal value: 31 850 Ω
Resistor leakage current: 10^{-10} A
Shielding: yes, AGND1

Resistor R_3: clustered ratio
$I_{max} = 19 \cdot 10^{-6}$ A
Temperature range: −30 °C to +90 °C
Parasitic capacitance: don't care
Tolerance: 0.5 per cent
Resistor nominal value: 17 290 Ω
Resistor leakage current: 10^{-10} A
Shielding: yes, AGND1

Resistor R_4: clustered ratio
$I_{max} = 19 \cdot 10^{-6}$ A
Temperature range: −30 °C to +90 °C
Parasitic capacitance: don't care
Tolerance: 0.5 per cent
Resistor nominal value: 10 000 Ω
Resistor leakage current: 10^{-10} A
Shielding: yes, AGND1

Resistor R_5: ratioless
V_{max}: 1 V
Temperature range: −30 °C to +90 °C
Parasitic capacitance: don't care
Tolerance: 50 per cent
Resistor nominal value: 100 kΩ
Resistor leakage current: $0.1 \cdot 10^{-6}$ A
Shielding: no

In the next step descriptors (tolerance, absolute value, maximum voltage, leakage, and shielding) determine the resistor type. When the resistor type is selected the minimal resistor width is calculated, based mostly on the requested tolerance, given technology and design rules. The selected technology is 3 μm P-well analog CMOS process.

After this the total resistor length is calculated and finally it is broken into a whole number of unity resistors. If this cannot be achieved because the unity resistor cell requested is impractically small, a good approximation can be achieved by spreading the non-unity value using small deviations from the nominal unity value resistors as shown in the example. Resistors

R_1, R_2, R_3, R_4 are selected to be polysilicon resistors types while the resistor R_5 is made a P-well type.

Minimum width for poly resistors is 4 μm for the given tolerance, as seen from technology database (Table 4.4). However, the selected width was 6 μm to compensate for parasitic contact resistance variations. Plate 4.6 shows the compiled layout of the cell. For the final evaluation a report on the achieved characteristics is given as well as files, which can be used for simulation or further processing, including placement, routing and layout versus schematic verification.

Table 4.4 Resistor technology table

Minimum resistance per square	Maximum resistance per square	Minimum resistor width	Maximum current density	Parasitic contact resistance	
				3 x 3 (μm^2)	4 x 4 (μm^2)
15 Ω	28 Ω	3 μm	0.2 mA/μm	2 – 15 Ω	1 – 4 Ω

W	Capacitance to substrate per kΩ (pF/kΩ)	Voltage coefficient	Leakage current	Temperature coefficient	Ratio tolerance
3 μm	---	very small	NA	800 ppm/°C	0.8 %
4 μm	0.035 pF/kΩ	very small	NA	800 ppm/°C	0.5 %
6 μm	0.080 pF/kΩ	very small	NA	800 ppm/°C	0.2 %
10 μm	0.225 pF/kΩ	very small	NA	800 ppm/°C	0.1 %

It is important to note that the layout compilation also takes into account the interconnecting parasitic resistance which occurs mainly at the contacts and interconnecting bridges. This interconnecting resistance is calculated on the basis of the requested tolerance. If this is not met during the phase of layout generation the procedure has to be repeated.

4.6 Matched capacitor network layout synthesis

The majority of matched capacitor network applications are in the domain of switched-capacitor circuits. These circuits are very popular because integrated capacitors can achieve a matching ratio accuracy in the order of 0.1 per cent. In addition the associated charge redistribution techniques usually require much less power consumption than continuous time solutions.

These advantages make switched-capacitor circuits very attractive, even though they suffer from the normal problems of sampled discrete time systems including higher noise, lower operating frequency, the need for additional antialiasing and smoothing filters, and the requirement for multiphase clocks.

No general switched-capacitor circuit synthesis method currently exists, however some switched-capacitor filter synthesis programs do exist. An example of a complete switched-capacitor filter silicon compiler is described in Chapter 6.

The integrated capacitor normally used in advanced analog CMOS processes is the inter-polysilicon capacitor as shown in Fig.2.1(b) in Chapter 2. Matching characteristics of integrated capacitors are analysed in the literature.[3] The matching accuracy is mainly a function of SiO_2 quality and uniformity of thickness as well as the control of the parasitic effects.

Although some switched-capacitor circuit designers feel that they can control matching accuracy simply by making constant ratios of capacitor areas (including the perimeter), this approach is adequate only when the sensitivity of the circuit is very low. To achieve higher matching accuracy the unity capacitor approach should be used. Here the desired capacitor C is implemented as follows:

$$C = m\, C_u + C_{nu} \tag{4.1}$$

where:

$$m = \text{integer}\ (C/C_u - 1)$$
$$C_u = \text{unity capacitor}$$
$$C_{nu} = \text{non-unity capacitor}$$

The non-unity capacitor can have a value between one and two unity capacitors. Its layout has to conform to the rule of constant area to perimeter ratio. The layout of capacitor networks when broken into the unity and related non-unity capacitors has the following benefits:

1. A centroid placement of the capacitors is easier to implement
2. The rule to avoid the neighbouring effect can be fully obeyed (i.e. each cell borders on to the same geometry)
3. Interconnecting parasitics can be equalized

The last two effects are very often overlooked, although they can significally affect the circuit accuracy when the unity capacitor geometry is very small.

The procedure for the layout synthesis of switched-capacitor networks consists of the following steps which are illustrated in Fig.4.3.

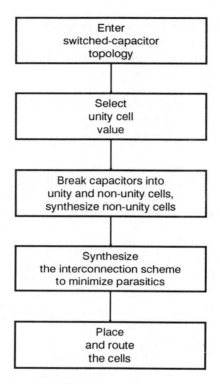

Fig. 4.3 Switched-capacitor network synthesis procedure

The switched-capacitor topology can be entered either via a schematic editor or directly synthesized . The unity cell value is selected by the use of two criteria:

1. Maximum circuit sensitivity of capacitor ratio accuracy
2. Requested noise level

To comply with the first criterion experimental results for a given process can be used. Fig.4.4 shows the measured results for capacitor matching accuracy for the 3 μm CMOS analog process. As can be seen from the figure, the smallest value for unity capacitor (0.25 pF) can be used only when the total sensitivity of the circuit requires only 0.2 per cent average capacitor matching. To ensure that the design meets the requirements, a tolerancing analysis is recommended. The second criterion can be met by observing the relation given in the literature:[1]

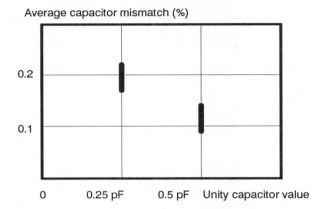

Fig. 4.4 Capacitor matching characterization results using two different sizes of unity cell

$$R_{on}C > 0.05/f_c \qquad (4.2)$$

where R_{on} is the "on" resistance of the transistor switch and f_c is the sampling frequency.

When the unity cell is selected the non-unity cell can be calculated and synthesized.

The interconnecting parasitic is equalized if the interconnecting metals crossing non-unity capacitors are scaled according to the non-unity capacitor value:

$$W_u/W_{nu} = C_u/C_{nu} \qquad (4.3)$$

where W_u is the metal width crossing the unity capacitor, while W_{nu} is the metal width crossing the non-unity capacitor. By using crossing in all four directions the parasitic capacitor is made insensitive to masking misalignment.

4.6.1 Non-unity capacitor (NUCAP)

The problem consists of finding a layout of a non-unity capacitor with a given capacitance (or, equivalently, its area) between 1 and 2 capacitances of a unity capacitor and a prescribed constant area-to-periphery (A/P) ratio equal to the ratio of a unity capacitor, so that it fits into the space for two unity capacitors. The layout should have no sharp edges (i.e. only 135° edges are allowed; in particular, 90° edges are not allowed because of technology limitations). It should be such as to minimize the "neighbour effects".

Fig.4.4 shows the measured results for the 3 μm CMOS process. The first two requirements (area, periphery) could be satisfied by a rectangle with cut corners as shown in Fig.4.5; however, in order to satisfy the perimeter requirement, such a capacitor expands so much as to violate the space requirement (more than the space of two unity capacitors). So a mechanism must be

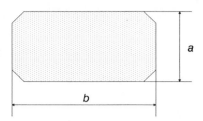

Fig. 4.5 Non-unity capacitor with cut corners

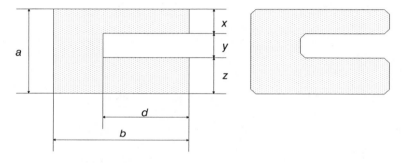

Fig. 4.6 Non-unity capacitor with a cut

provided to increase artificially the perimeter of the capacitor. This is possible by making a cut into the rectangle as illustrated in Fig.4.6.

Each such cut could, however, cause "neighbour effects", so we want as few cuts as possible. (In fact it turns out that one such cut is always enough.) Moreover, we want such a cut to be centred ($x = z$), so that the smaller of x, z is the maximum possible. Ideally, we would also want $y = x = z$. We have chosen y to be 1/3 of maximum NUCAP height which yields satisfactory results since in most cases this is also equal to 1/3 of actual NUCAP height.

So far, we are able to meet all the specified requirements on the NUCAP. However, the dimensions of our capacitor must be multiples of grid size, so they must be rounded. This rounding can introduce intolerable errors in the capacitor area. Therefore, as a final step, we must fine-trim our capacitor, so that the area requirement is satisfied as precisely as possible. This is done by adding or deleting a small strip on the longer side of the capacitor (Fig.4.7(a,b)). When the strip being added is too small, some special trimming has to be implemented as shown in Fig.4.7(c).

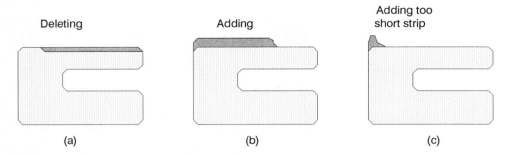

Fig. 4.7 Non-unity capacitor fine trimming technique

Deleting a band obviously preserves periphery whereas adding a band changes (increases) the periphery of the capacitor slightly. However, this change is very small and turns out to be negligible in practice. Note also that the capacitor area has greater influence on its capacitance than does the periphery, so a high precision in area remains our primary goal.

In summary the layout of a NUCAP has three phases:

1. RECTANGLE—find a suitable rectangle which would solve the problem.
2. CUT—make a cut into the rectangle (and expand it so as to preserve area) if necessary, so as to satisfy the A/P ratio requirement.
3. REFINE—fine-trim the capacitor so as to make its area as close to desired one as permitted by the technology.

4.7   Design and layout of matched transistor networks

Matched transistor networks are very often used in analog design. Typical examples are input stages of operational amplifiers, current mirrors and D/A converters using transistors as current sources or active resistors.

The synthesis of such networks is more complicated than resistor network synthesis, since the matching characteristics do not depend only on the selection of the device sizes, but also on their operating point.

It is not a general practice to characterize the matching characteristics of analog CMOS processes fully. However, a first order approximation of the mismatch behaviour is given in the literature.[2] This gives an analysis of the two most important transistor parameters; the threshold voltage V_T and the conduction constant K'.

It is shown in the above reference that the standard deviation of the MOS transistor threshold voltage is inversely proportional to the square root of effective channel area. The major cause of the mismatch is a non-uniform distribution of the dopant in the bulk material. The other significant source of the mismatch results from differential doping at the surface, which occurs during the compensating threshold adjustment implant.

Figs.4.8 – 4.11 show the characterization data of transistor matching for the 3 μm analog digital process.

Fig.4.8 shows the normalized P-channel transistor threshold voltage mismatch versus transistor area. The slope of the straight line is a process dependent parameter obtained by the measurement as proposed in Ref.2.[2] Fig.4.9 shows the normalized N-channel characteristic threshold voltage mismatch versus transistor area. Fig.4.10 and Fig.4.11 show the normalized conductance constant mismatch versus effective transistor channel width and length for N-channel and P-channel device respectively. The process parameters were measured for the 3 μm analog CMOS process. Fig.4.12 shows the synthesis procedure for automatic generation of transistor networks.

The most important layout and process dependent descriptors affecting unity transistor cell dimension are the following: input offset-voltage, current ratio accuracy, equivalent low frequency $1/f$ noise voltage. Flicker noise (or $1/f$ noise) is an important parameter when input transistors for operational amplifiers are being considered. The transistor noise voltage is given by the approximate expression:

$$V_n^2 = \frac{K_n}{C_{ox} W L} \frac{\Delta f}{f}$$

(4.4)

where K_n is a constant dependent on the temperature and fabrication process. Fig.4.13 and Fig.4.14 show the average of measured results for transistor noise voltage density for two different channel dimensions for P-channel transistors. Fig.4.15 and Fig.4.16 show the results for N-channel transistors. The characterization data is again for the 3 μm analog digital CMOS process.

The technology database for layout-dependent transistor parameters obtained from the characterization information presented consists of the following data: K_{nN}, K_{nP}, α_n, a_n, α_p, a_p, β_{1n}, β_{2n}, β_{1p}, β_{2p}. This data together with the electrical specification data of the transistor operating point is the basis of the layout compilation of simple transistor networks for some analog applications. Beside this other information such as high frequency behaviour, output impedance, wide frequency thermal noise and switching characteristics can be of interest. Unfortunately there is no general rule for the synthesis of transistor dimensions, layout compilation and choice of operating point which would be valid for every possible application. To determine the appropriate transistor operating point, its parasitics and its behaviour for specific applications, analog simulation is still the best approach to verify heuristic designs.

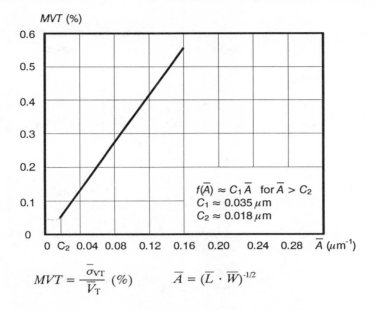

$$MVT = \frac{\overline{\sigma}_{VT}}{\overline{V}_T} \ (\%) \qquad \overline{A} = (\overline{L} \cdot \overline{W})^{-1/2}$$

Fig. 4.8 Normalized threshold voltage variation versus P-channel transistor area

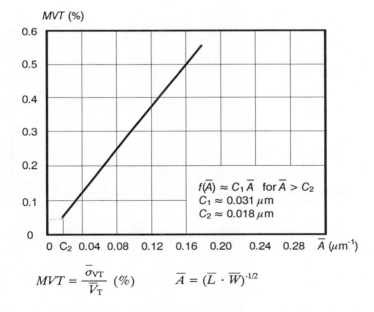

$$MVT = \frac{\overline{\sigma}_{VT}}{\overline{V}_T} \ (\%) \qquad \overline{A} = (\overline{L} \cdot \overline{W})^{-1/2}$$

Fig. 4.9 Normalized threshold voltage variation versus N-channel transistor area

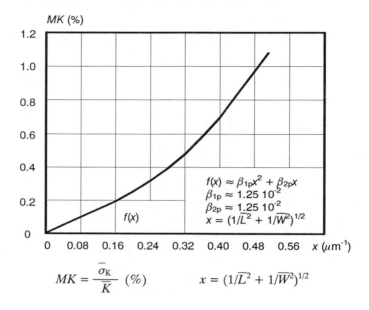

Fig. 4.10 Normalized K' variation versus P-channel transistor dimensions

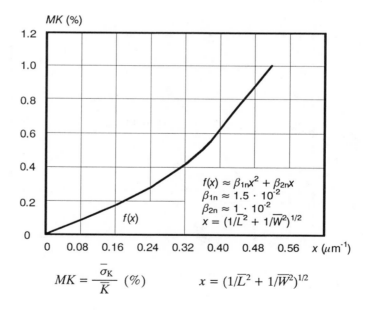

Fig. 4.11 Normalized K' variation versus N-channel transistor dimensions

Noise density (nV/√Hz)

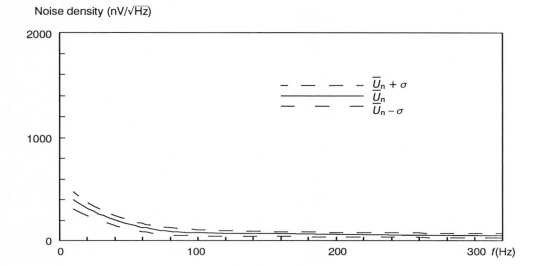

Fig. 4.13 Noise characterization results for P-channel transistors of 3 μm analog digital
CMOS process, transistor dimensions $W/L = 100/10\,\mu$m

Noise density (nV/√Hz)

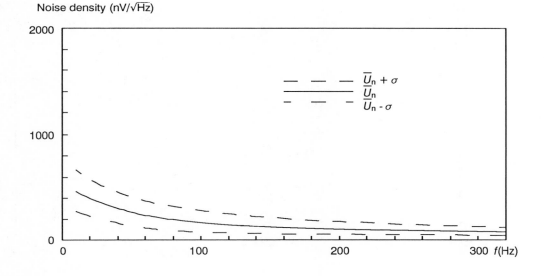

Fig. 4.14 Noise characterization results for P-channel transistors of 3 μm analog digital
CMOS process, transistor dimensions $W/L = 100/3\,\mu$m

Noise density (nV/√Hz)

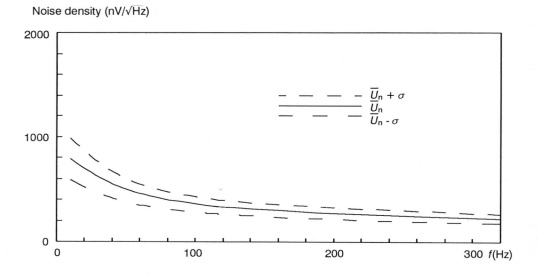

Fig. 4.15 Noise characterization results for N-channel transistors of 3 μm analog digital CMOS process, transistor dimensions $W/L = 100/10\,\mu$m

Noise density (nV/√Hz)

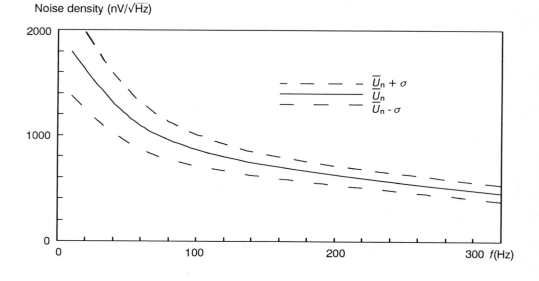

Fig. 4.16 Noise characterization results for N-channel transistors of 3 μm analog digital CMOS process, transistor dimensions $W/L = 100/3\,\mu$m

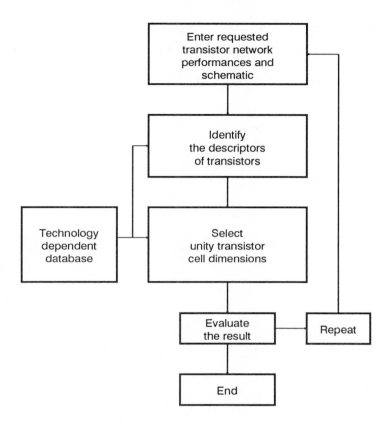

Fig. 4.12 Procedure for automatic matched transistor network generation

References

1. Gregorian, R., Temes, G.C., *Analog MOS Integrated Circuits for Signal Processing*, John Wiley & Sons, Inc., New York, 1986.
2. Larsmikumar, K.R., Madaway, R.A., Copelend, M.A., Characterization and modeling of mismatching in MOS transistors for precision analog design, *IEEE Journal of Solid State Circuits*, **SC–21**, No.6, 1986.
3. McReary, J.L., Matching properties and voltage and temperature dependence of MOS capacitors, *IEEE Journal of Solid State Circuits*, **SC–16**, No.6, 1981.

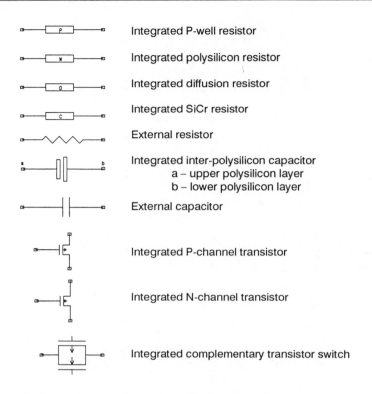

	Integrated P-well resistor
	Integrated polysilicon resistor
	Integrated diffusion resistor
	Integrated SiCr resistor
	External resistor
	Integrated inter-polysilicon capacitor a – upper polysilicon layer b – lower polysilicon layer
	External capacitor
	Integrated P-channel transistor
	Integrated N-channel transistor
	Integrated complementary transistor switch

Appendix Subset of schematic editor symbols

5. Macrocell synthesis and layout compilation

5.1 Introduction

Different levels for macrocell synthesis and compilation can be used in the design of complex analog digital integrated circuits. The highest level is automatic macrocell circuit topology and layout generation from the functional specifications of the macrocell, while the lowest is manual schematic entry of the macrocell topology. In the case of manual design the use of an interactive simulator is necessary for verification when using cut and try design techniques. The layout generation can be semiautomated using the tools for primitive circuit elements generation as described in Chapter 4.

In this chapter some of the most popular methods for macrocell synthesis and layout generation are presented.

As an example of the highest level of macrocell synthesis and layout compilation, a CAD tool for automatic S–C filter generation is described. A synthesis tool for the automatic layout generation of a predefined analog library based operational amplifier topology, incorporating automatic transistor sizing, is shown as an efficient medium level approach. Some analog library data is included to support the described methods.

5.2 Digital macrocell generation

5.2.1 The tasks of a macrocell generator

Before studying different types of digital macrocell generators it is useful to review the set of tasks that must be performed to generate a library of digital macrocells.

5.2.2 Specification

Firstly a requirements specification that defines the required properties of both the set and the individual macrocell elements must be written. A typical specification should include:

1. Behavioural or functional descriptions
2. Electrical requirements (timing, voltage and power levels)
3. Size constraints (fixed height or absolute dimensions)

4. Boundary issues (where can connections be made, what process layers can be at or near the boundary, etc.)
5. Process portability. The ability to port the macrocell to a new process
6. Parametrization. This is the ability to define a parameter of the macrocell performance or implementation as a parameter, e.g. number of bits, transistor size, etc.

5.2.3 Feasibility analysis

Before attempting a design implementation, an analysis of the requirements should be made with respect to previous knowledge. Failing this, some trial cell designs should be made and simulated. This will help to determine feasibility and steer the design approach, e.g. suggest architectural or circuit solutions, power versus speed and area and hence cost trade-offs. An existing library of macrocells that can be compared with the requirements is a valuable starting point, as is any indication of the limits of circuit performance. This analysis should help to prevent the generator of macros which cannot meet a required electrical specification.

5.2.4 Design implementation

This should be a full design exercise that creates a circuit and layout implementation, and performs simulations on the design at various levels. Provision should be made for simulation under actual operating conditions expected in the chip as illustrated by the following extract from IMP's digital cell library documentation. "Provision is made under worst case conditions for tester resolution of 100 mV and for an IR voltage drop of 250 mV along the internal chip V_{DD} bus. So at V_{DD} minimum of 4.5 V the actual supply voltage across the device under test (DUT) is $4.5 - 0.25 - 0.1 = 4.15$ V. An IR voltage drop of 150 mV along the V_{SS} bus is allowed for by reducing the input voltage swing to the DUT by 150 mV. These provisions make the delay times obtained through HSPICE quite conservative." The situation is shown graphically in Fig.5.1.

The process can either be a highly automated one, in which a set of linked programs take a set of data through a design loop and present a result, or can be interactive with a designer. Many systems today can be operated in either mode.

5.2.5 Characterization

This can be accomplished in one of two ways: either by extracting the model parameters from a variety of process runs and performing extensive simulations over different conditions (so-called "soft" characterization), or by producing silicon for each macrocell over a range of different processing runs and measuring the resultant macrocells (so-called "hard" characterization). In either case the characterization is a large task, consuming many man months of effort.[1]

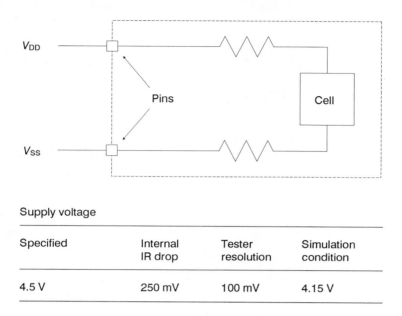

Supply voltage

Specified	Internal IR drop	Tester resolution	Simulation condition
4.5 V	250 mV	100 mV	4.15 V

Fig. 5.1 Worst case provisions for IMP digital cell library

5.2.6 Documentation

This should be produced in a way that is most useful to a new designer approaching the macrocell library for the first time. Many systems attempt to offer the data in a similar way to that used by the manufacturers of standard catalogue ICs. This is a reasonable approach as it presents a format familiar to systems designers. The data must, however, contain sufficient information such that a new user can easily satisfy himself that the macrocell does actually comply with the specifications. It should also present modelling data so that the macrocell can be used as a "component" in a larger design.

5.3   Types of macrocell generators

Digital macrocell generators can be classified into "soft" and "hard" generators. A "soft" generator produces, as an intermediate output, a gate-level netlist which can be placed and routed on a gate array or some other regular layout structure. The generation process is then completed on the particular structure chosen. A "hard" generator produces an "all-layer" layout of the macrocell which is normally unique to the particular generation instance.

5.3.1 Soft macrocell generators

A large number of approaches have been proposed that synthesize behavioural or functional descriptions of Boolean logic.[2] These approaches, as well as existing MSI and LSI gate-level implemented designs, can be used to generate a large number of macrocells relatively quickly compared with the design of "hard" macrocells. This approach is used by several gate array vendors and very complex designs are now being targeted with this solution.[3]

The advantage of "soft" macrocells as described in Chapter 3.1. is the potential speed of generation and characterization. The disadvantage is the loss of performance and silicon density. The "hard" macrocells target particular layout structures to optimize these parameters.

5.3.2 Hard macrocell generators

Many researchers have developed tools to generate the common digital memories and logic arrays such as ROMs, RAMs and PLAs. A number of tools have come from the University of California at Berkeley that interface with a graphical layout editor.[4] They include a program for generating semi-regular modules by assembling "tiles" or small pieces of layout designed with the graphics editor. The end result is a module generator that can generate different styles of modules depending on the set of tiles used.

Also available is:

1. A tool that compiles a "high level" description of a finite state machine into logic equations. These logic equations can be fed into the PLA tools for automatic layout and optimization of the finite state machine.
2. A technology independent generator of split and folded PLAs built using the tile assembler.

It should be clear from the above descriptions that each tool fulfils only one part of the total task of a macrocell generator, as described in Section 5.1. The development and maintenance of such a complete tool is a major undertaking. One commercial product that approaches this requirement is "GDT" from Silicon Compiler Systems of San Jose, California.[5]

GDT consists of a closely coupled set of tools for all of the design tasks. It starts with a behavioural modelling language based on "C" structure and proceeds down to a set of layout tools that allow for the design of parametrizable layouts and schematics. This uses a procedural layout language, "L", that supports electrical as well as geometric objects and is capable of describing the physical and electrical inter-relationships between circuit elements. Fig.5.2 shows the different tools contained within GDT and the links of circuit information and verification between the different design steps.

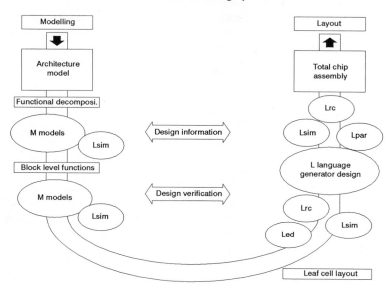

Fig. 5.2 GDT silicon compiler tools

GDT can be used in several different modes. The designer is supplied with a "starter" library of simple logic generators which can be expanded to include RAMs, ROMs, PLAs, datapaths, etc. For these macrocells certain parameters of the design have been identified as variables. The user can choose either to input these variables and control the design process himself, or he can program the system to attempt to find a design solution and report on the results. Alternatively, he can input a new schematic or layout and choose the parameters he wishes to be variables. Here in fact is the major problem, i.e. the choice of variables. To choose too many can seriously extend the design cycle, and to choose too few restricts the future use of the macrocell. This is where real design experience and skill is needed.

5.4   Operational amplifier synthesis and compilation

The analysis of different types of operational amplifier has been widely reported. A good background can be obtained by reading.[6,7] However a description of full automatic synthesis and layout compilation is not currently available. There are two major reasons for this. Firstly, a large number of parameters determine operational amplifier behaviour. Secondly, it is not possible to specify optimization criteria which would be valid for every possible application.

A further reason, valid for sensitive analog cell design, is the influence of layout characteristics. As a consequence, no synthesis of high performance cells can be performed without optimizing the layout for parasitics, matching, process variations etc. An approach to personalizing an existing analog cell schematic and layout has been proposed in the literature.[8,9] This approach was more or less followed by others,[10] where all the elements were sized in the pre-selected schematic. In theory this could give slightly better flexibility of the cell, with the penalty of a non-optimal automatic layout and solution for a specific application. This is because no provision is made for the extraction or generation of cell specifications from the system requirements.

Our present objectives for the synthesis and compilation of operational amplifiers based on the personalization of standard analog cells are the following:

1. Operational amplifier characteristics are derived automatically from system specifications, including cell environment and loading. Such an approach prevents the overspecification of cell characteristics, most often the case in present analog designs. This incurs a penalty of larger silicon area and larger power dissipation than actually needed.
2. Operational amplifier synthesis is based on a deterministic sizing of preselected cell components. This approach facilitates the optimization strategy.
3. The layout expertise is held in a predetermined cell composition which is manually created by an expert.
4. Those cell characteristics which are most difficult to simulate or predict accurately are extracted from the characterization data collected from prefabricated library cells. This approach is particularly useful where high cell performance is essential to successful analog function integration.

The personalized cell elements can be sized according to a specific ASIC's requirements. This approach minimizes the layout dependence of the cell performance, since it is based on a predetermined and manually optimized layout and on a cell layout strategy which uses characterized cell data. The sizing algorithm fully respects all the layout rules established in the previous chapters.

The advantage of this approach is a reduction of the number of degrees of freedom available to the designer when performing the cell topology and layout synthesis. Only the reduced number of circuit elements which control the requested circuit characteristics are sized.

The effectiveness of this personalization approach is demonstrated with three examples for automatic synthesis and layout compilation of operational amplifier cells.

As examples a general purpose class A–B operational amplifier, a low power low voltage class A operational amplifier and a cascode operational amplifier have been chosen. For each cell both the electrical topology (i.e. schematics without component values) and the cell floorplan have been fixed. In addition a set of sizing and layout descriptors are identified and calculated to comply with the specifications. To prevent errors or to avoid overspecification, the required cell characteristics are deduced from the system aspect. The closed loop behaviour of the operational amplifier designed for an ASIC, with all specific loading conditions of input and output pins, are the basis of the cell synthesis.

5.4.1 General purpose class A–B operational amplifier synthesis and layout compilation

The schematic of this operational amplifier type is shown in Fig.5.3. As shown it can be divided in the following sub-circuits :

1. Differential input stage
2. Voltage level translator
3. Phase compensation circuit
4. Output stage
5. Bias generator

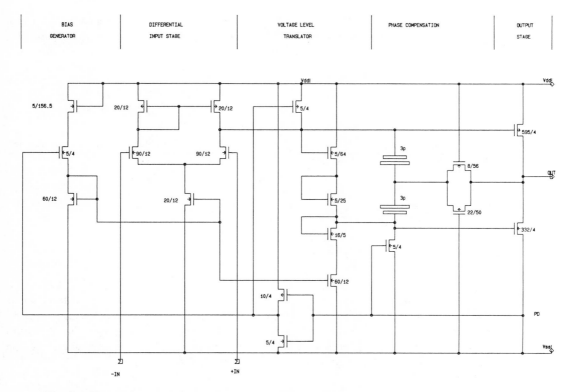

Fig. 5.3 General purpose class A-B operational amplifier

The differential input stage, voltage level translator and phase compensation circuits are designed to operate over a wide power supply voltage range and cover a large common mode input voltage range. It is possible to cover a large number of applications by cell personalization merely by sizing the output stage and bias generator. This is done by introducing the incremental output stage and bias stage as shown in the cell layout in Plate 5.1. The cell descriptor X is the number of increments in the output stage and Z is the number of increments in the bias stage.

For every specific application, the cell size descriptors X and Z have to be calculated. For the cell characterization purposes the cell with $X = 10$ and $Z = 3$ was fabricated. It was characterized by using typical process parameters and the so-called "four corner" process parameters, i.e. the process parameters extended to the limits in each of four directions. Some of the measured characteristics are given in Tables 5.1, 5.2, and 5.3.

In Tables 5.1 and 5.2 the characterization results for the most distant process parameter corners A and E are given, while Table 5.3 presents characterization results over full process and temperature range.

The characterization was performed to obtain some of the cell parameters which are not available from simulations. Some of the data which is difficult to predict because of poor models, unknown process parameters and layout dependence are:

1. Input offset-voltage
2. Input offset-voltage drift
3. Input noise-voltage and its temperature and frequency dependence

The most important parameters determining the output stage sizing descriptor X and bias stage sizing descriptor Z are the following :

1. Power supply operating voltage
2. Load conditions
3. Output voltage swing
4. Closed loop gain and its accuracy
5. Closed loop 3 dB gain drop frequency
6. Slew rate

A deterministic algorithm has been developed to calculate the cell descriptors X and Z. This automatically produces the cell layout together with predicted open-loop cell characteristics, and a SPICE file which can be used for documentation and verification purposes. The algorithm for the calculation of the cell descriptors is based on the combination of small and large signal operational amplifier models, and of the matrix of measured data.

Table 5.1(a,b) Print-out of characterization data of operational amplifier OA4 for process parameter corner A for power supply voltages (a) ±4.5 V, (b) ±5 V

```
ELECTRICAL CHARACTERISTICS :4A() 9 V,25 C;  09/21/87
   SYMBOL      MIN     TYP     MAX    UNITS        σ(N)

   VOS        -1.89    1.66    5.52   mV           2.02
   AO30Hz     86.12   87.28   88.10   dB           0.58
   AO80Hz     79.10   81.32   84.52   dB           1.36
   AO10kHz    39.80   40.31   40.70   dB           0.29
   AO100kHz   16.90   17.50   17.90   dB           0.32
   BW          0.83    0.88    0.92   MHz          0.03
   EN100Hz   182.00  203.08  230.00   nV/√Hz      15.25
   EN1kHz     80.80   88.78  104.00   nV/√Hz       5.57
   EN10kHz    35.40   39.08   43.00   nV/√Hz       1.81
   OVRP        4.66    4.68    4.69   V            0.01
   OVRN       -4.41   -4.36   -4.31   V            0.02
   IVRP        3.75    3.75    3.75   V            0.00
   IVRN       -4.45   -4.39   -4.35   V            0.05
   PM         80.02   83.65   87.84   deg          2.25
   CMRR      -120.9  -91.16  -83.65   dB           8.05
   THD         0.01    0.02    0.04   %            0.01
   PSRR      -72.42  -69.47  -66.20   dB           1.60
   FTOP        3.25    3.25    3.25   MHz          0.00
   ROUT       13.01   15.99   17.76   kΩ           1.45


ELECTRICAL CHARACTERISTICS :4A() 10 V,25 C;  09/21/87
   SYMBOL      MIN     TYP     MAX    UNITS        σ(N)

   VOS        -2.25    1.23    5.12   mV           1.90
   AO30Hz     85.80   86.87   87.98   dB           0.66
   AO80Hz     80.10   82.41   84.16   dB           1.19
   AO10kHz    41.30   41.87   42.28   dB           0.31
   AO100kHz   18.70   19.33   19.80   dB           0.35
   BW          1.00    1.07    1.12   MHz          0.04
   EN100Hz   179.00  209.58  233.00   nV/√Hz      15.18
   EN1kHz     76.40   86.60   98.40   nV/√Hz       5.96
   EN10kHz    36.60   40.10   43.40   nV/√Hz       1.90
   OVRP        4.65    4.69    4.70   V            0.01
   OVRN       -4.60   -4.56   -4.52   V            0.02
   IVRP        4.20    4.25    4.30   V            0.05
   IVRN       -4.80   -4.72   -4.70   V            0.05
   PM         94.24   96.97  100.39   deg          1.81
   CMRR      -127.8  -95.96  -81.47   dB          13.51
   THD         0.01    0.02    0.03   %            0.00
   PSRR      -71.48  -68.54  -65.61   dB           1.35
   FTOP        3.25    3.25    3.25   MHz          0.00
   ROUT        9.44   11.44   13.19   kΩ           1.05
```

```
ELECTRICAL  CHARACTERISTICS  :4A()  11 V,25 C;   09/21/87
   SYMBOL      MIN      TYP      MAX     UNITS       σ(N)

    VOS       -2.67     0.92     4.73     mV         1.88
   AO30Hz     84.78    85.81    87.06     dB         0.68
   AO80Hz     80.10    82.50    84.78     dB         1.15
   AO10kHz    42.58    43.06    43.50     dB         0.30
   AO100kHz   20.12    20.71    21.20     dB         0.35
    BW         1.17     1.25     1.31     MHz        0.05
   EN100Hz   176.00   202.85   238.00    nV/√Hz     18.22
   EN1kHz     72.00    85.06    94.00     nV/√Hz      5.04
   EN10kHz    38.40    40.29    44.00     nV/√Hz      1.50
   OVRP        4.66     4.68     4.69     V          0.01
   OVRN       -4.61    -4.57    -4.53     V          0.03
   IVRP        4.45     4.45     4.45     V          0.00
   IVRN       -4.45    -4.45    -4.45     V          0.00
    PM        67.15    97.57   107.85     deg       14.62
   CMRR     -110.2    -89.76   -76.87     dB         7.59
   THD         0.01     0.02     0.04     %          0.01
   PSRR      -70.15   -67.25   -64.77     dB         1.24
   FTOP        3.25     3.58     4.88     MHz        0.66
   ROUT        7.09     8.38     9.92     kΩ         0.80
```

Table 5.1(c) Print-out of characterization data of operational amplifier OA4 for process parameter corner A for power supply voltage ±5.5 V.

The abbreviations are the following:

VOS: input offset voltage
AO30Hz, AO80Hz, AO10kHz, AO100kHz: open loop gain at 30Hz, 80Hz, 10kHz, 100kHz
BW: gain bandwidth product
EN100Hz, EN1kHz, EN10kHz: input noise density at 100 Hz, 1 kHz, 10 kHz
OVRP: positive output voltage range at $R_L = 100$ kΩ
OVRN: negative output voltage range at $R_L = 100$ kΩ
IVRP: common mode positive input voltage range
IVRN: common mode negative input voltage range
PM: phase margin at unity gain
CMRR: input common mode rejection ratio
THD: total harmonic distortion at 1 V_{RMS} output level
PSRR: power supply rejection ratio
FTOP: unity gain frequency
ROUT: output impedance

Table 5.2(a,b) Print-out of characterization data of operational amplifier OA4 for process parameter corner E for power supply voltages (a) ±4.5 V, (b) ±5 V

```
ELECTRICAL CHARACTERISTICS :4E() 9 V,25 C;  09/21/87
     SYMBOL      MIN      TYP      MAX    UNITS        σ(N)

     VOS       -2.65     0.83     3.35    mV           1.47
     AO30Hz    88.94    89.34    89.96    dB           0.23
     AO80Hz    81.24    83.49    87.32    dB           1.51
     AO10kHz   42.30    42.65    42.96    dB           0.14
     AO100kHz  19.52    20.05    20.46    dB           0.20
     BW         1.11     1.17     1.22    MHz          0.02
     EN100Hz  152.00   174.80   207.00    nV/√Hz      12.87
     EN1kHz    61.20    70.42    82.80    nV/√Hz       5.89
     EN10kHz   34.20    36.29    38.80    nV/√Hz       1.55
     OVRP       4.66     4.67     4.69    V            0.01
     OVRN      -4.43    -4.40    -4.37    V            0.02
     IVRP       4.05     4.05     4.05    V            0.00
     IVRN      -3.85    -3.77    -3.75    V            0.03
     PM        43.99    53.19    70.18    deg          9.94
     CMRR    -117.8    -92.51   -79.57    dB           8.25
     THD        0.01     0.01     0.05    %            0.01
     PSRR     -81.65   -73.14   -69.76    dB           2.59
     FTOP       4.06     4.61     4.88    MHz          0.37
     ROUT       9.92    11.30    12.95    kΩ           0.77


ELECTRICAL CHARACTERISTICS :4E() 10 V,25 C;  09/21/87
     SYMBOL      MIN      TYP      MAX    UNITS        σ(N)

     VOS       -2.96     0.51     3.04    mV           1.35
     AO30Hz    88.34    88.71    89.24    dB           0.24
     AO80Hz    81.86    83.46    85.42    dB           1.08
     AO10kHz   43.60    43.92    44.20    dB           0.14
     AO100kHz  21.00    21.51    21.90    dB           0.21
     BW         1.30     1.37     1.41    MHz          0.02
     EN100Hz  159.00   181.40   207.00    nV/√Hz      12.79
     EN1kHz    60.00    70.96    76.40    nV/√Hz       4.02
     EN10kHz   34.40    37.22    42.00    nV/√Hz       2.00
     OVRP       4.66     4.68     4.69    V            0.01
     OVRN      -4.60    -4.57    -4.52    V            0.03
     IVRP       4.50     4.50     4.50    V            0.00
     IVRN      -4.10    -4.04    -4.00    V            0.05
     PM        45.12    57.24    67.41    deg          8.56
     CMRR    -116.6    -92.28   -78.19    dB          10.23
     THD        0.01     0.01     0.02    %            0.00
     PSRR     -79.18   -71.84   -68.95    dB           2.22
     FTOP       4.88     5.21     5.69    MHz          0.39
     ROUT       7.29     8.20     9.04    kΩ           0.53
```

```
ELECTRICAL CHARACTERISTICS :4E() 11 V,25 C;  09/21/87
  SYMBOL      MIN      TYP      MAX    UNITS       σ(N)

  VOS         -3.28     0.26     2.77   mV         1.51
  AO30Hz      87.26    87.75    88.32   dB         0.25
  AO80Hz      81.86    84.01    87.24   dB         1.23
  AO10kHz     44.62    44.97    45.26   dB         0.17
  AO100kHz    22.20    22.67    23.00   dB         0.23
  BW           1.48     1.55     1.61   MHz        0.03
  EN100Hz    153.00   171.25   200.00   nV/√Hz    11.39
  EN1kHz      62.80    69.54    82.80   nV/√Hz     4.96
  EN10kHz     34.20    36.59    40.60   nV/√Hz     1.54
  OVRP         4.66     4.67     4.69   V          0.01
  OVRN        -4.61    -4.57    -4.53   V          0.02
  IVRP         4.45     4.45     4.45   V          0.00
  IVRN        -4.35    -4.29    -4.25   V          0.04
  PM          41.57    55.33    75.57   deg        9.51
  CMRR      -121.9    -91.74   -77.38   dB        10.00
  THD          0.01     0.01     0.02   %          0.00
  PSRR       -76.77   -70.46   -67.85   dB         1.92
  FTOP         4.88     5.89     6.50   MHz        0.49
  ROUT         5.55     6.22     7.01   kΩ         0.37
```

Table 5.2(c) Print-out of characterization data of operational amplifier OA4 for process parameter corner E for power supply voltage ±5.5 V.

The abbreviations are the following:

VOS: input offset voltage
AO30Hz, AO80Hz, AO10kHz, AO100kHz: open loop gain at 30 Hz, 80 Hz, 10 kHz, 100 kHz
BW: gain bandwidth product
EN100Hz, EN1kHz, EN10kHz: input noise density at 100 Hz, 1 kHz, 10 kHz
OVRP: positive output voltage range at R_L = 100 kΩ
OVRN: negative output voltage range at R_L = 100 kΩ
IVRP: common mode positive input voltage range
IVRN: common mode negative input voltage range
PM: phase margin at unity gain
CMRR: input common mode rejection ratio
THD: total harmonic distortion at 1 V_{RMS} output level
PSRR: power supply rejection ratio
FTOP: unity gain frequency
ROUT: output impedance

Table 5.3(a,b) Print-out of characterization data of operational amplifier OA4 for all parameter corners (A, B, C, D, E, F) for power supply voltage ±5 V at (a) 25 °C and (b) 80 °C

```
ELECTRICAL CHARACTERISTICS :4() 10 V,25 C;  05.03.89
   SYMBOL      MIN      TYP      MAX    UNITS       σ(N)


   VOS        -3.53     0.67     5.62    mV          1.80
   AO30Hz     85.76    88.23    91.58    dB          1.40
   AO80Hz     80.10    83.53    88.50    dB          1.61
   AO10kHz    41.30    44.03    46.70    dB          1.60
   AO100kHz   18.70    21.80    25.00    dB          1.84
   BW          1.00     1.43     1.96    MHz         0.28
   EN100Hz   126.00   192.01   249.00    nV/√Hz     28.04
   EN1kHz     56.40    77.73    99.60    nV/√Hz     11.48
   EN10kHz    33.40    39.28    48.80    nV/√Hz      3.50
   OVRP        4.65     4.69     4.70    V           0.01
   OVRN       -4.61    -4.56    -4.52    V           0.02
   IVRP        4.20     4.42     4.60    V           0.14
   IVRN       -4.80    -4.31    -3.90    V           0.35
   PM         36.30    71.81   101.69    deg        21.89
   CMRR     -127.8    -92.60   -77.14    dB         11.00
   THD         0.01     0.02     0.04    %           0.01
   PSRR      -79.18   -70.28   -65.39    dB          2.34
   FTOP        3.25     4.46     5.69    MHz         1.03
   ROUT        6.85     9.91    14.37    kΩ          1.84



ELECTRICAL CHARACTERISTICS :4() 10 V,80 C;  05.03.89
   SYMBOL      MIN      TYP      MAX    UNITS       σ(N)


   VOS        -3.33     0.49     5.42    mV          1.67
   AO30Hz     81.90    86.38    90.26    dB          1.65
   AO80Hz     77.64    81.99    86.88    dB          2.09
   AO10kHz    38.84    41.67    44.44    dB          1.61
   AO100kHz   15.60    18.76    22.10    dB          1.84
   BW          0.73     1.04     1.45    MHz         0.21
   EN100Hz    98.00   145.86   205.00    nV/√Hz     24.18
   EN1kHz     49.80    64.38    80.80    nV/√Hz      8.11
   EN10kHz    34.20    39.09    52.00    nV/√Hz      3.12
   OVRP        4.62     4.65     4.66    V           0.01
   OVRN       -4.73    -4.68    -4.62    V           0.03
   IVRP        2.60     4.47     4.60    V           0.29
   IVRN       -4.70    -4.11    -2.80    V           0.37
   PM         43.80    79.48   121.82    deg        21.97
   CMRR     -125.0    -91.10   -76.04    dB         10.04
   THD         0.01     0.02     0.15    %           0.03
   PSRR      -77.17   -69.31   -64.43    dB          2.33
   FTOP        1.63     3.48     4.88    MHz         1.02
   ROUT        6.34     9.40    14.19    kΩ          1.69
```

```
ELECTRICAL CHARACTERISTICS :4() 10 V,-40 C;  05.03.89
    SYMBOL     MIN      TYP      MAX    UNITS        σ(N)

    VOS       -8.49     0.39     5.85    mV          2.35
    AO30Hz    88.02    90.72    94.92    dB          1.41
    AO80Hz    82.62    86.03    89.30    dB          1.52
    AO10kHz   45.00    47.65    50.36    dB          1.59
    AO100kHz  23.32    26.22    29.16    dB          1.72
    BW         1.61     2.26     3.07    MHz         0.43
    EN100Hz  210.00   317.05   414.00    nV/√Hz     50.23
    EN1kHz    80.80   111.35   154.00    nV/√Hz     16.74
    EN10kHz   32.20    42.30    51.00    nV/√Hz      4.60
    OVRP       4.14     4.90     4.93    V           0.08
    OVRN      -4.55    -4.43    -4.31    V           0.07
    IVRP       2.70     4.30     4.50    V           0.23
    IVRN      -5.00    -4.43    -3.80    V           0.34
    PM        25.83    44.03    65.10    deg         6.57
    CMRR    -138.7    -93.53   -78.87    dB         11.76
    THD        0.01     0.03     0.12    %           0.03
    PSRR     -83.49   -71.98   -66.25    dB          2.82
    FTOP       3.25     7.01     8.13    MHz         0.62
    ROUT       6.39    10.49    16.83    kΩ          2.47
```

Table 5.3(c) Print-out of characterization data of operational amplifier OA4 for all process parameter corners (A, B, C, D, E, F) for power supply voltage ±5 V at −40 °C.

The abbreviations are the following:

VOS: input offset voltage
AO30Hz, AO80Hz, AO10kHz, AO100kHz: open loop gain at 30 Hz, 80 Hz, 10 kHz, 100 kHz
BW: gain bandwidth product
EN100Hz, EN1kHz, EN10kHz: input noise density at 100 Hz, 1 kHz, 10 kHz
OVRP: positive output voltage range at $R_L = 100$ kΩ
OVRN: negative output voltage range at $R_L = 100$ kΩ
IVRP: common mode positive input voltage range
IVRN: common mode negative input voltage range
PM: phase margin at unity gain
CMRR: input common mode rejection ratio
THD: total harmonic distortion at 1 V_{RMS} output level
PSRR: power supply rejection ratio
FTOP: unity gain frequency
ROUT: output impedance

5.4.1.1 Example A, accurate closed-loop gain stage

Fig.5.4 shows the example which was used in one of the designs.

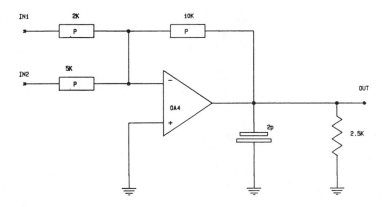

Fig. 5.4 Closed loop gain stage

The design was very sensitive to total power consumption, so no overspecification was allowed. The input data to the program were the following:

$V_{DD} - V_{SS} = +4.5\ \text{V} -4.5\ \text{V}$	power supply voltage
$R_L = 2\ \text{k}\Omega$	load resistance
$C_L = 15\ \text{pF}$	load capacitance
$V_o = 3\ \text{V}$	peak output voltage swing
$G = 5$	maximum closed loop gain
$G_r < 0.2$ per cent	maximum gain tolerance
$f_{3dB} > 10\ \text{kHz}$	minimum 3 dB corner frequency
$SR = x$	slew rate (not requested)

The cell was synthesized and fabricated with the descriptors $X = 8$ and $Z = 3$. The selected increment of the input cell of $16\,\mu\text{m}$ resulted in the output transistor dimensions of $W/L = 480/4$ μm for P-channel transistor and $W/L = 192/4\ \mu\text{m}$ for N-channel transistor. The overall amplifier cell size was $536\ \mu\text{m} \times 178\ \mu\text{m}$ using the sizeable operational amplifier cell OA4S. The cell had the characteristics shown in Table 5.4.

Table 5.4 Target and measured electrical characteristics for the synthesized operational amplifier cell in example A

Cell parameter	Target value	Measured value	Deviation from target value
Offset voltage range	+2 mV /–2 mV	1 mV	0 %
Offset temp.coeff.	6 μV/°C	5 μV/°C	–16 %
1/f noise at 100 Hz	192 nV/$\sqrt{\text{Hz}}$	220 nV/$\sqrt{\text{Hz}}$	14 %
1/f noise at 1 kHz	78 nV/$\sqrt{\text{Hz}}$	100 nV/$\sqrt{\text{Hz}}$	28 %
1/f noise at 10 kHz	48 nV/$\sqrt{\text{Hz}}$	55 nV/$\sqrt{\text{Hz}}$	14 %
Noise temp.coeff.	1.4 nV/$\sqrt{\text{Hz}}$/°C	1.6 nV/$\sqrt{\text{Hz}}$/°C	14 %
Open loop DC gain	88 dB	91 dB	–3.4 %
Open loop gain at 70 Hz	83 dB	85.5 dB	–3 %
Open loop gain at 200 Hz	78 dB	81 dB	3.8 %
Gain bandwidth	2 MHz	1.9 MHz	–5 %
Phase margin at C_L = 15 pF	71 °	78 °	10 %
Total harmonic distortion	0.02 %	0.02 %	0 %
PSRR	–70 dB	–66 dB	–6 %
CMRR	–90 dB	–84 dB	–7 %
Input voltage range	–4.2 V / +4.0 V	–4.4 V / +4.2 V	5 %
Output voltage swing at R_L = 2 kΩ	–3.2 V / +3.2 V	–3.0 V / +3.0 V	–6 %
Slew rate at C_L = 15pF	3.5 V / μs	3.3 V/μs	–6 %
Output resistance	19 kΩ	21 kΩ	10 %
Power consumption at supply ±5 V	5.6 mW	5.2 mW	–7 %

5.4.1.2 Example B, heavily loaded output buffer

The required schematic is shown in Fig.5.5.

The input data are the following :

$V_{DD} - V_{SS}$ = +5 V, –5 V	power supply voltage
R_L = 600 Ω	load resistance
C_L = 30 pF	load capacitance
V_o = 3.8 V	peak output voltage swing
G = 1	maximum closed loop gain
G_r < 1 per cent	maximum gain tolerance
f_{3dB} > 10 kHz	minimum 3 dB corner frequency
SR = < 6 V/s	slew rate

The cell descriptor X was calculated to be X = 26 and cell descriptor Z = 3 with the results summarized in Table 5.5.

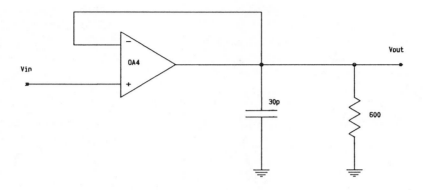

Fig. 5.5 Heavily loaded output buffer

Table 5.5 Measured and target electrical characteristics for the synthesized operational amplifier cell in example B

Cell parameter	Target value	Measured value	Deviation from target value
Offset voltage range	+2 mV /–2 mV	1.5 mV	0 %
Offset temp.coeff.	7 μV/°C	8 μV/°C	14 %
1/f noise at 100 Hz	192 nV/√Hz	225 nV/√Hz	17 %
1/f noise at 1 kHz	78 nV/√Hz	95 nV/√Hz	9 %
1/f noise at 10 kHz	49 nV/√Hz	55 nV/√Hz	12 %
Noise temp.coeff.	1.6 nV/√Hz/°C	1.6 nV/√Hz/°C	0 %
Open loop DC gain	88 dB	91 dB	3.4 %
Open loop gain at 70 Hz	83 dB	85 dB	2.4 %
Open loop gain at 200 Hz	78 dB	80 dB	2.5 %
Gain bandwidth	1.6 MHz	1.65 MHz	3.1 %
Phase margin at C_L = 15 pF	75 °	78 °	4 %
Total harmonic distortion	0.02 %	0.02 %	0 %
PSRR	–70 dB	–65 dB	–7 %
CMRR	–90 dB	–86 dB	–5 %
Input voltage range	–4.2 V / +4.3 V	–4.1 V / +4.2 V	2.5 %
Output voltage swing at R_L = 600 Ω	–4.0 V / +4.0 V	–3.8 V / +4.0 V	–5 %
Slew rate at C_L = 30 pF	5.3 V/μs	5.1 V/μs	–4 %
Output resistance	7.3 kΩ	7.6 kΩ	4 %
Power consumption at supply ±5 V	9.6 mW	9.2 mW	–4.2 %

5.4.2. Low power, low voltage class A operational amplifier synthesis and layout compilation

Fig.5.6 represents the schematic diagram of the selected amplifier. Similarly to the previous example it consists of the following sub-circuits:

1. Differential input stage
2. Phase compensation circuit
3. Output stage
4. Bias generator

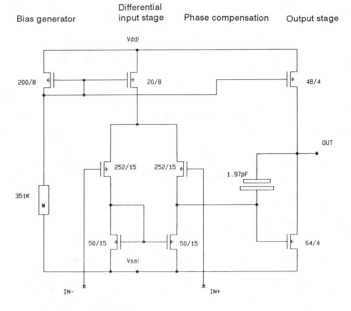

Fig. 5.6 Low power, low voltage class A amplifier

The cell was designed to operate from single or dual supply voltage ranging from 1.2 V to 10 V. Four cell descriptors were assigned to the cell:

1. X incremental sizing of output stage
2. Y incremental sizing of input stage
3. Z incremental sizing of bias generator
4. W incremental sizing of phase compensation circuit

The characterization of the cell was performed by using the following descriptors: $X = 6$, $Y = 1$, $Z = 1$, $W = 1$. Its layout with descriptors $X = 6$, $Y = 1$, $Z = 1$ and $W = 1$ is shown in Plate 5.2. Tables 5.6, 5.7 and 5.8 show some of the characterization results. The synthesis algorithm calculates the descriptors on the basis of the following closed loop characteristics:

Table 5.6(a,b) Print-out of characterization data of operational amplifier OA13 at 25 °C for process parameter corner A for power supply voltages (a) ±1.1 V, (b) ±1.2 V

```
ELECTRICAL CHARACTERISTICS :13A( ) 2.4 V,25 C;   23.10.87
    SYMBOL      MIN      TYP      MAX     UNITS        σ(N)

    VOS        -5.19    -1.50     2.36     mV          1.67
    AO30Hz     83.40    84.06    85.48     dB          0.51
    AO80Hz     72.52    74.30    76.40     dB          1.23
    AO10kHz    41.04    41.58    42.00     dB          0.22
    AO100kHz   20.88    21.42    21.82     dB          0.22
    BW          1.12     1.19     1.25     MHz         0.03
    EN100Hz   140.00   169.60   187.00     nV/√Hz     13.96
    EN1kHz     85.60    94.50   102.00     nV/√Hz      3.70
    EN10kHz    54.40    60.32    63.60     nV/√Hz      2.80
    OVRP        1.03     1.10     1.30     V           0.08
    OVRN       -1.04    -1.03    -0.99     V           0.02
    IVRP        0.94     0.94     0.94     V           0.00
    IVRN       -0.84    -0.84    -0.84     V           0.00
    PM *        0.00     0.00     0.00     deg         0.00
    CMRR     -109.4    -86.43   -76.70     dB          7.99
    THD         0.04     0.06     0.18     %           0.03
    PSRR     -110.4    -93.80   -79.03     dB          9.03
    FTOP        0.61     0.64     0.71     MHz         0.04
    ROUT *      0.00     0.00     0.00     kΩ          0.00


* NOT MEASURED



ELECTRICAL CHARACTERISTICS :13A( ) 2.4 V,25 C;   23.10.87
    SYMBOL      MIN      TYP      MAX     UNITS        σ(N)

    VOS        -3.90    -1.48     2.33     mV          1.51
    AO30Hz     84.08    85.29    87.00     dB          0.75
    AO80Hz     73.68    75.79    77.94     dB          1.10
    AO10kHz    42.08    42.68    43.08     dB          0.21
    AO100kHz   22.12    22.66    23.10     dB          0.22
    BW          1.27     1.36     1.43     MHz         0.04
    EN100Hz   143.00   170.70   200.00     nV/√Hz     13.86
    EN1kHz     85.60    92.90    98.40     nV/√Hz      3.89
    EN10kHz    51.60    58.04    63.60     nV/√Hz      3.20
    OVRP        1.15     1.21     1.31     V           0.05
    OVRN       -1.16    -1.15    -1.10     V           0.02
    IVRP        1.10     1.10     1.10     V           0.00
    IVRN       -0.90    -0.90    -0.90     V           0.00
    PM *        0.00     0.00     0.00     deg         0.00
    CMRR     -113.4    -88.17   -77.64     dB          9.61
    THD         0.03     0.04     0.06     %           0.01
    PSRR     -113.9    -93.86   -79.74     dB          8.70
    FTOP        0.71     0.71     0.76     MHz         0.01
    ROUT *      0.00     0.00     0.00     kΩ          0.00


* NOT MEASURED
```

```
ELECTRICAL CHARACTERISTICS :13A() 2.6 V,25 C;  23.10.87
  SYMBOL     MIN      TYP      MAX     UNITS        σ(N)


VOS        -5.02    -1.47     2.32     mV           1.63
AO30Hz     85.46    86.40    87.96     dB           0.68
AO80Hz     74.44    75.87    78.18     dB           1.18
AO10kHz    43.18    43.66    44.04     dB           0.22
AO100kHz   23.10    23.68    24.02     dB           0.23
BW          1.44     1.53     1.59     MHz          0.04
EN100Hz   145.00   167.15   181.00     nV/√Hz       8.47
EN1kHz     77.20    89.20    97.20     nV/√Hz       4.42
EN10kHz    53.60    58.40    64.40     nV/√Hz       2.94
OVRP        1.28     1.31     1.33     V            0.01
OVRN       -1.28    -1.26    -1.23     V            0.02
IVRP        1.26     1.26     1.26     V            0.00
IVRN       -1.06    -1.06    -1.06     V            0.00
PM *        0.00     0.00     0.00     deg          0.00
CMRR     -125.8    -89.95   -78.55     dB          11.10
THD         0.03     0.04     0.05     %            0.00
PSRR     -120.2    -94.83   -80.08     dB           9.48
FTOP        0.81     0.81     0.81     MHz          0.00
ROUT *      0.00     0.00     0.00     kΩ           0.00


* NOT MEASURED
```

Table 5.6(c) Print-out of characterization data of operational amplifier OA13 at 25 °C for process parameter corner A for power supply voltage ±1.3 V.

The abbreviations are the following:

VOS: input offset voltage
AO30Hz, AO80Hz, AO10kHz, AO100kHz: open loop gain at 30 Hz, 80 Hz, 10 kHz, 100 kHz
BW: gain bandwidth product
EN100Hz, EN1kHz, EN10kHz: input noise density at 100 Hz, 1 kHz, 10 kHz
OVRP: positive output voltage range at $R_L = 100$ kΩ
OVRN: negative output voltage range at $R_L = 100$ kΩ
IVRP: common mode positive input voltage range
IVRN: common mode negative input voltage range
PM: phase margin at unity gain
CMRR: input common mode rejection ratio
THD: total harmonic distortion at 1 V_{RMS} output level
PSRR: power supply rejection ratio
FTOP: unity gain frequency
ROUT: output impedance

Table 5.7(a,b) Print-out of characterization data of operational amplifier OA13 at 25 °C for process parameter corner F for power supply voltages (a) ±1.1 V, (b) ±1.2 V

```
ELECTRICAL CHARACTERISTICS :13F() 2.2 V,25 C;  23.10.87
    SYMBOL      MIN     TYP     MAX    UNITS       σ(N)

    VOS        -6.03   -1.40    1.83    mV         1.92
    AO30Hz     86.64   87.72   88.50    dB         0.49
    AO80Hz     73.58   75.38   77.64    dB         1.13
    AO10kHz    39.38   39.80   40.36    dB         0.25
    AO100kHz   19.10   19.54   20.02    dB         0.24
    BW          0.92    0.96    1.02    MHz        0.03
    EN100Hz   140.00  159.69  184.00    nV/√Hz    11.37
    EN1kHz     99.60  106.89  119.00    nV/√Hz     5.76
    EN10kHz    59.20   65.70   72.00    nV/√Hz     3.18
    OVRP        1.03    1.06    1.09    V          0.02
    OVRN       -1.05   -1.04   -1.00    V          0.02
    IVRP        1.14    1.14    1.14    V          0.00
    IVRN       -1.14   -0.76   -0.64    V          0.16
    PM *        0.00    0.00    0.00    deg        0.00
    CMRR      -97.07  -81.01  -68.16    dB         7.51
    THD         0.04    0.18    2.39    %          0.50
    PSRR      -98.52  -82.65  -69.19    dB         8.53
    FTOP        0.51    0.51    0.51    MHz        0.00
    ROUT *      0.00    0.00    0.00    kΩ         0.00


 * NOT MEASURED


ELECTRICAL CHARACTERISTICS :13F() 2.4 V,25 C;  23.10.87
    SYMBOL      MIN     TYP     MAX    UNITS       σ(N)

    VOS        -5.86   -1.39    1.82    mV         1.89
    AO30Hz     88.10   89.27   90.56    dB         0.71
    AO80Hz     73.44   76.86   78.50    dB         1.36
    AO10kHz    42.14   42.62   43.22    dB         0.29
    AO100kHz   22.00   22.57   23.30    dB         0.32
    BW          1.27    1.35    1.46    MHz        0.05
    EN100Hz   131.00  159.40  187.00    nV/√Hz    15.89
    EN1kHz     82.00   93.74  113.00    nV/√Hz     7.22
    EN10kHz    60.00   65.14   71.20    nV/√Hz     3.21
    OVRP        1.17    1.20    1.23    V          0.02
    OVRN       -1.17   -1.16   -1.12    V          0.02
    IVRP        1.20    1.29    1.30    V          0.02
    IVRN       -1.30   -0.84   -0.70    V          0.12
    PM *        0.00    0.00    0.00    deg        0.00
    CMRR     -101.7   -86.70  -73.39    dB         8.37
    THD         0.03    0.05    0.21    %          0.04
    PSRR     -118.4   -86.87  -72.79    dB        10.51
    FTOP        0.71    0.71    0.71    MHz        0.00
    ROUT *      0.00    0.00    0.00    kΩ         0.00


 * NOT MEASURED
```

```
ELECTRICAL CHARACTERISTICS :13F() 2.6 V,25 C;   23.10.87
  SYMBOL     MIN      TYP      MAX     UNITS       σ(N)

 VOS        -6.14    -1.42     1.82    mV          1.94
 AO30Hz     88.86    90.09    91.00    dB          0.54
 AO80Hz     75.24    76.87    78.62    dB          0.86
 AO10kHz    43.52    44.12    44.82    dB          0.33
 AO100kHz   23.60    24.14    24.82    dB          0.32
 BW          1.51     1.61     1.74    MHz         0.07
 EN100Hz   132.00   149.30   168.00   nV/√Hz     10.36
 EN1kHz     78.00    86.58    92.80    nV/√Hz      4.01
 EN10kHz    57.20    62.86    68.80    nV/√Hz      3.14
 OVRP        1.29     1.31     1.33    V           0.01
 OVRN       -1.29    -1.28    -1.24    V           0.02
 IVRP        1.36     1.36     1.36    V           0.00
 IVRN       -0.86    -0.86    -0.86    V           0.00
 PM   *      0.00     0.00     0.00    deg         0.00
 CMRR     -127.4    -93.48   -80.79    dB         10.63
 THD         0.03     0.04     0.06    %           0.01
 PSRR     -122.0    -92.86   -77.66    dB         11.87
 FTOP        0.81     0.81     0.81    MHz         0.00
 ROUT *      0.00     0.00     0.00    kΩ          0.00

 * NOT MEASURED
```

Table 5.7(c) Print-out of characterization data of operational amplifier OA13 at 25 °C for process parameter corner F for power supply voltage ±1.3 V.

The abbreviations are the following:

VOS: input offset voltage
AO30Hz, AO80Hz, AO10kHz, AO100kHz: open loop gain at 30 Hz, 80 Hz, 10 kHz, 100 kHz
BW: gain bandwidth product
EN100Hz, EN1kHz, EN10kHz: input noise density at 100 Hz, 1 kHz, 10 kHz
OVRP: positive output voltage range at $R_L = 100\,k\Omega$
OVRN: negative output voltage range at $R_L = 100\,k\Omega$
IVRP: common mode positive input voltage range
IVRN: common mode negative input voltage range
PM: phase margin at unity gain
CMRR: input common mode rejection ratio
THD: total harmonic distortion at 1 V_{RMS} output level
PSRR: power supply rejection ratio
FTOP: unity gain frequency
ROUT: output impedance

Table 5.8(a,b) Print-out of characterization data of operational amplifier OA13 for all parameter corners (A, B, C, D, E, F) for power supply voltage ±1.2 V at (a) 25 ˚C, (b) 80 ˚C

```
ELECTRICAL CHARACTERISTICS :13() 2.4 V,25 C;  19.01.89
   SYMBOL      MIN      TYP      MAX     UNITS       σ(N)

VOS           -5.86    -1.38     2.33     mV         1.48
AO30Hz        80.22    85.35    90.56     dB         3.40
AO80Hz        69.54    75.13    78.64     dB         2.23
AO10kHz       30.04    38.34    43.22     dB         4.98
AO100kHz       8.92    17.98    23.30     dB         5.43
BW             0.30     0.94     1.46     MHz        0.44
EN100Hz      131.00   183.97   276.00     nV/√Hz    30.93
EN1kHz        82.00   109.35   163.00     nV/√Hz    22.56
EN10kHz       41.40    60.48   183.00     nV/√Hz    22.54
OVRP           1.14     1.19     1.31     V          0.04
OVRN          -1.18    -1.16    -1.10     V          0.02
IVRP           1.10     1.24     1.30     V          0.08
IVRN          -1.30    -0.94    -0.70     V          0.19
PM *           0.00     0.00     0.00     deg        0.00
CMRR        -116.2    -86.75   -69.87     dB         8.81
THD            0.03     0.04     0.21     %          0.02
PSRR        -118.4    -88.50   -70.09     dB        10.04
FTOP           0.20     0.53     0.76     MHz        0.22
ROUT *         0.00     0.00     0.00     kΩ         0.00

* NOT MEASURED


ELECTRICAL CHARACTERISTICS :13() 2.4 V,80 C;  19.01.89
   SYMBOL      MIN      TYP      MAX     UNITS       σ(N)

VOS           -5.37    -1.20     2.26     mV         1.39
AO30Hz        76.90    82.83    87.72     dB         3.71
AO80Hz        66.96    73.32    77.26     dB         2.98
AO10kHz       27.04    35.67    41.00     dB         5.31
AO100kHz       5.10    14.85    20.60     dB         6.06
BW             0.20     0.69     1.10     MHz        0.34
EN100Hz      113.00   160.71   241.00     nV/√Hz    33.13
EN1kHz        85.60   122.29   183.00     nV/√Hz    31.49
EN10kHz       39.60    57.99    77.20     nV/√Hz    10.66
OVRP           1.13     1.18     1.20     V          0.01
OVRN          -1.18    -1.15    -1.10     V          0.02
IVRP           1.10     1.25     1.30     V          0.08
IVRN          -1.10    -0.90    -0.80     V          0.14
PM *           0.05    10.33   103.14     deg       13.03
CMRR        -140.3    -91.94   -77.25     dB        11.08
THD            0.03     0.05     0.13     %          0.02
PSRR        -121.1    -92.86   -77.75     dB         8.57
FTOP           0.15     0.67    13.00     MHz        1.85
ROUT *         0.00     0.00     0.00     kΩ         0.00

* NOT MEASURED
```

```
ELECTRICAL CHARACTERISTICS :13() 2.4 V,-40 C;  19.01.89
   SYMBOL      MIN      TYP      MAX    UNITS       σ(N)

   VOS        -7.36    -1.93     2.31    mV         1.91
   AO30Hz     72.54    87.20    93.52    dB         3.68
   AO80Hz     70.02    74.69    78.02    dB         1.72
   AO10kHz    32.68    40.24    46.24    dB         4.50
   AO100kHz   12.24    20.09    26.14    dB         4.71
   BW          0.24     1.15     2.04    MHz        0.53
   EN100Hz   196.00   291.22   680.00    nV/√Hz    84.92
   EN1kHz     68.00   110.42   152.00    nV/√Hz    18.48
   EN10kHz    39.60    54.07    65.60    nV/√Hz     5.16
   OVRP        1.00     1.09     1.13    V          0.03
   OVRN       -1.19    -1.17    -1.16    V          0.01
   IVRP        0.80     1.14     1.30    V          0.16
   IVRN       -1.30    -0.94    -0.70    V          0.24
   PM *        0.00     0.00     0.00    deg        0.00
   CMRR     -125.6    -79.85   -58.47    dB        11.33
   THD         0.00     0.00     0.00    %          0.00
   PSRR     -110.1    -80.25   -58.61    dB        10.45
   FTOP        0.00     0.00     0.00    MHz        0.00
   ROUT *      0.00     0.00     0.00    kΩ         0.00

   * NOT MEASURED
```

Table 5.8(c) Print-out of characterization data of operational amplifier OA13 for all process parameter corners (A,B,C,D,E,F) for power supply voltage ±1.2 V at −40 °C.

The abbreviations are the following:

VOS: input offset voltage
AO30Hz, AO80Hz, AO10kHz, AO100kHz: open loop gain at 30 Hz, 80 Hz, 10 kHz, 100 kHz
BW: gain bandwidth product
EN100Hz, EN1kHz, EN10kHz: input noise density at 100 Hz, 1 kHz, 10 kHz
OVRP: positive output voltage range at $R_L = 100$ kΩ
OVRN: negative output voltage range at $R_L = 100$ kΩ
IVRP: common mode positive input voltage range
IVRN: common mode negative input voltage range
PM: phase margin at unity gain
CMRR: input common mode rejection ratio
THD: total harmonic distortion at 1 V_{RMS} output level
PSRR: power supply rejection ratio
FTOP: unity gain frequency
ROUT: output impedance

1. Power supply operating voltage and current
2. Load conditions
3. Output voltage swing
4. Closed loop gain and accuracy
5. $1/f$ input noise voltage
6. Closed loop 3 dB gain drop frequency
7. Slew rate

The degrees of freedom for sizing all sub-circuits in the cell are limited by the synthesis algorithm.

A few examples of the synthesis and sizing of this cell are presented in Chapter 9.

5.4.3 Cascode operational amplifier synthesis and compilation

This type of operational amplifier is particularly suitable for S–C filter applications. The schematic of the cell is shown in Fig.5.7. The output transistors are sized according to cell descriptor X, differential input transistors according to descriptor Y, and bias transistor according to descriptor Z, as shown in Plate 5.3. For the characterization the following descriptors were chosen: $X = 1$, $Y = 3$ and $Z = 1$. The sizing algorithm is incorporated as a part of the automatic filter synthesis program, described in Section 5.5.

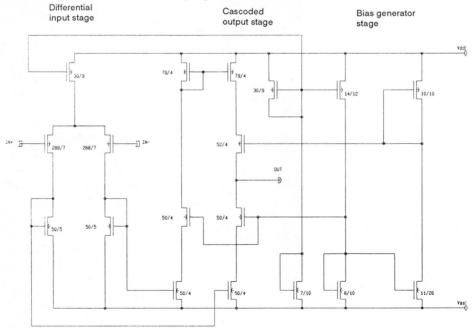

Fig. 5.7 Cascode operational amplifier

5.5   S–C filter synthesis

5.5.1   Introduction

Amplitude transfer function synthesis is based on an analytical approximation of the transfer function with the ratio of two polynomials. The theoretical background is given in Ref.11.

The input data necessary to define the transfer function is given to the program from a user friendly graphic entry system. The output is coefficients of the required transfer function given as a product of second order stages, and possibly first order stage for odd order filters.

5.5.2   Basic definitions

The basic types of amplitude transfer functions and their templates are given in Fig.5.8(a) for low-pass (LP), in Fig.5.8(b) for high-pass (HP), in Fig.5.8(c) for band-pass (BP) and for band stop (BS) in Fig.5.8(d). The types of amplitude transfer functions are:

1.   Butterworth
2.   Chebyshev
3.   Elliptic

The transfer function is synthesized in the s domain and is given as a cascade of biquadratic sections. For S–C filters it is transformed into the z domain using bilinear s–z transformation:[11]

$$s = \frac{2}{T} \frac{z-1}{z+1} \tag{5.1}$$

5.5.3   Synthesis algorithm

The amplitude transfer function synthesis algorithm flowchart is shown in Fig.5.9.

The synthesis procedure starts with the selection of the filter type and its transfer function. The next step is the entry of the border amplitude and frequency points according to the definitions, and if the S–C filter is required, the sampling frequency has to be selected.

If the required transfer function is in the z domain, then prewarping is performed to correct for the bilinear transformation non-linearity. From the prewarped specifications, the parameters for LP normalized transfer function are determined and then appropriate positions of poles and zeros in the frequency domain are calculated according to the transfer function type. In the next step, the denormalized transfer function coefficients are calculated using poles and zeros of the normalized LP transfer function. This transfer function is useful for antialiasing and smoothing filters synthesis. For S–C filters built of cascaded biquadratic sections the bilinear s–z transformation is performed.

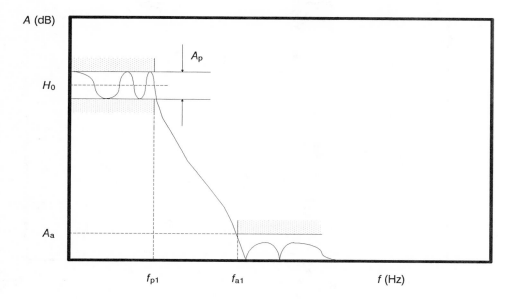

Fig. 5.8(a) Amplitude transfer function of low-pass filter

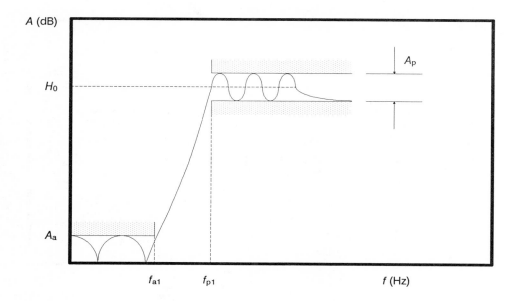

Fig. 5.8(b) Amplitude transfer function of high-pass filter

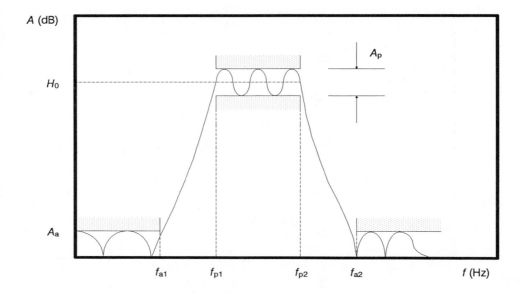

Fig. 5.8(c) Amplitude transfer function of band-pass filter

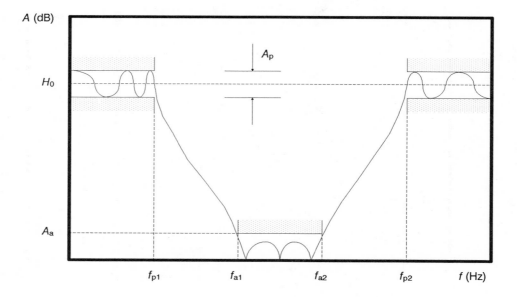

Fig. 5.8(d) Amplitude transfer function of band-stop filter

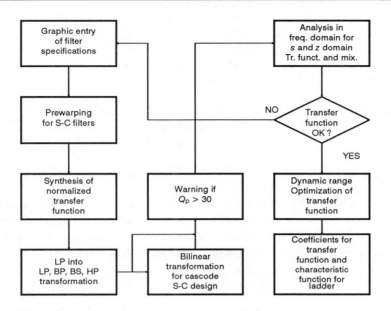

Fig. 5.9 Flowchart for amplitude transfer function synthesis

The transfer function dynamic range is optimized for cascaded sections with the following algorithm:

Step one: pairing of all poles and zeros for the elliptic transfer functions to make the amplitude transfer function of the pairs as flat as possible.

Step two: ordering of sections so that the section with the flattest transfer function is the first and the one with the worst ripple is the last in the cascade.

Step three: constant factors of each biquadratic stage are calculated to equalize the output levels.

The procedure is the same for all types of transfer functions except for step one which is only necessary for elliptic filters.

This optimization algorithm yields a dynamic range which is very close to optimum. It is also very fast and can be completed in real time.

At the end the transfer function is given as a table of coefficients used in equation (5.2).

$$H(w) = \prod_{l=1}^{l=s} h_0[l] \quad \frac{A[2,1]\, w^2 + A[1,1]\, w + A[0,1]}{B[2,1]\, w^2 + B[1,1]\, w + B[0,1]} \tag{5.2}$$

- where $w = s$ for the s domain transfer function, and
- $w = z$ for the z domain transfer function

The program analyses the gain, phase and delay of the synthesized transfer function in s or z domain or in a combination of the two. This combination is useful for the analysis of the complete filter as the cascade of the antialiasing filter, the S–C filter and the smoothing filter.

5.5.4 Aliasing

If the required transfer function is in the z domain a continuous time antialiasing filter is usually necessary, in order to prevent high frequency components of the input spectrum being folded into the baseband. The pole frequency and the order of the filter are determined from the sampling frequency, border points of S–C filter and the requirements of noise and distortion.

5.5.5 Smoothing

A smoothing filter is required if the output is connected to the analog environment where the spectrum of output signal is strictly defined. Since the output signal of S–C filters is a sampled and hold signal, the spectrum is composed of the baseband spectrum and image frequencies about multiples of the sampling frequency, and of multiples of the sampling frequency itself. Such a spectrum is very rich and must be attenuated with a smoothing filter, usually a single pole passive or second order active filter.

5.6 Continuous time filter synthesis

5.6.1. Integration of antialiasing and smoothing filters

In this section only integrated antialiasing and smoothing filters are discussed. The average requirements for such filters are the following:

1. Second order low-pass filter
2. Accurate, process and temperature independent passband gain
3. Low passband ripple
4. High stopband attenuation
5. Inaccurate pole frequency
6. Loose pole frequency accuracy requirements

Two predefined filter topologies are chosen to meet the listed requirements.

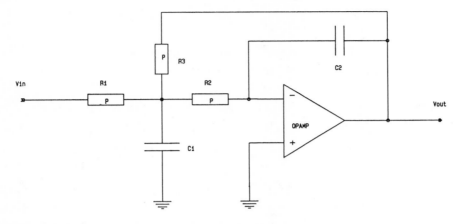

Fig. 5.10 Negative feedback low-pass filter topology

The circuit shown in Fig.5.10 using a single operational amplifier is known as a negative feedback topology. The relevant filter parameters are calculated according to the following equations — for pole frequency ω_p:

$$\omega_p{}^2 = \frac{1}{C_1\,C_2\,R_1\,R_2} \tag{5.3}$$

for passband gain H_o:

$$H_o = \frac{R_3}{R_1} \tag{5.4}$$

and filter quality Q_p:

$$Q_p = \frac{((C_1\,R_3)/(C_2\,R_2))^{1/2}}{1 + (R_3/R_1) + (R_3/R_2)} \tag{5.5}$$

The second, so-called positive feedback low-pass topology is shown in Fig.5.11. Filter parameters are given as pole frequency ω_p:

$$\omega_p{}^2 = \frac{1}{R_1\,R_2\,C_1\,C_2} \tag{5.6}$$

Passband gain H_o is in this case:

$$H_o = 1 \tag{5.7}$$

and filter quality Q_p is given as:

$$\frac{1}{Q_p} = (\frac{R_1 C_2}{R_2 C_1})^{1/2} + (\frac{R_2 C_2}{R_1 C_1})^{1/2} \tag{5.8}$$

The selection of the appropriate topology is performed according to Table 5.9 where the positive and negative features of both topologies are compared.

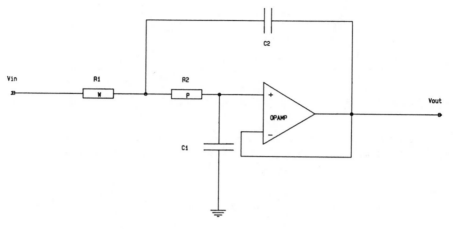

Fig. 5.11 Positive feedback low-pass filter topology

Table 5.9 Features of positive and negative feedback filter topologies

	NEGATIVE FEEDBACK low-pass filter topology	POSITIVE FEEDBACK low-pass filter topology
ADVANTAGES	Programmable passband gain Good high frequency characteristic Insensitive OP–AMP design regarding input common range and stability	Low sensitivity of Q_p and H_o Low distortion in spite of P-well resistor voltage coefficient Smaller silicon area
DISADVANTAGES	More elements requiring larger silicon area Larger sensitivity of H_o and Q_p Large distortion due to resistors' voltage coefficient	Non-programmable passband gain Degraded high frequency characteristic Demanding OP–AMP design regarding its stability and common mode voltage range

5.6.2 Continuous time filter design automation

In Fig.5.12 a flowchart for the automatic design of antialiasing and/or smoothing filters is given.

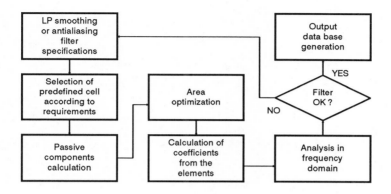

Fig. 5.12 Flowchart for automatic design of antialiasing and/or smoothing filter

5.7 S–C filter synthesis using cascaded biquadratic stages

The simplest solution for S–C filter topology synthesis is the approach based upon cascaded biquadratic stages. This solution is not the best for sensitivity, noise, area and dynamic range; however the design procedure is time effective and automatic. It also gives structures which are modular and very good for VLSI implementation. It is appropriate for mid and low order filters with a maximum Q of the section lower than approximately 30.

5.7.1 Transfer functions

The amplitude transfer function is given as a product of the second and first order transfer functions in the z domain according to the formulas given previously. The number of stages S is equal to $n/2$ for even order transfer function S, and $S = n/2+1$ for odd order transfer function. The approximation of given transfer functions is acceptable if the ratio between sampling frequency and the pole frequency is greater than approximately 5.

5.7.2 Biquadratic stages

5.7.2.1 First order stage

The structure for the first order section is given in Fig.5.13.

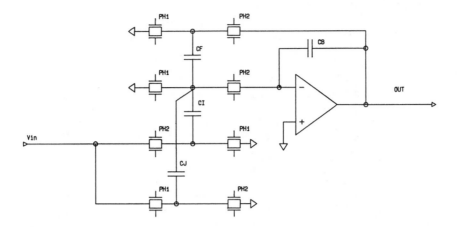

Fig. 5.13 First order stage filter topology

The proposed first order stage can exactly realize the first order HP transfer function, however it can realize the generic LP transfer function only approximately. (The approximation is acceptable if the ratio of sampling frequency to pole frequency is large enough, at least $f_s/f_p > 5$.)

5.7.2.2 Second order stage

The basic topology which can realize all types of second order transfer functions is shown in Fig.5.14. The letters CA, CB, CC, CD, CE, CF, CG, CH, CI, CJ represent capacitor names and their values.

5.7.3 Poles for second order stage

In the first step the capacitors which determine the poles (denominator of transfer function) are calculated for each biquadratic stage in a cascade. Since there are more capacitors than necessary, some of them may take fixed values for the first iteration. This freedom is used later for optimization of some parameters. Because only the capacitor ratio is important the integrating capacitors CB and CD are set to 1.0, i.e. to a unity value capacitor. The capacitor CA is also set to 1 and is recalculated later during the optimization of dynamic range. Since the remaining number of capacitors is still redundant to form the poles of the second order circuit, two basic topologies are used: E-topology with capacitor CF = 0 and F-topology with capacitor CE = 0.

Equating the denominator coefficients at the same power of z in the synthesized transfer function with the transfer function obtained from the S–C topology from Fig.5.14 results in the values of pole capacitors (CA, CB, CC, CD, CE, CF).

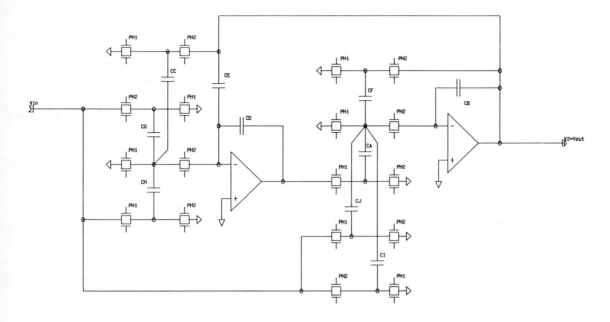

Fig. 5.14 General filter topology for second order biquadratic stages

5.7.4 Pole for first order stage

For the first order stage the pole is defined with the definition of capacitors CB and CF, while all other capacitors are set to zero.

5.7.5 Zeros for second order stage

The "zeros" capacitors are determined for all exact and approximate transfer functions for each biquadratic stages in cascade by equating their numerator coefficients with those of the required transfer function.

Three equations are given for the six capacitors CI, CIJ, CJ, CG, CH, CGH. Hence three of the capacitors can be preset to optimize some particular performance parameter.

5.7.6 Zero for first order stage

For the first order stage two equations can be written and three capacitors have to be determined.

5.7.7 Dynamic range optimization

The gain of internal outputs must be determined for the given transfer function. To get the optimum dynamic range for an S–C filter which is driven with a white noise input signal, the maximum levels at all outputs (also internal outputs) should be equal to the level at the main output. The selection of the optimization algorithm is very important when an efficient real time synthesis is required.

5.7.8 Scaling

The performance of an S–C filter is determined by the ratio of capacitors in each integrating stage. The capacitors in the biquadratic stages which can be scaled are divided in the two groups: capacitors CD, CE, CC, CG, CH, CGH from one group and capacitors CB, CF, CA, CI, CJ, CIJ from the second. The minimum capacitor in each group is chosen as the unity value while other capacitors are divided by this value.

5.7.9 Area optimization

The optimization of area can be performed using one of two procedures. In the first, parallel combination of S–C stages CI and CJ are transformed into:

1. Parallel stages CIJ = CJ, CI = CI – CJ, CJ = 0; for CI > CJ
2. Parallel stages CIJ = CI, CJ = CJ – CI, CI = 0; for CI < CJ
3. Capacitor CIJ = CI, CI = 0, CJ = 0; for CI = CJ

The transformation of parallel combinations of switched-capacitors CI and CJ or CG and CH is possible if the input signal is a full sample and hold signal with the proper phase.

The same procedure is used for the combination of capacitors CG and CH. Which combination will be used is dependent on the total area of the resultant circuit, where the total area is composed of the capacitor area, the area of switches and the area of interconnect. Usually the last solution gives the smallest area and has the lowest sensitivity, since the number of capacitors is reduced.

The second procedure for area optimization is to compute all possible versions and to choose the solution which gives the smallest area for each biquadratic stage. This procedure, while capable of producing optimum results is not used in practice because of the unacceptable long computation time required.

5.7.10 Definition of clock phases

In the synthesis procedure it is assumed that all biquadratic stages have the same clock phase, which is defined as a phase when all switched-capacitors in that stage are discharged to the virtual ground of the operational amplifier. This solution is possible only if the sampling frequency is very low and/or the S–C filter does not have many stages in cascade, and if we neglect the real performance of the elements. If real elements are taken into account it is necessary to prevent signal propagation through more than one biquadratic stage during one half of a clock cycle; otherwise the performance will be degraded.

The phase in the biquadratic stage will be the same as in the previous stage provided that it does not have the capacitors CI and/or CIJ, and different if one of these capacitors is present. For the first biquadratic stage the phase is defined from the input signal phase. When changing the phases according to the described rules an error in gain occurs. However, it is negligible if the ratio of pole frequency to sampling frequency is small enough (at least $f_p/f_s = 0.2$).

5.7.11 S–C filter library cell organization and selection

Each biquadratic stage is composed of two integrators, some S–C stages, and capacitors which are connected either between the two integrators or between the signal input and the first integrator or to both. By comparing the electrical topology of both integrator stages in the biquadratic cell, and the topology of the first order stage, the basic integrator stages given in Table 5.10 can be derived. From these stages all possible second order and first order

Table 5.10 Integrator stages

First integrator stage					Second integrator stage				
CC	CG	CH	CGH	NAME	CF	CA	CI	CJ	CIJ
0	0	x	0	BU2AYZ	0	x	0	0	0
0	x	0	0	BU2BYZ					
x	x	0	0	BU3BYZ					
x	0	x	0	BU3DYZ	0	x	x	0	0
x	x	x	0	BU4AYZ					
x	0	0	x	BU2SYZ	0	x	0	0	x
x	0	0	0	BU2BYZ					
				BU3AYZ	x	x	0	0	0
				BU3SYZ	x	x	0	0	x
				BU4BYZ	0	x	x	x	0
				BU4CYZ	x	x	x	0	0
				BU4DYZ	x	x	0	x	0
				BU5AYZ	x	x	x	x	0
				BU2HYZ	x	0	0	0	x
				BU3GYZ	x	0	0	x	0
				BU3FYZ	x	0	0	x	x
				BU3IYZ	x	0	x	0	0
				BU3JYZ	x	0	x	0	x
				BU3LYZ	0	x	0	x	0
				BU4AYZ	x	0	x	x	0

biquadratic stages can be realized for all E- and F-type circuits from all exact and approximate transfer functions.

The following data is necessary for the definition of the integrator stage name:

1. A set of capacitors for every integrator. The capacitors may have value 0 or different from 0 (in the table non-zero capacitors are marked with an x).
2. Integrator position within the biquadratic stage
3. Phase of the biquadratic stage

Each integrator stage is described by the name (BUNXYZ) in the first row, while in the next rows the capacitances of all non-zero capacitors are given. The name is composed as follows:

1. BU is the generic library name of a half biquadratic stage or an integrator stage.
2. N is the number of fixed seeds[14] needed for the integrator stage, where a fixed seed is necessary for all switched-capacitors stages and integrating capacitors.
3. X is the letter showing the type of inputs to the integrator stage.
4. Y is the number representing the phase of integrator stage.
5. Z is the number which shows the position of integrator stage within the biquadratic stage and can be 1 or 2.

In Table 5.10 the capacitor CE is not mentioned because it is a so-called "floating capacitor" and does not have a fixed seed, so it can be connected to any integrator stage. Secondly it is connected to the analog bus outside the biquadratic cell.

5.7.12 Automatic synthesis procedure

The complete synthesis algorithm of S–C filters based on the cascaded biquadratic section approach is represented by the flowchart shown in Fig.5.15.

5.8   S–C ladder filter synthesis principles

Ladder filters are known for producing transfer functions with very low sensitivity. This is true also for S–C filters obtained by transformation of a passive ladder structure. Because of this ladder filters are very useful for high performance and demanding filters. Theoretically, every type of filter (LP, HP, BP, BS) can be transformed into a ladder S–C topology; however, only the low-pass (LP) is really useful. S–C ladder filter synthesis is performed in two steps:

1. Doubly terminated passive LC ladder structure synthesis (RLC)
2. Transformation of passive RLC circuit into S–C topology

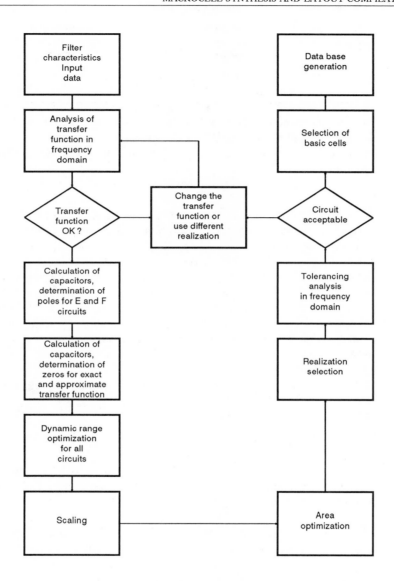

Fig. 5.15 S-C filter synthesis flowchart with cascaded biquadratic section approach

Two transfer functions are needed for passive ladder filter synthesis: The transfer function between output and input of the filter, and the characteristic function. Both can be calculated with existing programs and are given as a table of coefficients for polynomials in the s domain.[14]

The synthesis procedure for a passive doubly terminated ladder structure is performed in the following steps:[12]

1. From the known transfer and characteristic functions the immitance parameters y_{11}, y_{22} and z_{11}, z_{22} are calculated.
2. The positions for poles in the ladder structure are determined so that the lower poles are in the middle of the structure and the higher poles are located at the beginning and at the end of the ladder structure. This is necessary for elliptic filters only.
3. Calculation of elements using the driving point synthesis procedure and the zero shifting technique.
4. Calculation of terminating resistances.

The passive doubly terminated LC filter structure is then transformed into a S–C circuit using the lossless discrete integrator (LDI) transformation of branch currents and node voltages. The procedure is different for Butterworth/Chebyshev and elliptic filters. Each equation is realized using one of the S–C integrators from Table 5.9. The cells used for the S–C ladder filter design are as follows: input cell is BU4DYZ, middle cells are BU3BYZ, BU3DYZ, BU3LYZ (not used in cascaded S–C filter approach), and end terminating cells BU3CYZ, BU3AYZ.

When the capacitances have been calculated, the dynamic range optimization and the scaling is performed so that maximum levels on the integrators are made equal, or can be determined by the user.

At the end a tolerancing simulation is performed to analyse and predict the behaviour of the fabricated filter.

5.9   S–C filter design example

An example of advanced analog design tool for S–C filters synthesis and layout compilation will be described.[14] This allows automatic high performance ASIC layout generation from filter specifications within a few minutes.

The designer only needs to provide the filter specifications as seen in Table 5.11. This can be done using either an interactive graphical entry or a text file.

The transfer function is synthesized and analysed in the frequency domain. Two possible syntheses were analysed as shown in the schematics in Figs.5.16 and 5.17.

For filter topology synthesis, a cascaded biquadratic filter stage approach was selected. Table 5.12 shows the print-out of the calculated filter coefficients.

The schematic shown in Fig.5.16 is the result of a non-area optimized approach realizing the exact transfer function, while Fig.5.17 represents the filter topology which resulted from area

Table 5.11 Print-out of filter specifications

```
SC
Bandpass
Chebyshev
fa1 = 736Hz          ** first frequency in stopband
fa2 = 1635Hz         ** second frequency in stopband
fp1 = 1000Hz         ** first frequency in passband
fp2 = 1200Hz         ** second frequency in passband
fs  = 48kHz          ** sampling frequency
H0  = 0dB            ** gain in passband
AP  = 0.5dB          ** passband ripple
AA  = -60dB          ** attenuation in stopband
```

Table 5.12 Print-out of filter coefficients for filter, specified in Table 5.11

```
afil.s
sc
4                                    ** number of biq. stages
4.800000e+04                         ** sampling frequency
1.023293e+00                         ** gain in passband


1st BIQUADRATIC STAGE


+1.249162965196358e-02               ** constant factor
     NUMERATOR              DENOMINATOR
-1.000000000000000e+00 +9.877885974731362e-01  ** coefficients at power 0 of z
+1.000000000000000e+00 -1.965738347635092e+00  ** coefficients at power 1 of z
+0.000000000000000e+00 +1.000000000000000e+00  ** coefficients at power 2 of z


2nd BIQUADRATIC STAGE


+2.138546763871364e-02               ** constant factor
     NUMERATOR              DENOMINATOR
-1.000000000000000e+00 +9.886917346224007e-01  ** coefficients at power 0 of z
+1.000000000000000e+00 -1.969806226195491e+00  ** coefficients at power 1 of z
+0.000000000000000e+00 +1.000000000000000e+00  ** coefficients at power 2 of z


3rd BIQUADRATIC STAGE


+1.250936099452638e-02               ** constant factor
     NUMERATOR              DENOMINATOR
-1.000000000000000e+00 +9.955655196664763e-01  ** coefficients at power 0 of z
+1.000000000000000e+00 -1.978581647262729e+00  ** coefficients at power 1 of z
+0.000000000000000e+00 +1.000000000000000e+00  ** coefficients at power 2 of z


4th BIQUADRATIC STAGE


+5.693200990533544e-02               ** constant factor
     NUMERATOR              DENOMINATOR
-1.000000000000000e+00 +9.946602271682136e-01  ** coefficients at power 0 of z
+1.000000000000000e+00 -1.969974977320385e+00  ** coefficients at power 1 of z
+0.000000000000000e+00 +1.000000000000000e+00  ** coefficients at power 2 of z
```

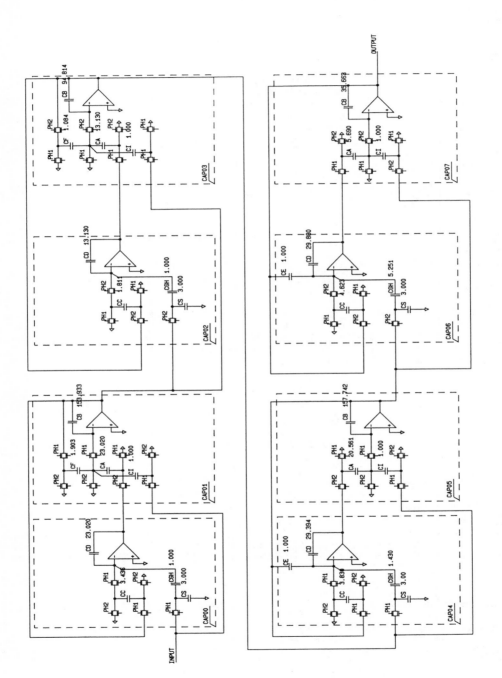

Fig. 5.16 Schematics for 8th order S–C Chebyshev filter

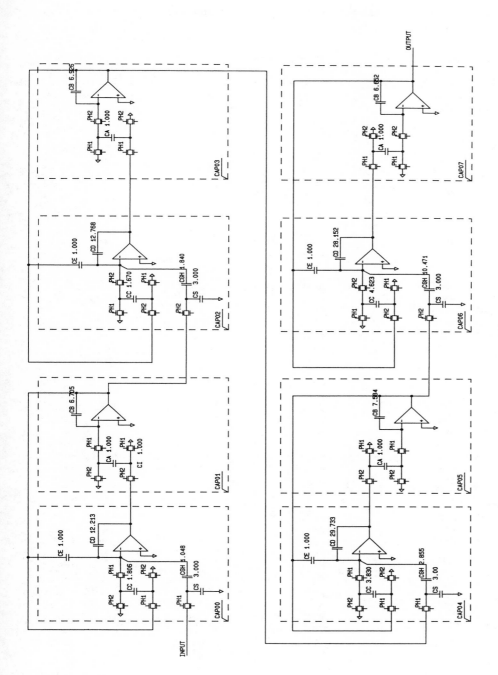

Fig. 5.17 Schematics for 8th order S–C Chebyshev filter, second alternative

Table 5.13(a,b) Capacitor values print-out for (a): area optimized filter, (b): non-optimized filter

```
(a)  afil.anc              (b)  fil.anc
*                          *
*  CAPACITOR TABLE         *  CAPACITOR TABLE
*  OPTIMIZED BY            *  BEFORE
*  APPROXIMATION           *  APPROXIMATION
*                          *
8                          8
BU2S21                     BU2S11
CD      12.213             CD      23.020
CC       1.806             CC       3.436
CE       1.000             GH       1.000
CGH      1.048             E
E                          BU4C12
BU2A22                     CB     153.933
CB       6.705             CF       1.903
CA       1.000             CA      23.020
E                          CI       1.000
BU2S21                     E
CD      12.768             BU2S21
CC       1.670             CD      13.130
CE       1.000             CC       1.811
CGH      1.840             CGH      1.000
E                          E
BU2A22                     BU4C22
CB       6.926             CB      94.814
CA       1.000             CF       1.084
E                          CA      13.130
BU2S21                     CI       1.000
CD      29.733             E
CC       3.830             BU2S11
CE       1.000             D       29.394
CGH      2.855             CC       3.830
E                          CE       1.000
BU2A22                     CGH      1.430
CB       7.584             E
CA       1.000             BU3D12
E                          CB     157.742
BU2S21                     CA      20.561
CD      28.152             I        1.000
CC       4.623             E
CE       1.000             BU2S21
CGH     10.471             CD      29.880
E                          CC       4.623
BU2A22                     CE       1.000
CB       6.652             GH       5.251
CA       1.000             E
E                          BU3D22
                           CB      35.663
                           CA       5.690
                           CI       1.000
                           E
```

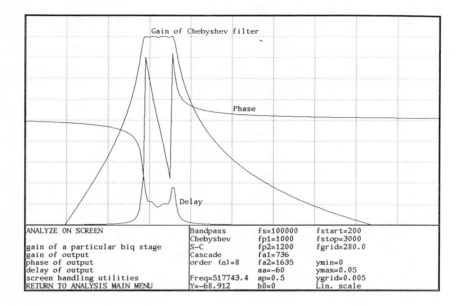

Fig. 5.18 Amplitude transfer function, phase and delay for 8th order S-C Chebyshev filter

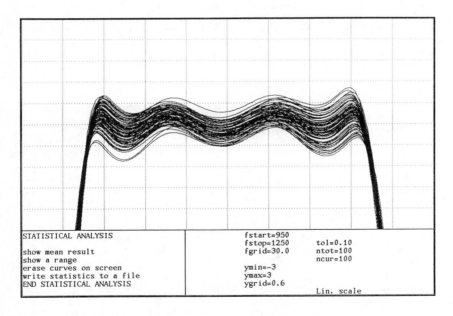

Fig. 5.19 Tolerancing analysis for 8th order S-C Chebyshev filter with optimized topology

optimization. The effectiveness of optimization can be seen from capacitor tables shown in Table 5.13(a) which show capacitor values for the optimized case, while Table 5.13(b) shows the non-optimized capacitor values. The amplitude transfer function together with phase and delay are shown in Fig.5.18 for the mathematical form of the requested filter. Fig.5.19 shows the results of a tolerancing analysis for the optimized filter topology. The automatically generated layout of this filter is shown in Plate 5.4. A SPICE file which was used for layout generation was automatically extracted and is shown in Table 5.14.

Table 5.14 Extracted SPICE file for optimized filter

```
afil.spi
*
*  INPUT   NODE = 10
*  OUTPUT NODE = 18
*  INPUT PH1   = 50
*  INPUT PH1B = 51
*  INPUT PH2   = 52
*  INPUT PH2B = 53


* CIRCUIT
.MACRO MAIN
XCAP00 11 12 12 10   AGND CAP00
XCAP01 12 11   AGND CAP01
XCAP02 13 14 14 12   AGND CAP02
XCAP03 14 13   AGND CAP03
XCAP04 15 16 16 14   AGND CAP04
XCAP05 16 15   AGND CAP05
XCAP06 17 18 18 16   AGND CIJ CIJ
CAP06
XCAP07 18 17   AGND CAP07
.EOM MAIN


* SUBCIRCUITS
*    SCALING FACTOR = 0.50000PF
*    OPAMP INDEX    = 3
* LIBRARY CELL DEFINITION:
*
*
*/CELL CAP00
*    CELL NAME :    ABFS.SPI
.MACRO CAP00 10 1 2 3 AGND
M1 4 52 0 80 N W=10U L=4U
M2 4 53 0 90 P W=10U L=4U
M3 4 50 6 80 N W=10U L=4U
M4 4 51 6 90 P W=10U L=4U
M5 5 52 0 80 N W=10U L=4U
M6 5 53 0 90 P W=10U L=4U
M7 5 50 1 80 N W=10U L=4U
M8 5 51 1 90 P W=10U L=4U
M9 2 54 7 80 N W=10U L=4U
M10 2 55 7 90 P W=10U L=4U
*     - + OUT VDD VSS NAME
```

```
XAMP 6 0 10 90 80 OA3
CINT 6 10 12.213PF
CNNV 4 5 1.806PF
CFLT 3 6 1.000PF
CSMP 7 6 1.048PF
CS 7 0 1.4PF
.EOM CAP00


*/CELL CAP01
*    CELL NAME :    AA.SPI
.MACRO CAP01 10 1 AGND
M1 4 52 0 80 N W=10U L=4U
M2 4 53 0 90 P W=10U L=4U
M3 4 50 6 80 N W=10U L=4U
M4 4 51 6 90 P W=10U L=4U
M5 5 50 0 80 N W=10U L=4U
M6 5 51 0 90 P W=10U L=4U
M7 5 52 1 80 N W=10U L=4U
M8 5 53 1 90 P W=10U L=4U
*     - + OUT VDD VSS NAME
XAMP 6 0 10 90 80 OA3
CINT 6 10 6.705PF
CINV 4 5 1.000PF
.EOM CAP01


*/CELL CAP02
*    CELL NAME:    ABFS.SPI
.MACRO CAP02 10 1 2 3 AGND
M1 4 52 0 80 N W=10U L=4U
M2 4 53 0 90 P W=10U L=4U
M3 4 50 6 80 N W=10U L=4U
M4 4 51 6 90 P W=10U L=4U
M5 5 52 0 80 N W=10U L=4U
M6 5 53 0 90 P W=10U L=4U
M7 5 50 1 80 N W=10U L=4U
M8 5 51 1 90 P W=10U L=4U
M9 2 54 7 80 N W=10U L=4U
M10 2 55 7 90 P W=10U L=4U
*     - + OUT VDD VSS NAME
XAMP 6 0 10 90 80 OA3
CINT 6 10 12.768PF
CNNV 4 5 1.670PF
```

```
CFLT 3 6 1.000PF
CSMP 7 6 1.840PF
CS 7 0 1.4PF
.EOM CAP02


*/CELL CAP03
*    CELL NAME :    AA.SPI
.MACRO CAP03 10 1 AGND
M1 4 52 0 80 N W=10U L=4U
M2 4 53 0 90 P W=10U L=4U
M3 4 50 6 80 N W=10U L=4U
M4 4 51 6 90 P W=10U L=4U
M5 5 50 0 80 N W=10U L=4U
M6 5 51 0 90 P W=10U L=4U
M7 5 52 1 80 N W=10U L=4U
M8 5 53 1 90 P W=10U L=4U
*     - + OUT VDD VSS NAME
XAMP 6 0 10 90 80 OA3
CINT 6 10 6.926PF
CINV 4 5 1.000PF
.EOM CAP03


*/CELL CAP04
*    CELL NAME:    ABFS.SPI
.MACRO CAP04 10 1 2 3 AGND
M1 4 52 0 80 N W=10U L=4U
M2 4 53 0 90 P W=10U L=4U
M3 4 50 6 80 N W=10U L=4U
M4 4 51 6 90 P W=10U L=4U
M5 5 52 0 80 N W=10U L=4U
M6 5 53 0 90 P W=10U L=4U
M7 5 50 1 80 N W=10U L=4U
M8 5 51 1 90 P W=10U L=4U
M9 2 54 7 80 N W=10U L=4U
M10 2 55 7 90 P W=10U L=4U
*     - + OUT VDD VSS NAME
XAMP 6 0 10 90 80 OA3
CINT 6 10 29.733PF
CNNV 4 5 3.830PF
CFLT 3 6 1.000PF
CSMP 7 6 2.855PF
CS 7 0 1.4PF
.EOM CAP04


*/CELL CAP05
*    CELL NAME :    AA.SPI
.MACRO CAP05 10 1 AGND
M1 4 52 0 80 N W=10U L=4U
M2 4 53 0 90 P W=10U L=4U
M3 4 50 6 80 N W=10U L=4U
M4 4 51 6 90 P W=10U L=4U
M5 5 50 0 80 N W=10U L=4U
M6 5 51 0 90 P W=10U L=4U
M7 5 52 1 80 N W=10U L=4U
M8 5 53 1 90 P W=10U L=4U
*     - + OUT VDD VSS NAME
```

```
XAMP 6 0 10 90 80 OA3
CINT 6 10 7.584PF
CINV 4 5 1.000PF
.EOM CAP05


*/CELL CAP06
*    CELL NAME:    ABFS.SPI
.MACRO CAP06 10 1 2 3 AGND CIJ CIJ
M1 4 52 0 80 N W=10U L=4U
M2 4 53 0 90 P W=10U L=4U
M3 4 50 6 80 N W=10U L=4U
M4 4 51 6 90 P W=10U L=4U
M5 5 52 0 80 N W=10U L=4U
M6 5 53 0 90 P W=10U L=4U
M7 5 50 1 80 N W=10U L=4U
M8 5 51 1 90 P W=10U L=4U
M9 2 54 7 80 N W=10U L=4U
M10 2 55 7 90 P W=10U L=4U
*     - + OUT VDD VSS NAME
XAMP 6 0 10 90 80 OA3
CINT 6 10 28.152PF
CNNV 4 5 4.623PF
CFLT 3 6 1.000PF
CSMP 7 6 10.471PF
CS 7 0 1.4PF
.EOM CAP06


*/CELL CAP07
*    CELL NAME :    AA.SPI
.MACRO CAP07 10 1 AGND
M1 4 52 0 80 N W=10U L=4U
M2 4 53 0 90 P W=10U L=4U
M3 4 50 6 80 N W=10U L=4U
M4 4 51 6 90 P W=10U L=4U
M5 5 50 0 80 N W=10U L=4U
M6 5 51 0 90 P W=10U L=4U
M7 5 52 1 80 N W=10U L=4U
M8 5 53 1 90 P W=10U L=4U
*     - + OUT VDD VSS NAME
XAMP 6 0 10 90 80 OA3
CINT 6 10 6.652PF
CINV 4 5 1.000PF
.EOM CAP07
.END
```

References

1. Jones, I., Characterization of standard cell libraries, *Proceedings of the IEEE 1985 CICC*, IEEE, Portland, Oregon, pp.438–41, 1985.
2. Shiva, S.G., Automatic hardware synthesis, *Proceedings of the IEEE*, **Vol. 71**, (1), pp.76–87, Jan. 1983.
3. Man, H. De, *et al.*, Cathedral 11 — a silicon compiler for digital signal processing, *IEEE Design and Test*, Dec. 1986.
4. Scott, W., Hamachi, C., Ousterhout J., Mayo, R., Berkeley VLSI Tool: More works by the original artists, *Report No. UCB/CSD 85/225*, Feb. 1985.
5. *VLSI Book G.D.T.*, Silicon Compiler Systems, San Jose, Internal publication.
6. Grebene, A.B., *Bipolar and MOS Analog Integrated Circuit Design*, John Wiley & Sons, New York, 1984.
7. Allen P., Holberg, D., *CMOS Analog Circuit Design*, Holt, Rinehart and Winston, Inc., New York, 1987.
8. Pletersek, T., Trontelj, J., Trontelj, L., Jones, I., Shenton, G.,Sun, Y., Analog LSI design with CMOS standard cells, *Proceedings of the IEEE 1985 CICC*, IEEE, Portland, Oregon, pp.479–83, 1985.
9. Pletersek, T., Trontelj, J., Trontelj, L., Jones, I., Shenton, G., High performance designs with CMOS analog standard cells, *IEEE Journal of Solid State Circuits*, **SC–21**, (2), New York, 1986.
10. Degrauwe M.G.R. *et al*, IDAC an interactive design tool for analog CMOS circuit, *IEEE Journal of solid state circuits*, **SC–22**, (6), pp.1106–16, 1987.
11. Ghaussi, M.S., Laker, K.R., *Modern Filter Design*, Prentice-Hall, New York, 1981.
12. Temes, G.C., Lapatra, J.W., *Circuit Synthesis and Design*, McGraw Hill Book Company, New York, 1981.
13. Daryanani, G., *Principles of Active Network Synthesis and Design*, John Wiley and Sons, London, 1976.
14. Trontelj, L., Trontelj, J., Slivnik, T. jr., Sosic, R., Strle, D., Lucas, D., Analog silicon compiler for switched-capacitor circuits, *Proceedings of ICCAD, 1987*, pp.506–9.

6. Complete IC layout compilation

6.1 Introduction

A very important step in the design procedure is the creation of the complete integrated circuit layout. The purpose of this chapter is to describe the procedures and tools which are necessary for a high performance circuit layout.

At this point we assume that a full circuit schematic and netlist are available, and that the CAD tools exist which are capable of automatic or semiautomatic translation of the netlist into a physical layout. When considering complete IC layouts for the personalized standard cell methodology, it appears at first that the tasks to be accomplished are optimal cell placement and optimal cell routing. This is partly true for non-critical purely digital circuits. For this large category of digital IC designs a number of very effective design tools are available. The resulting layouts appear very dense with little silicon area penalty when compared to hand crafted full custom layouts. Since these tools cannot be used when demanding analog and mixed analog digital ICs are being considered, it is interesting to briefly review some of the principles used for non-critical digital placement and routing.

6.2 The role of autolayout

There are two main aspects to autolayout: synthesis and verification. During the synthesis phase, a circuit network is converted into a chip layout and in the verification phase the generated layout is checked for conformance to the design rules and for electrical integrity.

The most versatile autolayout systems employ a toolbox approach,[1] where the CAD system is flexible enough to accept many layout methodologies. Here the user can select one of many alternative layout strategies, each of which is optimized for a particular class of design. In a top–down chip layout, the starting point is a single hierarchical netlist which is usually extracted from a schematic entry system (Fig.6.1). The hierarchy of the netlist matches the hierarchy of the layout, and tools are used to partition the netlist into logical modules. The appropriate layout tool is then used to complete the design of each module. The next stage in the layout process is to link together the individual modules as the lowest level of the hierarchy. This is done by a block place and route system which produces a graphics block at the next higher level of the hierarchy. These higher level blocks can in turn be linked with the block place and route system, in so doing, each time completing the routing at one level of the graphics hierarchy. This process continues until the top level of the hierarchy is reached, where the pads and the

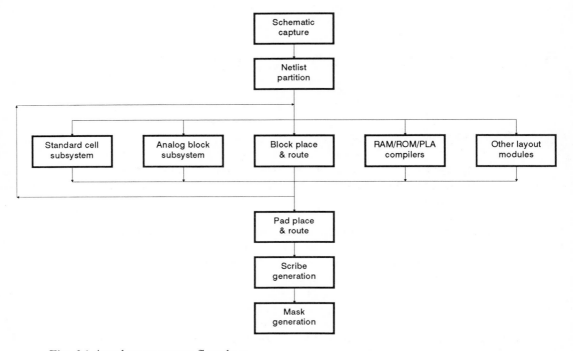

Fig. 6.1 Autolayout system flowchart

circuit are to be connected together. The synthesis phase is completed by the addition of IC manufacturer-dependent scribe and peripheral cells.

Although design verification may not be considered necessary if the layout has been completed by autolayout tools, in practice it is worth while checking to ensure that the software has performed correctly and to verify any manual layout intervention.

6.3 Standard cell placement

The most common layout scheme for autolayout is the arrangement of rows of standard cells (Fig.6.2). The standard cells are taken from a predefined library and all conform to the same rules for cell height, power connections, etc. The cells are designed such that when they are abutted, the power lines make connection between the cells.

The first task is to place the cells in the rows in an order which minimizes the routing area. As even the smallest deviation from an ideal placement can cause a very significant increase in the layout area. The placement task is perhaps the most critical phase of autolayout. A common

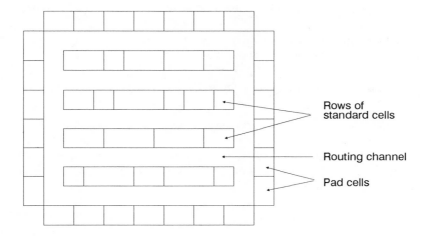

Fig. 6.2 Standard cell autolayout scheme

feature of placement algorithms is a trade-off between placement efficiency and computer time, and often the situation of diminishing returns is reached.

The seed and cluster approach to placement finds a single seed cell for each row.[2] These seed cells are chosen as being the set of cells which are least connected with each other. From each cell, clusters of highly connected cells are formed until all the cells in the layout have been allocated to a row. Constraints are applied to allow the rows to grow in width at an equal rate. The final stage in this method is to order the cells within the rows to minimize the routing area required between the rows. This class of algorithm can produce acceptable results, but usually requires a reasonably large amount of computer time.

The simulated annealing approach achieved popularity in the mid 1980s.[3] Random perturbations from an initial placement are tested, and the placement order kept if there was any placement improvement. This technique has been shown to give very good results but at the expense of vast amounts of computer time.

The min-cut algorithm successively divides the layout area by two and directs cells to one partition or another based upon its connectivity.[4] The advantage of this graphical technique is that it produces a very acceptable cell placement using the minimum of computer time.

During the placement phase it is possible to estimate the area of the standard cell core by making some assumptions for the size of the routing channels. Similarly it is possible to estimate the size of the pad ring and its associated interconnect. It can then be determined whether the pad ring or the standard cell core is the dominating factor governing the overall chip size. If it is a pad limited design then it may be possible to select a set of pads from the cell library having a different aspect ratio. Narrower but taller pads would reduce the total chip size. If it is a core limited design, then extra attention may be needed in achieving an acceptable standard cell placement as well as selecting wider shorter pads.

6.4   Standard cell routing

Over the years there have been as many papers written on standard cell routers as on any other design automation topic. With each new algorithm there is some alleged improvement over a previous technique, and this approvement may be an improvement in routing quality or an improvement in computational efficiency. Standard test cases have even been designed to measure the routing efficiency of new algorithms.

There are two phases to standard cell routing: global routing and channel routing. The global router must develop an overall routing plan for the chip. It must determine which nets pass though which channels. The global router is also responsible for inserting feed-through cells into the cell rows. The feed-through cells are used to drive a net across a row of cells from one routing channel to another. In certain technologies, some feed-throughs can be avoided by directly routing across the cell row rather than by inserting a special cell into the row (Fig.6.3).

Most standard cell libraries are constructed with the cells having equivalent pins at the top and bottom edges of the cells (Fig.6.4). Equivalent pins are defined as those pins which are connected to the same electrical node. By making use of equivalent pins the router can select the pins which result in the minimum routing area. Alternative pins are those pins which are functionally equivalent if not electrically equivalent. The three input pins on a three input NOR gate can be considered as alternative pins. The global router can minimize the routing in a routing channel by correctly selecting alternative pins.

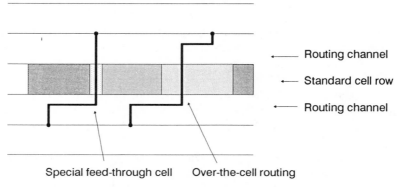

Fig. 6.3 Feed-through cell and over-the-cell routing

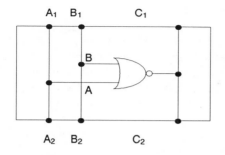

A_1 and A_2 are equivalent pins
B_1 and B_2 are equivalent pins
C_1 and C_2 are equivalent pins

A and B are alternate pins

Fig. 6.4 Equivalent and alternate pins

The result of the global routing phase is that the locations of all net connections at the borders of every routing channel are known. The effect of global routing therefore, is to reduce the overall chip routing problem to a number of smaller and independent routing problems, one per channel. The detailed channel router is then able to complete the routing for each channel.

There have been many channel routing schemes published. Some routers fail to complete the routing task when a particular topology is encountered. These constraints are well-known and routing strategies have been developed to overcome these problems.[5] However, probably the most widely adopted channel router is the Greedy Router which does not suffer from topological constraint problems and will always guarantee correct routing of all the nets in the channel.[6] It accomplishes this by allowing the channel to expand in both dimensions.

All the early routers were grid routers. That is, the routing tracks always followed a predefined technology grid. The pitch of this grid was usually the minimum contact to contact spacing of the processing technology. Assigning routes to the technology grid freed the router from any design rule constraints simplifying the implementation of the algorithm. The advantage of this technique is that the routes only need to be a whole grid distance apart when two contacts are adjacent, elsewhere a smaller spacing of tracks would suffice. So there is significant inefficiency of routing area when grid routers are used. The new breed of gridless routers do not employ a technology grid and generate a more compact layout by using a number of different process design rule spacings for different routing situations.

During the logic simulation phase of the design, it is usual for the engineer to make some assumptions of the signal delays to be introduced by the routing. With single metal/single polysilicon routing these delays can be considerable because of the large polysilicon RC time constant. They can be significantly reduced with double metal routing. Once the routing has been completed, it is possible to resimulate using the actual routing delay. The approximate signal delay can usually be computed from the length of each net; this information being obtained either directly from router, or from a parameter extraction program when running the design verification software.

6.5   Block placement and routing

The block placement and routing system has become one of the most important tools in the engineer's toolbox. This tool integrates the different layouts produced by the specialized layout generators in the IC compilation process. The system should be capable of integrating a variety of different types of blocks such as standard cell cores, RAMs and ROMs from a silicon compiler, and hand-drawn layout for highly customized components.

A number of such state-of-the-art block systems have been published and some are available commercially.[7] The features of these systems are:

1. Gridless routing. This is required for maximum routing density and to be able to connect routing to blocks with connection points not on a technology grid.
2. Preferred layer routing. For either electrical performance, packing density, or reliability reasons, routing on one layer may be preferred over another.
3. Power and critical net routing. It should be possible for power and critical nets to be identified and routed first.
4. Variable width nets. Nets should be able to be routed in different widths, either under program or user control.
5. Complete routing. The block system should ensure that all routes are completely routed.

Various block placement systems have been described in the literature and many use a modified form of the min-cut algorithm described in Section 6.2.2. Usually a manual interaction capability is also available. This placement activity can form part of a larger floorplanning phase of the chip design, where the relative positions of layout blocks can be fixed. The absolute locations of blocks will not be fixed until all the routing has been completed and the routing channels compacted.

The first stage of the clock routing phase defines the channels and the order of routing. Channel slices are found in the blocks, with preference being given to longer slices in the middle of the layout. As in standard cell routing there are topological problems in block routing that can prevent routing completion. Such a problem is the "pin-wheel" constraint which can be overcome by designating one of the channels in the pin-wheel cycle to be routed last by a switchbox router. A switchbox router is a special form of the channel router designed to route a channel which has fixed terminal locations on all sides.[8]

The channel slicing phase is followed by global routing. An expanding wavefront is generated from every terminal in a net. When wavefronts intersect, the shortest path for each net is found by back-tracking. Weighting can be applied to the wavefront expansion algorithm to favour the less congested channels.

A gridless router performs the detailed routing of each channel. The channels are allowed to expand or contract as demanded by the routing density in each channel, ensuring routing completion.

As in the standard cell design methodology it is important to extract the signal delays introduced by the routing. Again the delays can either be derived from path width and length information supplied by the router, or from the parameter extraction phase of a design verification tool.

6.6 Design verification

The purpose of design verification software at this point is to check the validity of the chip layout after the completion of the design engineering effort. It is important that this step is rigorously enforced even if design automation tools are used to generate the design. It will verify the correct operation of the design software and will check any manually generated portions of the layout.

There are some excellent commercial products available, as mentioned in Chapter 7. However, these products are only as good as the quality of the design rule data. In the design rule checking phase the process design rules are encoded in terms of Boolean layer operations. In practice a great deal of thought needs to be given to this activity to be sure that all possible layout configurations of the design rules are being tested. It is not usual for the semiconductor manufacturer's process design rules to be written with the encoding of the rules for design verification software in mind. Most silicon manufacturers, however, maintain design rule run sets for the commercially available verification tools and it is a good plan for the designer to obtain an official copy of this rather than to write a new one.

The layout versus schematics verification checks the connectivity as described in the circuit netlist with the physical layout. This step will only give a successful result if the netlist is a true transistor representation of the layout. A common problem is for the design engineer to make "simulation short-cuts" such as specifying a single invertor in the netlist when three invertors were used in the layout. Further complications arise when verifying mixed digital analog chips. Resistors and capacitors need to be marked as such on the layout (perhaps by some identifying shape on an information layer) and need to be interpreted as special devices by the software. Failure to do this will cause the software to mistake these devices for ordinary pieces of interconnect as they are produced from the same materials, e.g. polysilicon and diffusion.

6.7 Mixed analog digital placement and routing

The constraints of analog and mixed analog digital circuits require a different approach to layout compilation. The silicon area is still an important factor determining the cost of the final IC; however, the analog performance depends heavily on the layout. In other words, two different layouts representing the same schematic cannot be compared just by silicon area, as their resulting analog performance is very important.

Unfortunately it is very difficult to analyse and predict all layout-dependent analog performances before measurements are taken on the resulting silicon.

Because of this, the effectiveness of layout compilers and related design methodologies cannot be compared simply by measuring the silicon area consumed. In practice, an extensive analysis of the resulting circuit performance measured over a number of successful designs is necessary to establish the credibility of a mixed analog digital design method and layout compiler.

One methodology which has such proven designs is the personalized standard cell approach.

In order to avoid unpleasant surprises, unfortunately quite common today for designers involved in mixed analog digital projects, a strictly disciplined design procedure must be followed. This design procedure should be incorporated into the design tools from the very beginning of the design.

The hierarchical level of the circuit representation required for the final IC layout compiler for the personalized standard cell design consists of:

1. Personalized core cells and blocks
2. Analog signal interconnections
3. Digital signal interconnections
4. Power supply buses
5. Signal buses
6. Groundings
7. Input/output peripheral cells

Layout information is associated with all the listed circuit elements, together with interconnection information. The relevant layout information is entered at the level of the circuit topology creation, i.e. at the level of schematic entry.

6.8   Schematic entry for analog digital circuits

Beside the standard features commonly available in schematic capture systems developed for documentation, netlists and simulation files generation, a schematic entry tool which would be usable also for analog digital layout compilation should offer the following functions:

1. Different levels of interconnections
2. Possibility of supply bus positioning and attribute assignment
3. Possibility of grounding attribute assignment
4. Possibility to distinguish between interconnection signal types

5. Possibility of analog requirement attribute assignment on signal interconnections
6. Possibility of cell positioning attribute assignment
7. Provision of on line and final analog rule checking.

6.8.1 Interconnection levels for schematic entry

The concept of incorporating extensive information about the circuit under design in its schematic requires a structured form, to avoid the loss of information. To achieve this a multilayer approach is recommended. In this approach each layer is reserved for a certain class of interconnection.

In the schematic editor which is given as an example of this type of extended program, the layer assignment is shown in Table 6.1.[9]

Table 6.1 Layer assignment and attribute definition for schematic editor

Layer No.	Interconnection type	Comment	Attributes
1	power supply buses max resistance bus width	automatic interconnection	priority current level
2	signal buses	automatic interconnection	priority current level max resistance bus width
3	grounds	automatic or manual interconnection entry	common separate max resistance
4	digital signals	manual interconnection entry	max parasitic resistance capacitance sensitivity interconnection material(metal polysilicon...)
5	analog signals	manual interconnection entry	max parasitic resistance capacitance sensitivity interconnection material

The schematic can be plotted with layers shown in different colours or with any combination of layers which are of interest.

6.8.2 Schematic entry of power supply buses

Buses and common ground lines do not need to be entered manually. Their presence and type is implicit and defined in the symbol table. Additionally, selective displays can be generated on the basis of attributes or attribute parameters.

Buses such as ground or substrate connections do not need to be entered individually; their presence can be labelled in the symbol tables so that global connect commands can be used.

The user can, however, specify the attributes which will result in specific layout dimensions and organization.

The importance of the correct layout of power supply buses is very often overlooked and sometimes even misunderstood by designers, so the philosophy of the schematic capture program is to use an off-line rule checker, reporting errors if no attributes to the buses were assigned, i.e. if the designer did not verify the tolerable voltage drops, crosstalk, current densities, etc. of the supply buses to the core of the chip.

6.8.3 Analog ground in a mixed analog digital schematic entry

Other very important types of interconnections for analog circuits are the analog grounds. The schematic editor should be capable of distinguishing between non-critical grounds which can be shared by several analog functional blocks since there is no current flowing and hence no voltage drops, and very sensitive ground wires which should run separately from the ground pad and the specific macrocell. Again an analog checker built into the schematic editor reports errors if no attributes were assigned to the different ground lines.

6.8.4 Analog and digital interconnections

The distinction between analog and digital interconnections allows for the separation of analog and digital interconnection channels, which reduces to a great extent the digital crosstalk into the more sensitive analog portion of the circuit. Analog interconnections are defined as interconnections between analog nodes only. Digital interconnections connect digital nodes only, while mixed interconnections can be classified according to the designer's request. Each node is classified either as an analog or a digital type. This information is entered when the cells are created and is part of the library data base, so the designer does not need to pay attention to the interconnection type classifications, except for mixed types.

6.8.5 Analog requirements for signal interconnections

The provision for shielding sensitive analog interconnections is the attribute called sensitivity, which creates spacing around the specified sensitive line and provides parallel and bottom ground stripes, the equivalent of shielded cables in discrete component designs.

Another consideration for analog interconnections is the associated parasitic resistances, which can be several orders of magnitude larger than in printed circuits designs. The schematic editor should be capable of marking such critical interconnections and allowing for requests for maximum parasitic resistance, which will result in a layout with shorter interconnections with fewer bridges and with wider lines.

Since the resistances internal to the chip are much higher than encountered when designing with discrete components and printed circuit boards, it is mandatory to be able to monitor and modify the interconnection's parasitic capacitance.

All the above attributes which influence the final layout of the circuit are normally known during the beginning design phase and have an influence on the basic design approach. It is thus

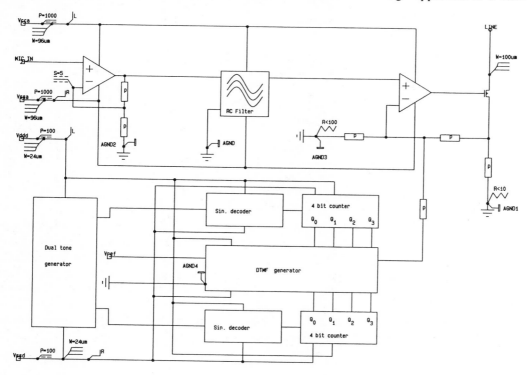

Fig. 6.5(a) Functional schematic diagram

completely unacceptable for design tools vendors to consider that tools for handling parasitics should be introduced only after the layout is finished. The present situation is that the designer extracts these parasitics when the layout is complete and adds the values to his models for resimulation. This approach can neither guarantee efficient cut and try procedures to achieve acceptable layout, nor can it identify all the critical parasitics since the simulation tools cannot accept such complex networks.

6.8.6 Cell positioning annotation in the schematic

In the front end design the information about requested placement of groups of sensitive analog cells and positioning of peripheral input output pads can be entered. Special parameters can be provided when the cell symbol is placed in the schematic.

Fig.6.5(a),(b),(c),(d) show an example of a module with mixed analog digital design. It represents a microphone (transmitter) amplifier, together with the audio filter and output power stage used in an integrated telephone IC. At the output stage a DTMF dialling signal has been added.

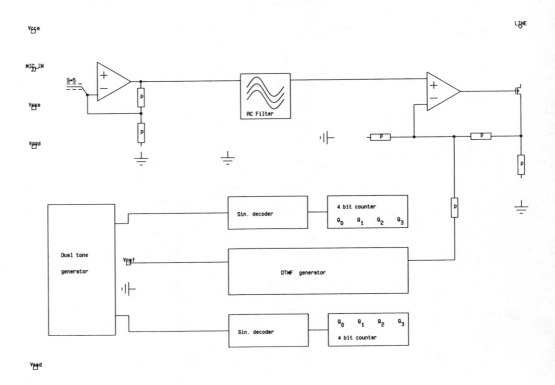

Fig. 6.5(b) Analog interconnections

Fig.6.5(a) shows the functional schematic combining all layers. Fig.6.5(b) shows interconnection layer 5 only with all the attributes known at that stage of the design. Fig.6.5(c) shows interconnection layer 4 with all the attributes known at that stage of the design. Fig.6.5(d) represents the power supply buses information, together with the information concerning grounding.

6.9   Mixed analog digital placement

As was mentioned earlier the floorplan of an integrated circuit consisting of both analog and digital blocks not only affects the silicon area of the chip, but also the functionality of the more sensitive analog parts of the circuit. This fact is made even more significant since the price of silicon die is constantly decreasing, with larger wafer sizes, process automation, etc. Consequently it is often worth while sacrificing a little silicon area to enhance or at least ensure meeting the full analog performance.

Fig.6.6 represents a generalized floorplan organization for mixed analog digital circuits which allows a fair degree of automation, but still gives sufficient confidence of the correct operation and silicon area conservation. The basic concept of this organization is the separation of the

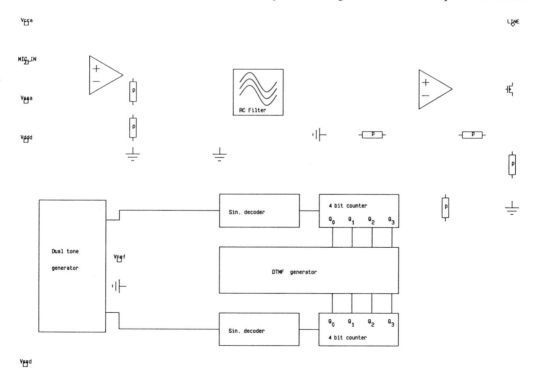

Fig. 6.5(c) Digital and analog digital interconnections

analog and digital portions of the chip wherever possible. This separation is performed not only in the core of the circuit but also in the circuit input/output periphery and power supply pads. This separation can only be accomplished in designs where the interaction of the analog and digital parts is limited.

When the interconnection between analog and digital parts of the circuit becomes greater, it is advisable to form analog and digital clusters in the core of the circuit while the periphery remains grouped into analog and digital parts as shown in Fig.6.6.

This organization still allows the separation of analog and digital routing channels. If the rule that digital signals route to the right hand side of the circuit and the analog signals route to the left hand side of the circuit is observed, the left vertical channel is completely analog and, vice versa, the right vertical channel is fully digital. This scheme very effectively eliminates one of the most important potential sources of digital crosstalk into the analog portion of the circuit from interconnection coupling.

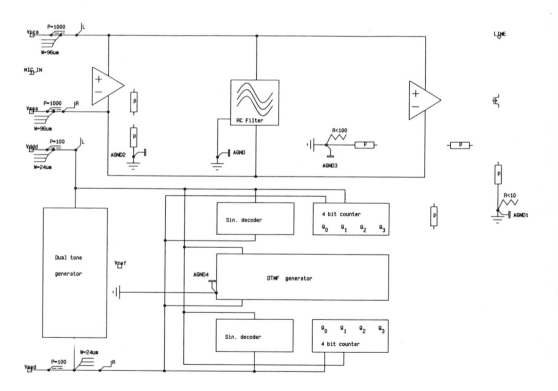

Fig. 6.5(d) Power supply and ground buses

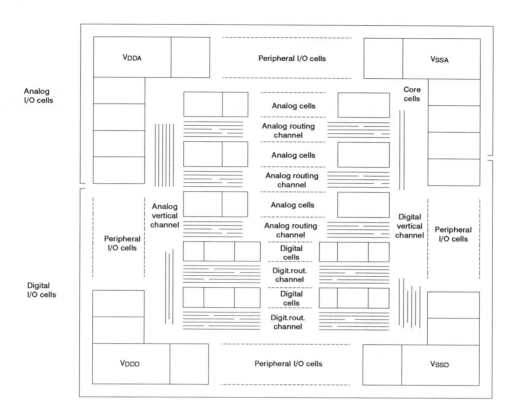

Fig. 6.6 Floorplan organization for mixed analog digital ASIC

6.10 Mixed analog digital routing

Comparisons of analog and digital routing show that the number of interconnections in the analog portion of the circuit is much smaller than in the digital portion. This statement appears to be true for the majority of designs, although no general rule can always be valid for the great variety of designs found in the field of mixed analog digital integration.

Although the number of interconnections in the analog portion is usually quite small, these interconnections deserve much closer attention that the less sensitive digital ones.

To illustrate the importance of the physical layout of the interconnection it is instructive to examine a few real design examples which suffered from poor layout.

6.10.1 False design example A

The design shown in Fig.6.7 suffered from a classical problem of power supply voltage drop. The designer had correctly designed the D/A converter by converting the digitally controlled output current into the output voltage by using a resistor connected to V_{SSA}. He also assigned the correct priority for V_{SSA}. The average current consumption of the analog portion of the circuit was 30 mA, so he used 40 micrometers V_{SSA} metal bus width—a conservative number for current density for the 3 μm CMOS process. He was also aware of the noise which could be introduced from the digital supply so he decided to use a separate digital V_{SSD}.

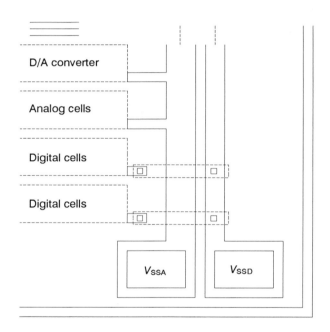

Fig. 6.7 False design example A

Unfortunately he forgot one important thing. His D/A was placed somewhere in the middle of the chip, so the V_{SSA} bus had to run over 2 mm to reach the V_{SSA} pad. A short calculation shows that there was a voltage drop V_{dr} of 60 mV, when using sheet resistance of aluminium wire $R_m = 40$ mΩ per square, with length $l = 2$ mm and width $w = 40\,\mu$m.

$$R_{ds} = R_m \frac{l}{w} = 40 \cdot 10^{-3} \frac{2 \cdot 10^{-3}}{40 \cdot 10^{-6}} = 2\ \Omega \tag{6.1}$$

$$V_{dr} = I_{DDA} \cdot R_S = 30 \cdot 10^{-3} \cdot 2 = 60 \cdot 10^{-3}\ V \tag{6.2}$$

This voltage drop not only introduced an offset-voltage error which varied with process variations in a ratio 1:2 but also caused a temperature dependence of 10 mV (LSB) because of temperature dependence of the analog supply current.

The remedy to the problem is to introduce a separate $V_{SS(D/A)}$, as shown in Fig.6.8. It can have a second priority since the LSB maximum current consumption of D/A converters is only 150 μA and a tolerable error of 1/2 LSB would occur at V_{SS} resistance $R_{VSS} = 5$ mV/150 μA = 33 Ω, which can easily be achieved even when using diffusion bridges in the power supply as shown in Fig.6.8.

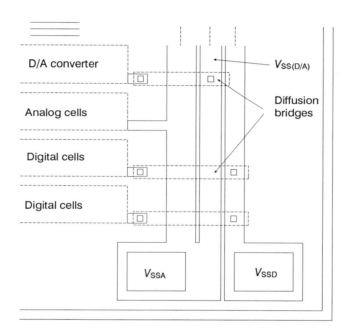

Fig. 6.8 Corrected design example A

6.10.2 False design example B

Another example shown in Fig.6.9 represents the influence of substrate induced digital noise—a very common source of malfunctions of analog digital circuits. In this case the designer had only one power supply available, so he had to use the same V_{DD} throughout the circuit. The digital portion of the chip used clock synchronized logic which turned off and on up to 1000 CMOS gates with minimal dimensions. Although the logic is fully complementary MOS, and no static current is flowing, the peak transients V_{drp} is:

$$V_{drp} = R_{DD} \cdot I_{tr} \qquad (6.3)$$

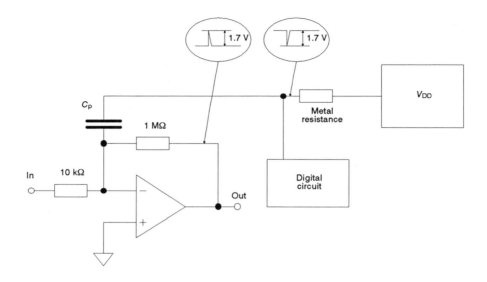

Fig. 6.9 False design example B

where R_{DD} is V_{DD} supply bus resistance and I_{tr} is the maximum simultaneous transient current.

In the design in question there is the following situation:

The V_{DD} bus is 40 μm wide and 4 mm long with a resulting $R_{DD} = 4\ \Omega$; I_{trmax} occurs in the synchronous counter chain and the associated synchronous logic resulting in approximately 400 transistors switching simultaneously. The calculated peak transient current is as high as 225 mA. Hence the V_{DD} voltage drop is:

$$V_{drp} = 4 \cdot 225 \cdot 10^{-3} = 0.9\ V \tag{6.4}$$

When microprobing the V_{DD} at the site of the operational amplifier from Fig.6.9 the result was as calculated in equation (6.4) and can be explained by the voltage drop during the transients. The op-amp used had a fairly good power supply rejection ratio, so the measured spikes at the output could not be attributed to it. At this point it is necessary to know that the design rules require V_{DD} to be connected to the substrate at least every 500 μm to assure an equipotential substrate to eliminate potential latch-up conditions and to assure proper operation of the devices. In this case the substrate was connected to V_{DD} which had superimposed spikes of 0.9 V at the amplifier site. When calculating the P-well junction capacitance of the feedback resistor in Fig.6.9 we can obtain its parasitic capacitance:

$$C_p = 1/3 \; W \cdot L \cdot C_j = 1 \text{ pF} \tag{6.5}$$

When entering this value into the SPICE simulation using the correct model of the operational amplifier we can see almost exactly the same results as seen from the measurements.

The solution to the problem is the following: Although external to the chip there is only one type of power supply V_{DD}, we have to create internally V_{DDA} and V_{DDD} as shown in Fig.6.10.

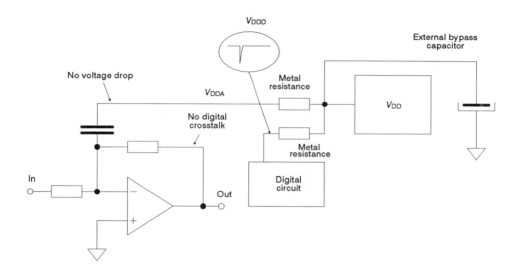

Fig. 6.10 Corrected design example B

The solution in Fig.6.10 runs a separate bus V_{DDA} directly from the V_{DD} pad which is filtered by an external bypass capacitor. All digital cells are reconfigured not to have any substrate contacts to V_{DDD}. The necessary substrate contacts are added separately on V_{DDA}. A more systematic solution is the following:

If a mixed analog digital design is being considered, all digital cells have to be modified to include V_{DDA} and V_{DDD} power supply buses as shown in the Plate 6.1. The digital cell represented here is of the type DIGA, i.e. a digital cell which is operating in mixed analog digital environments.

6.10.3 False design example C

In the example shown in Fig.6.11 the two gain channels had to be summed while the gain accuracy of each channel had to be accurate within 0.1 dB. Because of the strict noise and frequency band requirements a continuous time solution was selected. In Fig.6.12 the associate layout is presented.

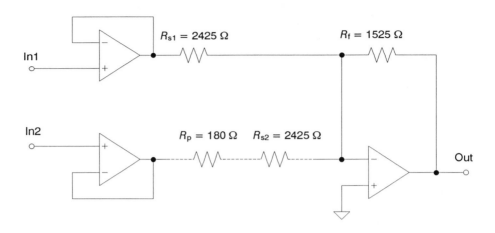

Fig. 6.11 Design example C

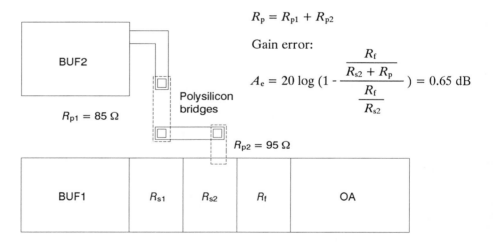

$$R_p = R_{p1} + R_{p2}$$

Gain error:

$$A_e = 20 \log \left(1 - \frac{\dfrac{R_f}{R_{s2} + R_p}}{\dfrac{R_f}{R_{s2}}}\right) = 0.65 \text{ dB}$$

Fig. 6.12 False layout for design example C

Since the input buffer 1 sits in the same row of analog cells as the resistor cells (using polysilicon resistors) for the summator the interconnection parasitic resistance is almost negligible. However, this is not true for the interconnection between buffer 2 and the summator. Since the designer forgot to specify the interconnection resistance the router took the default value and bridged the analog channel with a poly bridge only 5 μm wide, with a resulting parasitic resistance of 180 Ω. The resulting mismatch between the two channels was over 0.6 dB, more than specified.

The solution to the problem is either to increase the poly bridge width (a feature available with some analog routers) or to include the bridge resistance in the resistor R_{s2} (a feature which can be entered manually or included in an intelligent personalized cell compilation).

6.11 Systematic approach to mixed placement and routing

At this point it is assumed that the front end design is complete and that the schematic of the circuit is entered via a schematic editor or other netlist generation tool, for instance a SPICE file. All the necessary personalized cell synthesis or compilation is finished and entered in the user's temporary library.

In this section we discuss the CAD environment and the tools necessary to accomplish automatically the final stage of the design: placement and routing of the core and periphery of the circuit and layout data base generation.

6.11.1 Netlist file organization example

SPICE simulation file was selected for netlist extraction. The file describing the circuit should comply with SPICE syntax. The following additional information is added:

Identification of the subcircuits which exist at the personalized cell layout in the library. This information can be added as the first comment line of the subcircuit definition. The digital analog placer and router which was used as an example requires the addition of special layout information as comment lines starting with */.

For a subcircuit or macro which exists as a library cell, this information is entered in the following manner:

```
*/macro (cell name)
```

followed by the standard SPICE subcircuit definition.

The analog requirements dealing with parasitic resistances and capacitances are treated in a similar manner. This is accomplished with the statement:

```
*/LIMITS node X, node Y, R=(value)
```

This statement tells the router that the maximum resistance between node X and node Y introduced by the router connection cannot exceed the specified resistance.

The statement:

```
*/LIMITS node Z, C=(value)
```

specifies maximum parasitic capacitance of node Z.

Sensitive analog interconnection shielding is introduced by the statement:

```
*/LIMITS node X, node Y, S=(value)
```

This statement specifies the shielding width of the interconnection between node X and node Y.

Layout of power supply and other common buses is determined by an additional file BUSES.PRI with a statement for each bus as follows:

```
(BUS NAME),(POSITION),(PRIORITY),(WIDTH),(node 1,2....n)
```

This organization allows automatic bus positioning according to the specified priority (maximum priority means bus position closest to the core). Every node in the SPICE file with the bus name will be connected to that bus.

Bus width has to be specified either directly by entering the width in grids or it has to be calculated on the basis of maximum resistance or supply current using the technology parameters file for resistance per square or current density for the given technology.

A very important feature is the list of nodes names which can be added in the bus name statement. This node list forces the layout to run separately the interconnections which could cause analog interactions. These interconnections join only at the left or right buses where they are less likely to cause interactions. This feature is used, for instance, for sensitive ground lines which have to run separately to the pad. An example of such a SPICE file is shown in Chapter 9.

6.12 Cell library organization

A mixed analog digital placer and router does not need the full information about the cell layout. It can effectively work with the so-called "hollow cell" approach where the cell is represented by box of its boundaries with the pins at its periphery. For each cell two files are needed.

In the first file called "cell.type" the layout characteristics common to one class of cells are grouped. It is organized in the following manner:

```
cell type name, comment
cell height (value)
```

```
number of horizontal buses (value)
bus name 1, bus position (value), bus width (value)
bus name 2, bus position (value), bus width (value)
   .
   .
   .
bus name n, bus position (value), bus width (value)
```

The next file called "standard.clb" contains the specific information for the particular cell. It consists of cell type, cell origin, cell length, number of pins, pin orientation, position, dimension and type. Its organization is as follows:

```
cell name, comment
cell type
cell origin (x,y)
cell length (value)
number of pins (value)
pin 1 orientation (U,D,L,R, for Up, Down, Left, Right), position, width,
        type (A, D, for Analog, Digital)
pin 2 orientation, position, width, type
   .
   .
   .
pin n orientation, position, width, type
```

Examples for both files are given in Chapter 9.

6.13 Analog digital placement

The procedure for analog digital placement consists of two phases: automatic and manual. The placement algorithm is explained in Fig.6.13. The automatic portion of the placement consists of the following procedures: grouping the cells by their types, ordering the cells into the macrogroups Analog 1, Digital 1, Analog 2, Digital 2, ..., etc., as shown in Fig.6.14. This ordering is based on criteria:

1. Minimization of the interconnection area
2. Optimization of each row length to form an ideal square with all rows maximally filled
3. Finally optimization is performed within the row yielding the minimum interconnection channel width. This optimization does not destroy the formation of the groups of cells specified by the user during the front end phase of the design

The manual placement allows the user to perform manual optimization, leaving him, however, only two commands: "move cell" or "move the group of cells". This virtually prevents the user from making a mistake by removing the cell or by placing the cell into the row of the wrong type of cells.

Fig.6.14 shows the resulting placement of analog and digital groups of cells.

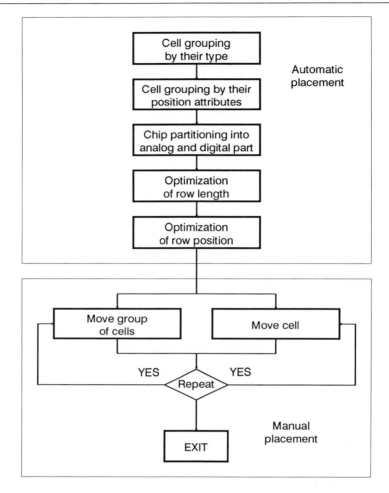

Fig. 6.13 Automatic and manual placement procedure

When the placement is finished the data is automatically transferred to an automatic router where no user intervention is allowed; however, all previously defined requests are automatically met. An example of placing and routing is shown in Chapter 9.

6.14 I/O structures

No attention has been paid so far to input/output structures, although they represent a very important part of the design effort.

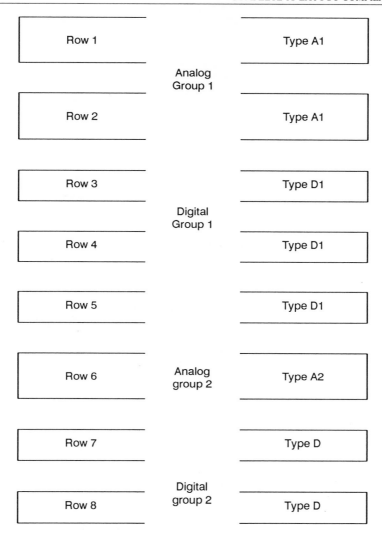

Fig. 6.14 Placement of analog and digital groups of cells

For digital input/output structures the situation is less complicated than for analog input/output structures. For digital input and output structures the following has to be observed when selecting the appropriate I/O cell from the library:

1. Input voltage level translation if necessary
2. Output voltage level translation
3. Digital fan-out

4. Provision for capacitive loads handling if necessary
5. Tristate outputs if necessary
6. Incorporation of the delay introduced by input/output cells in the complete circuit simulation

The following general rules should be observed:

1. Always use input and output buffers which are specially designed to handle the external environment.
2. Wherever possible use Schmitt-triggers structures at inputs. They guarantee better noise margins and false trigger prevention at the price of slightly increased propagation delays.
3. Use characterized I/O structures since the design for latch-up and electrostatic high voltage protection requires special know-how.

Fig.6.15 and Plate 6.2 show an example of a digital peripheral output cell designed for a mixed analog digital environment (dual supply). An example of a digital input cell is shown in Fig.6.16 and Plate 6.3. This cell is also suitable for mixed analog digital ASICs.

The situation for analog input/output structures is generally more complicated and needs additional attention. The most straightforward situation is when a simple unity gain amplifier can be used as the input or output buffer. However, even with moderate output current capability such a cell occupies the space for two I/O pads, as seen in Fig.6.17 and Plate 6.4.

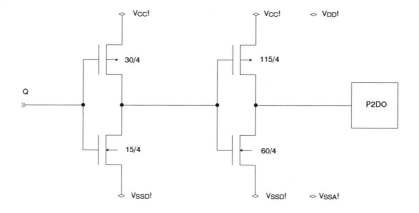

Description: Digital output buffer for use in circuits with separate analog and digital supply lines

Cell size: 288 μm × 432 μm

Fig. 6.15 Digital peripheral output cell

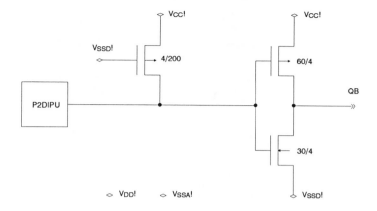

Description: Digital input pad with pull-up for use in circuits
               with separate analog and digital supply lines

Cell size: 228 μm × 432 μm

Fig. 6.16 Digital input cell schematic and specifications

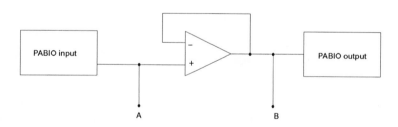

Description: General purpose dual pad cell for buffered analog
               input or buffered analog output

Cell size: 864 μm × 432 μm

Electrical specifications at $V_{DD} - V_{SS}$ = 10 V

Input voltage range: $(V_{DDA} - 0.5$ V$) - (V_{SSA} + 1.5$ V$)$
Output voltage range: $V_{DDA} - V_{SSA}$
Input offset-voltage: 5 mV maximum
Gain bandwidth: 2 MHz minimum at C_L = 0.5 pF
Output current: 10 mA at 1V_{RMS}

Fig. 6.17 General purpose analog input/output buffer peripheral cell schematic and
         characteristics

Description:	General purpose input output analog pad with variable serial resistance for use in circuits with separate analog and digital supply lines
Cell size:	288 μm × 432 μm

R_{min} = 275 Ω C_{min} = 0.48 pF
R_{max} = 572 Ω C_{max} = 0.83 pF

Latch-up protection: > 100 mA
ESD protection: > 2000 V

Fig. 6.18 General purpose input/output analog peripheral cell schematic and characteristics

Other factors which can prohibit the use of unity gain buffers is the presence of input noise, or unacceptable additional phase shift caused by such input of output buffers. For these cases specific I/O cells must be used providing the necessary latch-up-protection and electrostatic high voltage discharge immunity. To exacerbate the problem usually no voltage drop, i.e. no serial parasitic resistance, is allowed. Such I/O cell is shown in Fig.6.18 and Plate 6.5.

References

1. Lucas, D., Chiao, M., Srinivasan, S., An integrated low cost layout toolbox for custom IC design, *Proceedings of IEEE 1987 Custom Integrated Circuits Conference*, pp.502–6, Rochester, New York, 1987.
2. Kambe, T., Chiba, T., Kimura, S., Inufushi, T., Okuda, N., Nishioka, I., A placement algorithm for polycell LSI and its evaluation, *Proceedings of 19th Design Automation Conference*, p.655, Las Vegas, 1982.
3. Sechen, C., Sangiovanni-Vincentelli, A., The TimberWolf placement and routing package. *Proceedings of IEEE 1984 Custom Integrated Circuits Conference*, pp.522–7, Rochester, New York, 1984.
4. Lauther, U., A min-cut placement algorithm for general cell assemblies based on a graph representation, *Proceedings of Design Automation Conference*, p.1, San Diego, 1979.
5. Deutsch, D.N., A dogleg channel router, *Proceedings of 13th Design Automation Conference*, p.425, San Francisco, 1976.
6. Rivesta, R.L., Fiduccia, C.M., A greedy channel router, *Proceedings of 19th Design Automation Conference*, Las Vegas, 1982.
7. Lucas, D.W., Chiao, M., Srinivasan, S., Nguyen, J.P., Srinivasan, R., Pandya, A.L., An efficient routing system for block layout, *Proceedings of 22nd Asilomar Conference on Signals, Systems and Computers*, p.398, Pacific Groove, California, 1989.
8. Hamachi, G.T., Ousterhout, J.K., A switchbox router with obstacle avoidance, *Proceedings of 21st Design Automation Conference*, p.173, Albuquerque, 1984.
9. Trontelj, J., Trontelj, L., Slivnik, T., Pletersek, T., Shenton, G., Automatic circuit and layout design for mixed analog digital ASICs, *Proceedings of IEEE 1989 Custom Integrated Circuit Conference*, pp.17.1.1–4, San Diego, California, 1989.

7. Design control procedures and interface to silicon foundry

7.1 Introduction

In order to introduce an acceptable level of quality and accuracy to the IC design process it is necessary to establish a design procedure with many control points. This is true whether the design is being performed completely by a silicon vendor or solely by a system house or jointly.

The following description outlines the minimum control procedure.

7.2 Control procedures

The purpose of this section is to list the required design quality control procedures which must be followed, where applicable, during the design of an integrated circuit. If all the controls are strictly followed, it will help to minimize design mistakes and to maximize the probability of successful completion of the design task. It is advisable that a document be prepared on the basis of the listed activities regarding the design task. This document should show the design control. The check points should be dated and signed by the designer.

7.2.1 Feasibility study

As a result of the feasibility study the electronic system under design is partitioned into one or more ASICs. For the potential integrated circuits the following information should be acquired:

1. High level ASIC specification.
2. Detailed critical specifications regarding:
   (a) circuit complexity;
   (b) maximum digital clock speeds;
   (c) maximum analog signal frequencies;
   (d) maximum loads;
   (e) minimum analog signal levels;
   (f) maximum noise allowable;
   (g) power supply voltage range;
   (h) power dissipation;
   (i) analog function accuracy;

(j) temperature range;

(k) any other specific requirement.

3.   Process technology chosen.

4.   Chip size estimation.

5.   Testability evaluation.

6.   Encapsulation requirements.

The following questions should also be answered:

1.   Does the system specification comply with the ASIC specifications? Which specifications need to be further detailed? Is it overspecified?

2.   Are all critical specifications identified?

3.   Is the technology choice correct? Are all critical specifications feasible in the selected technology?

4.   Is the system partitioning into ASICs optimized regarding chip size, number of pins, testability, yield, encapsulation and power dissipation?

7.2.2 ASIC specifications development

The hierarchical nature of ASIC design requires the decomposition of functional block representations from higher to lower levels. This means that the specifications must also be decomposed to the respective levels. The decomposition of the specifications for each module must be made to the level where the simulation and synthesis tools can be used in the design procedure. A mapping of module specifications to input/output specifications of the ASIC is required to enable testability of module functions.

At completion of this design step the following checks should be performed:

1.   Verification of the conformity of modules specifications to the ASIC's and system specifications.

2.   Verification of the testability of each module.

7.2.3 Schematic capture

All circuits should be schematically captured. This assures that all netlists are software derived from the schematic database. In practice this means that the schematic is the master for all simulations and verification steps.

If the module or cell is synthesized its schematic is automatically represented by the resulting netlist. If the module is manually created its schematic may alter during the design procedure. It is important to develop design disciplines which do not allow differences between schematic and netlist. If a schematic editor does not allow modifications of the netlist using the text editor all modifications must be performed by altering the schematics. Than an appropriate netlist will be extracted from the schematic.

The following questions should be answered at this design step:

1. Are all netlists used for simulation identical to those extracted from the schematic?
2. Are all parts of the functional blocks specified and connected?
3. Is the necessary layout information (specific to either digital or analog part of the circuit) present in the schematic?

7.2.4 Simulations

7.2.4.1 Digital simulations

It is important to understand the effects of loading and the effects of parasitics of interconnections when doing personalized standard cell digital design. These effects and the process variations must be simulated by the use of maximum delay and minimum delay sets of values associated with each cell. All critical delay paths must be identified, together with allowable maximum interconnection parasitics, and specified in the schematic. All timing and potential race conditions should be analysed and verified by simulations. Maximum and minimum delay simulations should also be performed. Fast clocks and reset edges should also be tested by ensuring that the design rules have been observed.

7.2.4.2 Analog simulation

Analog simulation should model and predict circuit behaviour under varying process and environmental conditions.

1. Separate simulations should be performed to predict the performance of the analog circuitry at the lowest and at the highest specified temperature.
2. This should be repeated with the highest and the lowest specified operating voltage.
3. The simulations should be performed using best case process parameters specified at both temperature and operating voltage conditions and using worst case process parameters for both cases.
4. The effects of variations in circuit performance caused by uncorrelated changes in P-channel and N-channel transistors must be simulated using combinations of worst case N-channel transistor and best case P-channel transistors and vice versa.
5. The effects on matching characteristics should be simulated by the use of perturbations in device sizes, threshold voltages, and gain factors according to the analog process characterization data. A tolerancing analysis of the circuit against process parameter variations will give the designer a good feel of the circuit's sensitivity to subsequent manufacturing fluctuations.

6.   Layout descriptors and resulting parasitics should be incorporated in the above simulations.

7.2.4.3 Mixed-mode simulations

All mixed analog digital circuitry should be simulated. This is especially important where there is feedback between analog and digital sections. Different simulation tools may be used for different mixed analog digital functions incorporated in the ASIC; however, it is important that at least at the level of the behavioural descriptions the complete ASIC is simulated as one entity to verify input/output definitions.

1.   Switched-capacitor circuits may use simulations tools optimized for discrete time charge distribution techniques. These simulations should take into account circuit sensitivity to capacitor matching problems. Again, tolerancing analysis approach is preferable to a simple sensitivity analysis. The circuits should be verified for non-ideal operational amplifier and switch characteristics.

2.   Layout descriptors should also be verified in these simulations.

7.2.4.4 Checking procedures

The following points should be checked after completion of the simulation portion of the design task:

1.   Are the critical speed paths in the digital part of the circuit identified? How fast are they and what are the margins?
2.   Are the critical interconnection parasitic's attributes entered in the schematic?
3.   Are the race conditions properly avoided and what is the related time margin?
4.   Is there any timing condition which is not derived from the master clock of the ASIC? If so, is the asynchronization correctly simulated and analysed?
5.   Were all necessary analog simulations performed in both frequency and time domains?
6.   Are the dynamic range and noise level addressed correctly?
7.   Has the impact of non-ideal (not shown in simulations) input offset-voltage of the operational amplifiers been analysed?
8.   Are the sensitivities to digital and analog crosstalk identified and entered into the schematic as layout attributes?
9.   Is the grounding scheme correctly implemented? Are sensitive grounding buses separated? Are potential voltage drops caused by sharing the same ground bus eliminated?
10. Are the power supply lines designed for required digital noise immunity?
11. Is the separation of the digital and the analog power supplies complete and entered into the schematic diagram?
12. Is the influence of non-ideal power supply output impedance correctly simulated?

13. Are the tolerances of on-chip voltage reference, D/A and A/D converters properly simulated for the matching, process, power supply and temperature variations?

7.2.5 Test program definition

As described in Chapter 8, the designer must verify the testability of the ASIC. He may need to incorporate some built-in-test function or allow for a special mode of ASIC's operation, i.e. test mode. For the digital part he will need to specify the test pattern. The quality of this testing pattern should be verified by the use of fault simulation.

For the analog portion of the chip the designer has to specify the test method together with its input and output specification and tolerances. The quality of the test procedure cannot be measured directly; however, it is a function of the completeness of the tests of ASIC's analog modules and of their accuracy.

The following questions should be answered regarding testing:

1. Is there a general reset foreseen to put the digital logic into a known initial state?
2. Will the circuit power-up in a known state?
3. Is test time speed-up foreseen by using accelerated clock, and if so, was the circuit simulated for the test mode?
4. Is there a possibility of using a structural rather than a functional test approach, and what are the implications?
5. Are the analog specifications for testing realistic regarding the tester sensitivity resolution, dynamic range, noise, etc.?

7.2.6 Design for quality requirements

The designer can influence the ASIC's quality in the following ways:

1. Design for the lowest possible power dissipation of the ASIC
2. Design for the lowest voltage span on the device
3. Design for conservative current densities
4. Design for highest latch-up immunity
5. Design for highest electrostatic discharge
6. Observe all layout design rules
7. Add a design margin for tolerances, e.g. tester accuracy

The following questions should be answered to assure proper ASIC's design-dependent quality:

1. What is the worst case power dissipation of the ASIC, and what is maximum junction temperature for the maximum environment temperature and thermal resistance of the selected package?

2. Does any pin including V_{DD} or V_{SS} see a voltage larger than specified as maximum for the selected process? If not, does the design ensure that the devices maximum voltages are within the specified limits also during transients?
3. Is the sequence of turning on multiple supply voltages or other input voltages such that no latch-up condition can occur? If this cannot be guaranteed, is latch-up condition still prevented?
4. Are maximum DC and transient currents on power supply lines and on power outputs calculated and are the current densities below the specified maximum ratings?
5. Are the protection circuits employed correctly to protect for electrostatic discharge?

7.2.7 Final layout verifications

The final layout should be verified against the schematic to avoid any potential layout errors introduced either during manual editing of the graphic data base or caused by the operator or by a layout generator bug.

The following checks should be performed:

1. A full chip design rule check (DRC) showing no errors should be performed. If a specific design requires different DRC, it must be signed off and verified.
2. A full chip electrical rules check (ERC) has to be run on each design showing no errors.
3. A full layout versus schematic verification (LVS) must be performed showing no errors.

7.2.8 Project management

The complete specification, design and transfer to manufacturing is a complex process in which the penalties for errors are high. It is therefore essential to employ a disciplined project management approach that can accomplish the following:

1. Establish requirements
2. Define responsibilities
3. Schedule visibility
4. Review design

The complex design process is broken into a series of project phases. The project management technique recommended is to establish three parameters for each project phase. These are:

1. Entering phase—establish requirements and check status.
2. During phase—define responsibilities.
3. Completing phase—define transition mechanism.

Fig.7.1 shows a design process broken down into five phases. The three parameters for each of the five phases are given. Another way of representing the project management function is to look at the design flow and observe the control points within this design flow. Fig.7.2 illustrates where the control points given in Fig.7.1 occur, together with the additional control points in the "design engineering" phase.

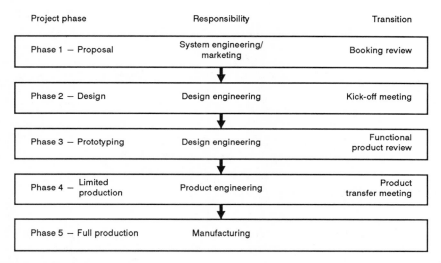

Fig. 7.1 Design process by project phases

7.3   Interface levels

There are two main points in the design procedure at which an interface is normally established between the design authority and the silicon foundry. These are the simulated schematic level and the so-called "clean database level".

7.3.1   Simulated schematic interface

This interface is a well proven route for digital ASIC designs. The silicon vendor provides the designer with digital libraries and model data; CAD tools are provided by either the silicon vendor or a CAD vendor or a combination of the two. In addition, in order to assure himself that the resulting design and simulation work will produce a design that can meet the overall objectives, the designer needs some other information from the silicon vendor. This concerns allowable chip sizes, package types and possible power dissipations, and ultimate design and unit cost. This information is important for initial feasibility studies and to ensure that the designer can check at various intervals, before he completes his final simulated design, that should meet the complete specification.

The other major interfaces involve the test program, mask making and the final chip assembly and packaging. In general, digital ASIC designers interface with a silicon vendor who organizes

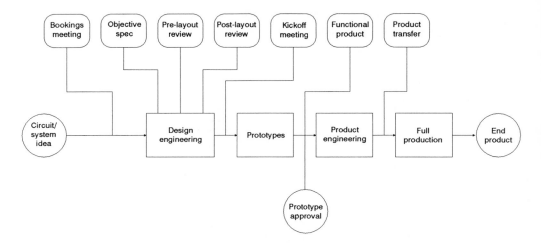

Fig. 7.2 Control points in design flows

the interface between these operations. The designer is required to provide a test pattern and a test plan which adequately covers the specification. This is described in more detail in the next chapter.

This same interface can apply to mixed analog digital designs, but they pose further problems to be solved than do purely digital designs. These relate to the critical performance often required from analog circuits and the significant impact of the layout on the final chip performance. The solution lies in providing the designer with an organized way in which to describe these layout issues to the foundry. This point was addressed in Chapter 6 in the discussion on the schematic capture program. In addition, with mixed analog digital designs, it will often be necessary to personalize some of the analog library cells and even to create entirely new cells. This means that a more comprehensive interface for mixed analog digital designs is required at the simulated schematic level. The designer must now be able to specify the new cell requirements accurately and to obtain models for them from the vendor for his simulation tools. This will mean in practice that the mixed analog digital vendor must have the capability rapidly and accurately to design and model new analog cells.

For the designer of a mixed analog digital system, who is also interfacing with a silicon vendor managing the interfaces between mask making, packaging and testing, the major additional interface is again that of the test program. The mixed analog digital test program is inevitably a more complex interface than a fully digital program. A clear understanding of the tester and its limitations and options available must be established as well as the best techniques for test time minimization. These points are discussed further in the cost considerations section and in Chapter 8.

Fig.7.3 shows a schematic representation of the described interfaces at the simulated schematic level.

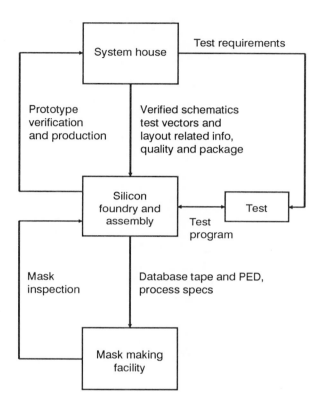

Fig. 7.3 Simulated schematic interface to silicon foundry

7.3.2 Layout database interface

Interfacing at this level means that the mixed analog digital designer has the full responsibility for the chip design. Consequently he needs an additional level of understanding of the design process particularly relating to circuit design and layout. He must receive from the silicon vendor more fundamental information concerning circuit modelling and layout rules and practices.

The designer needs the physical level of the silicon vendor's library and, ideally, access to his personalized cell CAD programs and silicon compilation tools. Additional useful information can be provided by the process validation module (PVM) or process evaluation device (PED). As described in Chapter 2 this is a test circuit containing a collection of device structures that is processed on each silicon wafer together with the final circuits. Measurements from these devices will tell the designer how the actual process parameters of his prototype devices compare with the processing limits. Table 2.6 shows a selection of typical parameters that are provided by silicon vendors to the designer from the PVM or PED. The relevant parameters that should be obtained for mixed analog digital design are discussed in Chapter 4.

Before releasing the final layout to the silicon vendor the designer should check the layout against both the schematic and the process layout rules as part of his design verification procedures, as described earlier. This is most accurately performed using one of the standard layout-versus-schematic (LVS), electrical rule checking (ERC), and design rule checking (DRC) programs. An example of a commercially available program is "Dracula" from Cadence.

To avoid potential discrepancies it is ideal for the designer to use both the same design rules checking (DRC) program and the same DRC run set as the silicon vendor. If this is not possible some discrepancies are likely which will take additional interface effort and cost to resolve.

The other interface points are really no different from the situation described for the simulation schematic interface except that the designer must check that the die fits the package and there are no bonding problems. Fig.7.4 describes the interfaces for the layout data base. If the designer is working with a silicon supplier who is not managing all the interfaces concerned with mask making, packaging and testing, then the interface issues expand significantly. The designer must then understand these issues in sufficient detail to insure that his complete packaged and tested product can be economically and repeatedly produced.

7.4   Cost considerations

Every silicon vendor will have his own method of calculating the final product price. This will be based not only on the anticipated production volume and his internal and external cost structures but also on his planned profit margins and current business strategy. Bearing this in mind it is nevertheless very important for the IC designer to be able to understand basic cost considerations to arrive at an economic design.

The final unit cost (U) of an IC is made up of three basic constituents:

1.   Die cost (D)
2.   Package and packaging cost (P)
3.   Test cost (T)

To understand how these costs are built up into the final cost U, it is necessary to remember that a die is normally first tested on the wafer using needle probes. Assuming this takes a time t seconds and produces a number $N \cdot \eta_s$ of good dies, where N is the total available number of dies on the wafer and η_s is the wafer sort yield. (Another way of expressing yield is through the concept of defect density which is a sum of all factors contributing to defective die.)

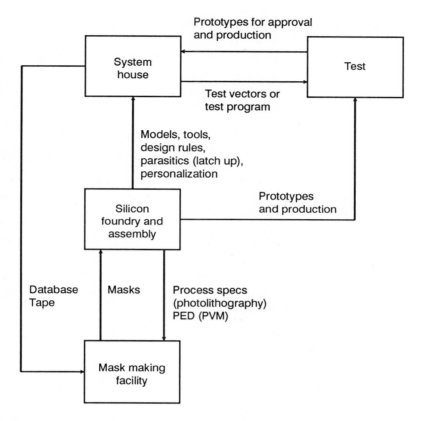

Fig. 7.4 Layout database interface to silicon foundry

The packaging cost P is made up of the cost of the package P_p plus the assembly cost per pin C_p times the number of pins N_p. It must now be remembered that both good packages and die that passed the wafer probe test will be discarded if they fail the final test. If we define the final assembly and test yield as η_f then the total cost of the unit can be expressed as:

$$U = D + P + T + F/V \tag{7.4.1}$$

or:

$$U = \frac{W}{N} \frac{1}{\eta_s \, \eta_f} + P_p \frac{1}{\eta_f} + C_p \cdot N_p \frac{1}{\eta_f} + C_T \cdot t \frac{1}{\eta_s} + C_T t \frac{1}{\eta_f} + F/V \qquad (7.4.2)$$

where C_T is the cost of testing per second and W is the processed wafer cost; F is the fixed cost factor for the silicon vendor to introduce a new product to his manufacturing facility. This can be a significant factor for low volumes V less than, say, 5 000 units per annum and is normally negligible for high volumes, say, greater than 100 000 units per annum, although in practice the determining factor is value of production not just the quantity.

For simplicity this formula assumes that the tester cost and time are the same for wafer probe and final test. Also for simplicity the cost formula does not take into account the fact that the detection of defective die and packaged parts do not take the full test time t.

By obtaining a range of the relative values for each of these key cost parameters the designer is able to make the important trade-offs in his design between die size, package pin count. package type, tester time and tester type. Chapter 8 gives the relative magnitude of cost of different tester types.

For many years the focus of IC design cost reduction was on die size minimization as die cost was the major cost factor. Recently, with smaller digital designs and more particularly with mixed analog digital designs, if a complex analog tester is required, this is less significant as test and package costs can dominate. First the designer should insure that a complete test can be accomplished in a few seconds. He should consider adding on-chip circuitry and additional package pins to achieve this. After ensuring that adequate testing can be performed in a few seconds, the designer can turn his attention to package cost reduction and finally die size reduction for cost savings.

7.5   Design acceptance

7.5.1   Definitions

In the process of enabling the designer to create his own mixed analog digital design the possibility has been introduced that although the design may for certain prototype units meet the complete design specification, it may not in fact be acceptable for production in any volume quantity. Such poor yielding designs consume the silicon foundry's capacity to produce other normal yielding die. It is hence essential for both the designer and the silicon manufacturer to establish a clear design acceptance procedure in which the tolerances of the design can be demonstrated to be acceptable for the manufacturer's process.

7.5.2   Responsibilities

The design control procedure described earlier has been constructed to not only provide quality control of the design process but also to ensure that sufficient tolerancing simulations are performed. If systematically applied, these procedures should give the designer a high degree of confidence that his design will be acceptable to the manufacturer. It should be clear that the ultimate responsibility for the manufacturability of the design rests with the designer. Equally clearly it is the responsibility of the silicon manufacturer to maintain the silicon manufacturing process within the published limits. Certain silicon vendors have yield criteria that the initial production batches must reach before the design is accepted as having a manufacturing status. If for any reason the yields of the design are below the expected values it is in both the designer's and the silicon vendor's interest to determine and rectify the causes. Should the cause not be readily determined by either an examination of the design or a check of the actual process parameters, the test program or test set-up should be suspected. If this does not reveal the cause, then an independent assessment by a product engineer is usually required. His task is to determine from the three variables, the design, the process and the test program, which variables are primarily contributing to the problem and what courses of action should be taken.

8. Test and evaluation

8.1 Types of test and evaluation

8.1.1 Introduction

There are many different silicon evaluation and test techniques and before looking into them in detail it is important to understand their different uses. They fall broadly into two classes: those associated with the evaluation and verification of the design, and those associated with testing production devices. Because of the limitations of system level modelling referred to in Chapter 3, the design verification testing may have to check both that the silicon meets the device specification, and that the device works in the system, i.e. that the device specifications were correct in the first place. In addition the design verification should include an evaluation of the production tolerance of the design against process parameter spreads. This process is called "characterization".

In considering the design verification technique to be used, and indeed the design methodology itself, apart from the points already mentioned one must consider that the chip might not function correctly on first silicon and thus diagnostic aids will be needed. With purely digital devices it has become common in the interest of saving test development time to proceed directly with the development of a program that can be used for final production units on automatic test equipment (ATE). If this approach is adopted, facilities for diagnostics and characterization will need to be built in for use at the appropriate point in the evaluation sequence and switched out again when not needed to minimize production test times.

8.1.2 Evaluation and test procedures

On receipt of first silicon or "prototypes", designers usually verify their designs with a combination of bench testing, system testing and using the test program written for the ATE. It is obviously important that the device should function correctly in its system tests, but often this is not a full test of the device specifications. In a system test it can be shown that a particular device will operate in a system with the other particular components used in that one system. It is often not practical or possible to evaluate the device in a range of systems that contain the other components with a complete spread of their specifications. Thus in a system test the device will not be evaluated over a complete range of input logic levels, timing and other parameters that one would expect over a high volume production run. In the absence of a real time emulation of the system, the device "system test" might be the first time the complete system has been tested and might show serious "high level" design flaws.

A bench test is often the most practical way of quickly extending the scope of tests and checking the conformance to specification for the analog sections of a device: measuring the performance of the D/As, op-amps, comparators and filters. For testing the digital section of an ASIC, however, the pattern set-up sequences are often too long to allow a comprehensive bench test and it is then a function of the ATE test program to evaluate the conformance to specification of the prototypes.

Having ensured that the prototypes conform to the design specification, the test program can now be used to characterize the device. To characterize a design, it is necessary not only to determine how a particular chip functions over temperature, speed and voltage, etc. but also to determine how different chips with a range of process parameters will operate under these different conditions. Often after the prototypes have been verified, wafer runs will be initiated that are planned to produce devices with a spread of the critical process parameters. These parts are then tested to ensure that there is a design margin at all "corners" of the process and thus ensure that yield problems will not occur in volume manufacture.

Once the design is verified and characterized the device can be given production status. At this point the test program will be used to test wafers so that the good die can be identified for assembly. After the die have been packaged the test program will be used to "final test" the devices prior to Quality Assurance checks and shipment. The test limits used throughout these programs will be set at different levels; for example the characterization test needs to be the most rigorous test to ensure that the design has margin over and above the specification limits for all wafers with parameters that conform to the process limits.

This must be true to ensure that the device will yield consistently throughout its production life. Also the wafer sort program requires tighter test limits than the final test program to maximize the final test yield. It is cheaper to throw away a die than a tested part. The test program will also be used by Quality Control who will take a sample of production and retest the packaged parts prior to shipment to the customer. An overall test program development flow is shown in Fig.8.1. For a more detailed discussion see Refs.1 and 2.

8.1.3 VLSI versus board testing

Some of the requirements and limitations are different when testing a VLSI device from those involved in testing a printed circuit board; others are similar.[3] A test program developed to test a board level analog digital system has firstly to provide a pass or fail decision as to whether the board meets the specifications. If a test of a board fails, the manufacturer will require to know which components, tracks or solder joints are giving the failure so that the board can be reworked. To give better observability of potential errors on a board it is common practice not only to monitor and force signals onto the board through the board connector pins, but also

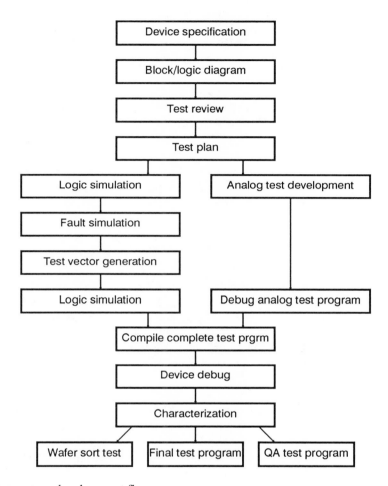

Fig. 8.1 Test program development flow

to add test probe points onto the board. These are then available via a bed of nails connection for the tester to force or monitor signals throughout the test program. Pressure to increase board densities is reducing the number of probe points that will be available, but when testing a VLSI it is important to remember that only package pins can be made available for test. Special wafer probe test pads can be used, but these are generally discouraged for production devices. Increasing the numbers of package pins to accommodate better testing can raise the package cost. Consequently, VLSI designers have to make a very careful choice between ensuring adequate testing, and use of pins. Additional on-chip circuitry can often be used to help solve this problem, e.g. the use of multiplexers which is described in Section 8.5.2. on test strategies.

The test program for a VLSI device also has the requirement to provide a pass or fail flag during production, but unlike a board level test we are not interested in repairing a failure at the production stage. It is, however, advantageous to both design verification and characterization if the test program can report the possible area of failure.

For the system designer who has the responsibility for both the VLSI chip and the board design, the use of a common integrated test philosophy has many advantages. This is especially true if the board contains several VLSI devices. In this case the use of one of the formal test techniques described in Section 8.5.3 for both the board and the VLSI devices allows the test program to be structured hierarchically. This can greatly aid the program development and the system diagnosis.

8.2   Mixed analog digital VLSI testing

8.2.1   Problems of testing mixed designs

As can be seen from the foregoing discussion, in designing a device with testing in mind, it is important to ensure that "observability" and "accessibility" are adequate.[4] Accessibility is defined as a measure of the ease of forcing a node to a particular level or with a particular signal, and observability is a measure of the ease of monitoring a signal or level on a node within the chip. It is also important to ensure that devices can be initialized and that long count sequences can be broken up to enable consistent test results and to shorten the test time respectively. The design-for-test strategies for analog and digital circuits share these same principles.

However, because mixed analog digital ICs implement complex matrices of macros and resistor/capacitor structures on the chip without providing access to each component's input or output, these devices lack controllability and observability. There can also be close interaction between logic and analog portions of a design, e.g. in a resistor string DAC where the most significant bit and subranging resistors are controlled by the digital word to be converted to the analog representation. Thus, in some cases, it is not possible to test the analog portion without adding complex logic functions.

There is usually a shortage of pins available for "complete" analog coverage. However, by partitioning the circuit into functional blocks, e.g. complete switched-capacitor filters rather than sections and using multiplexing at pin and analog digital boundaries it is possible to achieve much improved controllability and observability in mixed-signal designs.

Another problem associated with the testing of mixed analog digital ICs is related noise. Rapid transitions of logic signals from the tester's digital sections can be picked up by the sensitive analog circuitry, masking the analog measurements. Expensive tester technology can alleviate this problem, e.g. sensitive analog test circuitry near the pins in the test-head away from the tester. Alternatively, digital signal processing (DSP) techniques can be used,[5] or the digital tests and associated clocks can be halted while the analog measurements are being made. Halting the clocks can be expensive in test time but can enable a cheaper tester to be used. This is an important factor in test cost, as will be discussed in Section 8.4.

8.2.2 Analog and digital faults

The faults on a chip that cause it to misfunction arise from physical phenomena such as oxide defects, missing implants, lithographic defects, moisture accumulation, impurities contamination, static discharge and metal shorts and opens. A common method of modeling the effect of these faults for the digital section of the design is called the "stuck-at" model.[4] With this model a gate input is modelled as having a fault by that input being stuck-at 0 or stuck-at 1. An example is shown in Fig.8.2 where a missing contact has resulted in a node being stuck-at 0. This model is useful because it can be readily simulated by software that will check the effect of each node within the circuit being stuck-at 1 or 0, and comparing the resultant simulation output with a good simulation. By simulating the circuit using the proposed test program and these fault models it is possible to obtain a measure of the "fault coverage", i.e. the percentage of faults detected by the test pattern.

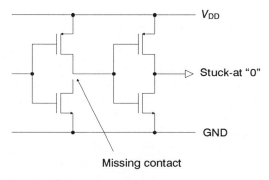

Fig. 8.2 Stuck-at "0" node due to missing contact

Not all faults are detectable with the stuck-at model.[6] These undetected faults usually involve circuits with parallel paths. One example is a CMOS transmission gate consisting of an n transistor and p transistor in parallel, where a stuck-at 1 on the p transistor gate will turn the p transistor permanently off. See Fig.8.3. The n transistor will still function as a pass gate; the only difference is that the output high level will be weak. Such a fault is undetectable by a stuck-at fault model; though it will be detectable by the change in the parametric performance of the device. Fig.8.4 shows a logic network containing a parallel path where a stuck-at 1 fault on node A is not detectable due to redundant logic. A number of proposals have been made to provide more comprehensive fault models to overcome these problems, but these complicate and worsen the fault simulation problem. The empirical evidence suggests that test vectors derived from the stuck-at model result in a low level of undetected defects.[4]

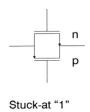

Stuck-at "1"

Fig. 8.3 Transmission gate with p transistor stuck-at "1"

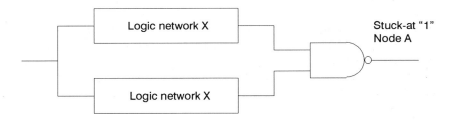

Fig. 8.4 Non-detectable stuck-at "1" fault

There is no simple direct equivalent to a fault model that can be used to check by simulation that a test of an analog circuit is comprehensive enough to find all processing faults.[7] Instead, parametric measurements are made that are designed to verify that the analog sections of the device operate to specification over the required voltage and temperature range. All the pullup and pulldown resistors, output drive currents, input threshold levels, voltage reference levels, op-amp gains, D/A and A/D performance, and frequency response of filters need to be checked parametrically to ensure that no devices with process faults, and thus out of specification devices, pass the test program. It is unfortunately up to the analog designer to specify for his circuit and system which faults are critical, particularly those that could occur on analog sections internal to the chip.

In practice it is usually not possible to test all parameters because of practical limits to pin-out and test-time. It is also difficult to carry out measurements such as offset-voltage or input-referred noise–voltage density for a high performance operational amplifier buried deep in a switched-capacitor modulator although these parameters would be critical to the harmonic content specification of this circuit. In this case measurement of the output of the modulator would show whether or not the harmonic distortion was within specification. The fact that it was poor behaviour of the op-amps that caused it to be out of specification could be argued to be irrelevant, for the final production test, but not of course for design verification and diagnosis.

The subtlety involved in defining "fault coverage" in the analog situation is best seen by reference to another example. Consider an operational amplifier buffer stage with output drive enhanced by the addition of an emitter follower Fig.8.5(a).

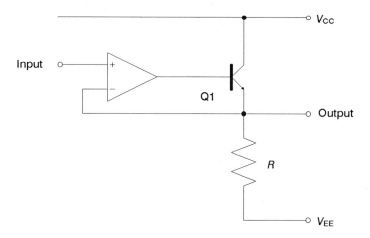

Fig. 8.5(a) Buffer stage with emitter follower

Obviously the output impedance is very low due to the Q1 stage. If, however, the collector of Q1 is, due to a processing error not connected to V_{cc} we have the situation depicted in Fig.8.5(b). A signal path is still maintained because of the diode, so an output will still be observed, but the output impedance of the circuit will be considerably higher and will probably render the block useless in terms of its intended function.

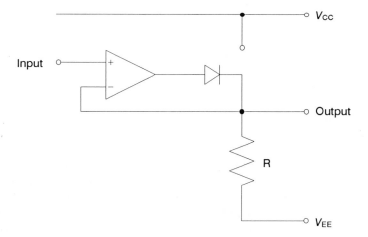

Fig. 8.5(b) Equivalent circuit of emitter follower with V_{CC} disconnected

The above example is equivalent to the transmission-gate case cited earlier in this section. The "fault" causes a resistance or "strength" deviation which can none the less be just as serious as a "hard" error in terms of the circuit functionality.

If, however, we treat the circuit in Fig.8.5 as a functional block, its function defined as a buffer with output resistance Z Ω, then the open circuit of collector Q1 will show as a fault in the block's operation. Testing parameters such as frequency response and output impedance under load of the whole block will, in practice, be adequate.

8.3   Quality of test

8.3.1   Cost of faults

The cost of a high quality test program is illustrated in Fig.8.6. This graph shows how the cost of detecting and correcting a fault increases throughout the development cycle of a project. For example a logic error detected at the design phase will cost an engineer just a few days extra work, whereas if that error is not detected until prototype evaluation, there is the much greater cost of masks and prototype fabrication incurred in addition to the engineering effort to correct

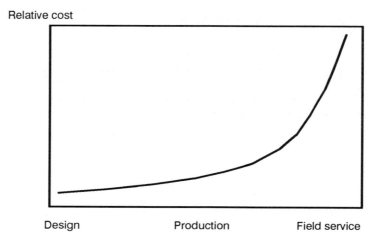

Fig. 8.6 Cost of faults

the design fault. Similarly in a production environment, if a faulty device is not detected at wafer sort but at final test, the package and assembly costs will be thrown away as well as the die costs. This can mean 10 times more cost for a failure to be detected at final test rather than at wafer sort. If the final test program passes devices that will fail when assembled into the final system, by the time the final system is repaired and retested this can result in the cost of a fault being again 10 times higher than the cost of detecting it at final test. If the system manufacturer does not find the faulty devices but ships bad product, this will result in field service calls which can again increase the cost of detecting and correcting the problem a further 10 times. It is clearly essential in a highly competitive, cost sensitive industry, to ship high quality product. This requires that the right quality of testing is applied at each point in the test cycle.

8.3.2 Average quality level, AQL

The average quality level of an ASIC device is defined as the number of defective parts shipped divided by the total number of devices shipped (see Fig.8.7). Thus AQL is the quality level of the ASIC supplier as measured by the customer. It is related, apart from other things, to the quality of the test program, and in turn to the fault coverage of the test program (see Fig.8.8).

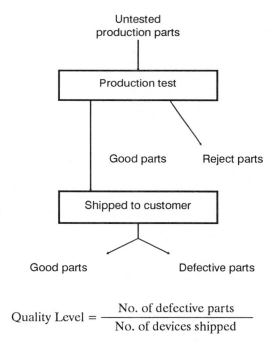

$$\text{Quality Level} = \frac{\text{No. of defective parts}}{\text{No. of devices shipped}}$$

Fig. 8.7 Average quality level

To consider an example of this, if 10 000 parts were shipped using a test program with only a 50 per cent fault coverage one would expect up to 750 of these parts to be defective; this assumed an overall yield for the process of about 30 per cent. Fig.8.9 shows how the number of defective parts could be expected to decrease if the fault coverage of the test program were to be increased. Many sectors of industry, such as automotive, are now requiring a minimum of 98 per cent fault coverage in order to diminish the number of potential field failures to an acceptably low level.

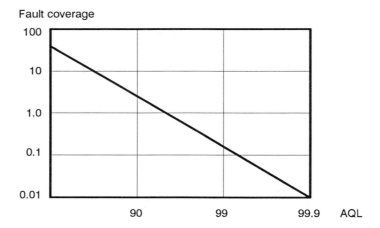

Fig. 8.8 Correlation of fault coverage versus average quality level

Fault coverage	Defective parts/ 10,000 shipped	Quality level
50	750	7.5 %
90	310	3 %
99	13	0.1 %
99.9	3	0.03 %

Assumption of 30 % overall yield

Fig. 8.9 Correlation of fault coverage versus defective parts

Because, as was stated earlier, there is no simple general model of an analog fault and hence no such concept as analog fault coverage, the designer must be sure that the system is designed in such a way that all critical analog parameters can be measured. As a consequence the analog sections of the design are usually tested with an exhaustive functional test to ensure that a high quality product results. Some techniques for developing analog tests are discussed in Section 8.5.2 on test strategies.

8.4 Choice of testers

Before considering the development of test strategies and test programs in more detail it is important to understand the options available in the choice of test equipment. The available equipment varies considerably in capabilities, in complexity and, of course, in cost. The options available can broadly be grouped into five classes:

1. Complex digital testers
2. Complex analog testers
3. Design verification testers
4. Bench-top test equipment
5. Special purpose test equipment

8.4.1 Complex digital testers

Examples are Fairchild Sentry S10, S20, S15 and S50 series, LTX Trillium, Teradyne J series, Megatest and GenRad GR125, GR130. The range of a complete system cost is $200K–$3M. The lower end of the price range is typically a machine that has been stripped of many features and options for use in a production test environment only. Complex digital testers provide logic pattern generation and data acquisition facilities. Realtime compare circuitry allows comparisons of acquired and reference (or expected output) data for functional verification of digital devices.

Timing or A.C. parameters such as propagation delays and set-up and hold times can also be measured. The results of these measurements are usually displayed in tabular and graphical formats. Very often a digital tester provides the ability to make these timing measurements over varying conditions of voltage, temperature and other variables for full device characterization.

In addition, a complex digital tester enables D.C. parametric measurements to be made to determine whether an IC's pin electronics conform to specifications. Typical D.C. measurements evaluate the load presented by a device's input pins, and the load that can be driven by the output pins. These D.C. measurements are performed by a parametric measurement unit (PMU) which can both force voltage and measure current and force current and measure voltage.

Complex digital testers can provide clock and data rates of up to 50 MHz, pin electronics for up to 512 pins, with per-pin programmability, timing edge resolution of 100 ps or less and the capabilities for accurate D.C. and A.C. parametric measurements. Typical digital tester resolutions are in the ranges 10–50 mV (voltage) and 1–5 μA (current) but accuracies can be as poor as ± 25 mV and frequency response measurements are, of course, very difficult. There are some exceptions; e.g. the Sentry S20 has a resolution of 1 mV. The ability to measure these values accurately is often spoiled by noise coupled from the digital stimuli. To avoid this the tester will have to be "stopped" during these measurements.

Complex digital testers may be used for certain mixed-signal IC situations and should always be considered as a first option because of availability, digital features and generally lower test cost than the complex analog testers. In practice this is limited to non-critical analog circuits which are part of a larger digital design and static measurements of ADCs, DACs, waveform generators such as DTMF systems, codecs, level-detectors and comparators. Often better results can be obtained by building special circuitry onto the load board to add test features not inherent in the digital machine.

8.4.2 Complex analog testers

Examples are LTX 77, Sentry Series 80 machines and Teradyne A500 series. Range of system costs is $1M–$4M. These testers allow measurements of voltages down to 10 μV, gains to 120 dB, dynamic range of more than 140 dB, voltage noise densities in the nanovolts per root hertz region, bias measurements down to 10 pA and frequency range from D.C. to 10 MHz. This type of tester consists of a collection of precision programmable signal sources and measurement systems built into a low noise environment. In all the more advanced complex analog digital testers extensive use is made of digital signal processing (DSP) techniques.

Complex analog testers are expensive, and analog test times are typically long. Consequently the unit test cost for ASICs with significant analog content can be much higher than for purely digital ICs of similar complexity. Using DSP techniques has the advantage that whether the device under test (DUT) is analog or digital or mixed, the measurements may be made in the digital domain. A good example of the use of DSP is in connection with filter ICs. Multitone testing combines all sinusoids needed for the analog stimuli into a single complex waveform. The responses for all passband frequencies are tested simultaneously. Thus test times can be significantly reduced (by as much as a factor of 10 to 20) since all the magnitudes and phases of all frequencies are analysed via a fast Fourier transform (FFT) from a single-pass measurement. Group delay is derived from the phase information provided by the FFT. Other filter characteristics such as bandwidth, harmonic distortion and dynamic range are derived from the same data set. There is a penalty in that analog testers with DSP capability are even more expensive than their pure-analog counterparts, but usually the savings in test times produce an overall test cost saving.

8.4.3 Design verification testers[8]

Examples are IMS Logic Master, ASIX-1 and 2, Hilevel-Topaz systems, Hewlett Packard 81805 and Cadic. Typical system price is $100 K–$300 K.

This new class of testers was introduced to assist digital ASIC designers in design verification and test program development. The machines provide a low cost, easy to use alternative to the complex digital testers. They do not require air conditioning and can easily fit into most small design laboratories. They can handle small prototype quantity tests, but are generally too slow for volume production testing, although some improvements are being seen in this area, e.g. ASIX-2.

Some systems can handle devices with 256 pins and 50–100 MHz clock and data rates for CMOS, ECL and even GaAs ASIC designs. Software control is aimed at providing a closer interaction between users and the device under test, and the ability to create "what if" situations to push the device to its performance limits.

Prototype verification provides functional, timing and D.C. parametric information from first silicon samples. If these characteristics meet expectations the design may be released to production. If this is the case the qualified simulation vectors must be transferred to production test equipment. It is clearly important that the test vectors from the design verification testers are easily transferable to production tester formats. While some tools to do this are being provided, many users still prefer to get access to a complex digital tester to avoid the translation effect.

Very limited analog testing can currently be achieved on design verification testers. The capabilities for analog testing are similar to those described for complex digital testers. It is thus important to consider other categories of tester for more complex analog or analog digital prototype evaluation.

8.4.4 Bench-top test equipment

This refers to equipment that is assembled as inter-connected instrumentation units from suppliers such as Hewlett Packard, Tektronix, Keithley, etc. These could be power-supplies, logic analysers, waveform generators, signal analysers or even oscilloscopes and voltmeters. The equipment can be very sophisticated and configured as a fully customized system and would then probably be connected together with a microcomputer or PC using a standard bussing arrangement such as IEEE-488 or GPIB/HPIB bus.

A typical set-up for testing a chip with a complex or high performance analog content could cost $100K–$300K depending on the specification of the instruments chosen. In addition one has to consider the cost of the user-generated software for the instrumentation control. The advantages and disadvantages of bench-top testing are discussed in Section 8.7 on bench-top testing.

8.4.5 Special purpose test equipment

After having considered the commercially available tester options just discussed, it could be that the most attractive solution for volume production testing a mixed analog digital design is a special purpose tester. This could be the case if, for example, a complex digital tester or a design verification tester did not have the capability and a complex analog tester was too expensive.

This solution was often used in the past for very high volume consumer chips where complex or high quality tests had to be performed at low cost. With more attention to design for test, better liaison between designers and manufacturers and the greater availability of a variety of complex analog testers, this solution is now not as often used. It is still worth considering when the other solutions look unattractive.

8.5   Design-for-test

8.5.1   Why design-for-test?

To control test costs it is essential that a "design-for-test", DFT philosophy is adopted as an integral part of the design methodology, as described in Section 3. The first aim is to ensure that a test of the desired quality can be performed and the test equipment chosen within the budgeted time and cost. The second aim is to reduce the complexity of the tests so that the test development schedule can be kept short, reducing test development costs and ensuring a faster time to market.

A test strategy and test plan for a device should be developed during the initial block development of the chip. To ensure that design-for-test has been incorporated into the design it is essential to have a DFT review checkpoint during the design phase. This is illustrated in Fig.8.1 in the test review phase.

8.5.2   Test strategies — general considerations

As was described in Section 3, a chip should be designed so that it can be simulated in blocks, because the individual blocks will be quicker to simulate and take less time to debug. The individual simulations can then be put together to provide a set of test vectors. The test vectors, having been generated on a per block basis, will themselves be easier to debug. This will assist the designer in providing better test program documentation, which will be useful to the product engineer in transferring the design to production. The simulation vectors should be designed to generate a test program that can be used to assist in the device debug as well as the production test, as mentioned earlier. The test program should have a high fault coverage to provide a high quality final test, but the test program runtime should be kept short to minimize test costs.

To achieve these aims it is necessary to develop a test strategy during the initial design phase. This should ensure that all nodes within the circuit can be initialized, that observability is maintained on all nodes, and long test sequences are broken up to minimize test pattern length. Testability circuitry may need to be added either to reduce test program length, or to ensure access is maintained to all internal functions, or to ensure that sufficient access is available to allow the analog sections to be checked to their parametric specifications.

Initialization is a way to be assured of knowing the state of the circuit when power is first applied during test. It is a special case of "controllability". Good initialization can greatly reduce test pattern lengths and hence test development time and test run time. The initialization of a circuit at power-up can be greatly improved by adding reset signals. Take the case of the divide by two circuit shown in Fig.8.10; the circuit is only testable by matching the tester to the output pattern,

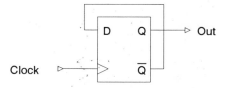

Fig. 8.10 Divide by two circuit

i.e. 00110011 or 11001100 are both acceptable outputs. If this circuit were to be embedded within a chip this could prove to be a very complex test problem. The addition of a reset signal as shown in Fig.8.11 simplifies the test program development by ensuring that the circuit can be initialized to a known state.

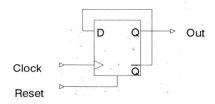

Fig. 8.11 Addition of reset signal for initialization

A second example where initialization is required to produce a testable design is shown in Fig.8.12. In this diagram, the counter cannot be initialized, so there is no way of knowing at what address the counter will start to access the ROM. This circuit is untestable as it stands because the match pattern would be too long and too complex to consider. The addition of a

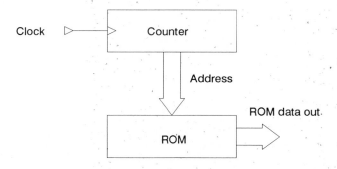

Fig. 8.12 Example of testable design using initialization

reset to the counter will make this circuit fully testable, by allowing the counter to be initialized to zero at the start of the test program.

A review should be made of the block diagram of the system at each level of the hierarchy to determine if all inputs to the block are readily controllable, and that the outputs of the block are readily observable. If this is not the case, long test sequences may be required to control or observe the input/output of the blocks within the system. One technique to improve the controllability of a node is to introduce multiplexors that either provide the circuit with its normal input or in test mode will provide an input signal from a more controllable point in the system, such as an input pad. In a similar way a multiplexor can be added to an output pad that will in test mode output a signal from an imbedded block.

Similarly for analog blocks, it is important that sufficient access is maintained so that the inputs can be readily controlled and the outputs easily observed to minimize the set-up time for each parametric test. It is good practice to provide test models to give access to intermediate analog signals produced within a block, e.g. after each stage of a filter in a multistage filter design. In this case the overall system can be readily tested by controlling the inputs to the filter and observing the outputs. During the evaluation stage of the silicon, however, it is often desirable to have data on the gain frequency response of each filter stage. This can best be measured by the addition of test modes that will give access to these internal nodes.

An extreme example of the problems of test if DFT techniques are not applied is the long counter chain. Fig.8.13 shows the block diagram of a 24 hour counter circuit. To test this circuit as shown fully would require $2.8 \cdot 10^9$ vectors, which with a clock rate of 32 kHz would take a test time of approximately 24 hours. At a test cost of $100/hour this would result in a test cost of $2400. If the counter chain is broken up as shown in Fig.8.14, the number of test vectors required will be reduced to 1440 and the test time would be less than 1 second. This would result in a test cost of less than $0.03. Generally it is aimed to keep digital ASIC test time down to less than 2 seconds, and a mixed A/D test time in the range of 5–10 seconds; though the economics depend also on other factors such as package cost, die cost and production volume as discussed in the last chapter.

No. of vectors: 2.8×10^9
Test time = 24 hours

Fig. 8.13 Block diagram of 24 hour counter circuit

It is important to remember at the design stage that the design must include a margin for all parametric and analog test measurements to allow for test technique and tester accuracy. An example is the design of an output stage specified as being able to sink 2.0 mA at 0.4 V. If the tester has an accuracy of ±50 mV, and the quality control requires a further 50 mV test margin

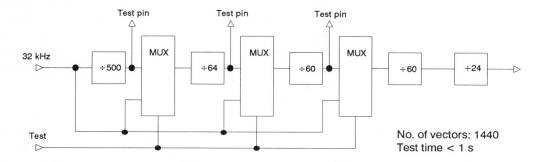

Fig. 8.14 24 hour counter chain broken for testability

to ensure repeatability of tests, then the output stage will have to be designed to sink 2.0 mA at 0.3 V. This is a design specification requiring 25 per cent more current than the customer's specification!

Similar examples can be given whether designing filters, op-amps, or other analog cells. Here the accuracy of the test measurement and the required test margin should be added to the specification so that they can be incorporated at the design stage. This is essential if a repeatable test program is to be produced. Compromises do have to be made, however, when testing analog components. For example, when testing a band pass filter, often no more than four frequencies are used to excite the filter during the test, one frequency for each stopband and one for either end of the passband. Here it is important to correlate the automatic test to the bench test measurements in order to quantify the completeness of the test.

8.5.3 Formal test techniques

The test strategies described so far outlined principals and *ad-hoc* procedures that will ensure testable circuits with the minimum of silicon area overhead. The assumption that has been stressed throughout is that the chip designer takes the DFT goals as part of the design specification and is successful in providing an adequate test coverage. In companies producing a large number of digital designs, e.g. mainframe computer manufacturers it is often considered desirable to use more formal DFT techniques. Many of these are based on the principle of partitioning the design into blocks of purely combinatorial logic. The storage elements, flip flops and latches, etc. naturally end up at the partitioning boundaries. With a small amount of additional circuitry these elements can be made to operate as shift registers in a test mode.

One such technique, introduced by IBM, is level sensitive scan design (LSSD).[9] In this technique flip flops throughout the circuit can be configured into a shift register to give access to internal nodes of the circuit, allowing the tester to either force or read signals on these points without having a long set-up sequence working through the rest of the circuit. A decision must be made early in the design cycle whether or not the more formal techniques will be used. They will usually result in a larger die size and hence higher die cost, but will minimize the test development time and will often result in a higher fault coverage. This may prove to be the determining factor in the decision if the cost of field failures is potentially very high. In addition LSSD techniques typically produce relatively long serial bit patterns and the chosen tester must be able to handle these.

An extension of LSSD for mixed designs is to provide an analog digital scan path to improve the controllability and observability of both the analog and digital sections. One technique is to provide a "boundary" around the digital section separating for testing purposes the analog and digital sections.[7] This enables the logic test pattern generation to proceed independently of the analog section. It also enables a simple set-up sequence to be used to provide the logic control while performing the analog tests. By using this technique both the test program development time and test program run times can be reduced with only a small increase in silicon area associated with the additional latches incorporated into the design.

A "built-in test technique" BIST that can be incorporated into a ASIC design is "signature analysis". This was developed from an electronic troubleshooting method developed by Hewlett-Packard.[10] The technique involves building a linear feedback shift register whose count sequence is controlled by the state of parallel inputs. After running through a sequence, a good part will have a particular number or "signature" in the counter; a bad part will have a different number in the register.

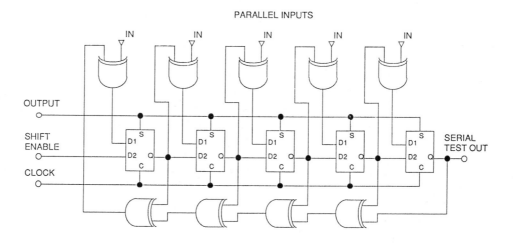

Fig. 8.15 BILBO structure

The signature analysis technique can be combined with LSSD to give a built-in logic block observation structure (Bilbo).[11] In a Bilbo structure (Fig.8.15) the registers in the linear feedback register can be shifted out in a serial mode during the test. One of the advantages of using this technique is that it allows good observation of internal nodes with a minimum of test mode set-up. The disadvantage can be that diagnostics of faults can become more difficult.

8.6   Test program development procedures

8.6.1   A team effort

The test program development is often best done as a team effort, between designer and test engineer. Together they can write an efficient test program for a complex mixed analog digital IC Firstly a test engineer may be required to assist in the choice of test system and to provide the knowledge of the capabilities of the chosen test system. At each stage of the project development, the test engineer will be able to ensure that the test methodology being developed will be viable on the chosen tester. The test engineer will also have the in-depth knowledge of the tester to be able to implement the agreed upon test plan. The design engineer while designing the ASIC is involved throughout in developing the test strategy during the design phase. He is also required as a consultant during the test program development on the chosen tester. The test engineer is the expert on the test system, and can implement an agreed test plan. He does not, however, have the in-depth knowledge of the ASIC that the chip designer will have and thus test program debug must often be a joint effort.

8.6.2   Test reviews

Throughout the system and chip design, regular test review meetings should be held to assist the designer in developing a design that has an adequate built-in test strategy. Once the logic and block diagrams have been finalized, a formal test review meeting should take place where the design engineer should explain in details his test strategy. The test engineer should be present at this meeting to give his formal concurrence with the strategy outlined. A check list is useful at such a meeting, so that for example initialization, controllability, observability, parametric and/or analog measurements and estimated test times are discussed in detail for each block.

8.6.3   The test plan

To formalize the interface between the design engineer and test engineer and to provide documentation of the test program contents it is advisable to produce a test plan. In this document will be specified the order of tests, the supply voltage, input levels and output sense levels used for each test. In addition there should be a list of the digital patterns to be used to test the digital sections of the design and a detailed description of the set-up and measurements to be made to implement each analog test. It is important to plan carefully the order of the tests, as this can impact test time. The test time of reject devices can be minimized by placing first those tests covering the widest area of the design. Generally the very first tests will be shorts and continuity tests which simply check that the device under test is correctly connected to the tester and that none of the pads are shorted that should not be. If a high proportion of devices are failing this test it will flag to production that a contact problem has arisen in the test set-up and the connections need to be inspected.

The digital tests are often completed prior to the analog tests, as they are generally quicker and thus find faults faster. This procedure keeps the average test time of a reject device down.

The production test program will have three switches so that it can be used as a wafer sort, final test or quality assurance test. The test plan should contain the test limits to be used for each of these options. The quality assurance limits will be the exact limits specified in the device specification and often measured at temperature. Final test is done at elevated temperature (e.g. 70 °C), if possible, together with wafer sort. In this case QA will be at room temperature. The wafer sort limits are often a compromize and depend greatly on the wire lengths to the probes. Ideally this test will be tighter than the final test so that any marginal device is rejected prior to being packaged.

8.6.4 Test program development

The digital test patterns can be created from the input and output files produced, respectively, for and by the logic simulator. Provided the principles described so far for DFT have been adhered to, and a thorough simulation of the circuit done, a high fault coverage should result. There are many simulators that can output data directly in a format acceptable to the major testers, or alternatively the files can be post processed by a reformatting program. These programs will ask which pins are inputs, outputs, or bidirectional to allow the correct tester set-up commands to be incorporated.

All inputs must be defined synchronously relative to some time interval or clock cycle. Each time interval or one half clock cycle will be defined as one test cycle, and inputs should be set so that they only change at the beginning of the test cycle. The automatic tester will apply the defined inputs simultaneously at the beginning of the test cycle and will strobe the output before the beginning of the next test cycle. The way that simulation results are collected must, therefore, conform to the way they will be read by the tester.

The test patterns for the digital circuitry can alternatively be generated automatically by a number of different techniques.[2] These can work well with the formal DFT techniques described earlier and do not require such a detailed involvement of the design engineer. The automatic techniques range from random pattern generation through a variety of uses of the D algorithm to intelligent knowledge-based systems.[12]

There is at present no equivalent to the digital test vectors that can be used to automate development of an analog section of a test program. Digital vectors are, of course, often required to set-up the analog circuit into the correct mode for measurement. Instead test techniques are built up for various analog modules such as filters, op-amps, D/A, A/D that can be modified to test the particular configuration in the ASIC under test. It should be possible in the future to develop analog test programs by combining the final results of the simulation of these analog modules, possibly using DSP techniques.[5]

8.7   Bench-top testing

For the design verification stage of an IC development a number of visually good die are taken from the centre of a wafer and packaged in ceramic packages. For digital ICs these can be evaluated using complex digital testers or design verification testers as described in Sections 8.4.1 and 8.4.3. For analog or mixed analog digital devices, however, the tests are often best carried out using bench-top testing.

Bench-top test equipment, as described in Section 8.4.4, consists of individual units, meters, power supplies, signal sources, analysers and data-logging equipment connected together by an appropriate bus, and controlled by an appropriate user-generated program resident in a microcomputer or PC. It is possible that the equipment will not be connected together at all but consist of hand-operated units with separate power supplies, sources and analysis units.

The big advantage of bench-top test equipment is that very specialized tests may be carried out on the IC while still giving a great deal of control and visability to the design engineer. For instance, special telecommunications measurement units are available for testing compliance with CCITT and ANSI standards. Also, no specialist test program knowledge is required for using this equipment. It is simply using electronics laboratory instrumentation and possibly a well-known language such as BASIC for control. The disadvantage of the bench-testing approach is the time involved for measurements. It can take many man days to characterize just one complex telecommunications IC. In addition the specialized equipment may be expensive but it is usually possible to hire this equipment when required.

During prototype testing if faults are detected it will be necessary to carry out fault diagnosis. This is best done using bench-top test equipment in order to make the measurements more directly. If access to internal nodes is not adequate from the IC pins it may be necessary to use a microprober workstation or a number of other more sophisticated tools.

8.8   Troubleshooting—measurements internal to chip

Some percentage of ICs will, unfortunately, fail on one pin or more to meet the target electrical or functional specification. Reasons for failure could be errors in device models, design or layout errors, or process defects. To de-bug the IC can require a large amount of engineering effort. Ideally, the design engineer would like to locate the fault in the same way one would on a printed circuit board using voltage sources, signal generators and oscilloscopes via probes and clips.

However, the integrated components are very small, in the order of microns as described in Chapter 2, and are not always accessible. They are formed in the silicon processing stages earlier than the polysilicon and metallization layers. Therefore methods for diagnosis of the IC must have the special resolution necessary for on-chip dimensions and may require that the designer be able to visualize the under-structures of the silicon.

In this section the following methods will be considered as they are all useful for various diagnoses of a faulty IC:

1.   Microprobing.
2.   Scanning electron microscopy (SEM).
3.   Voltage contrast electron microscopy.
4.   Thermal contrast analysis.

8.8.1 Microprobing

Microprobing is the most commonly used method for trouble shooting an IC. It enables the designer to get close to the PCB situation although there are problems associated with poor drive characteristics of on-chip components and the buried and often invisible structures that are inaccessible to the microprobes.

Very fine probes with tip diameters of a few microns are mounted onto steerable arms which are attached to solid blocks held on to the microprober bed. The bed is mounted on a heavy vibration-free table as it is important that the probes do not move when probing a narrow ($2-10\,\mu$m) width of metal on the IC. The probes are electrically connected to a distribution block and hence to the test equipment. The probes are located with the use of a powerful optical microscope and positioned by thumbscrew adjusters in three planes of movement. It must be remembered that the probes and connecting wires will add considerable loads to the components being measured on-chip. Capacitance can be as high as 40 pF per probe and this, of course, is too much for many digital and analog IC core circuits to drive. FET input buffered probes are available which present only a pF or so to the chip tracking. These are expensive and can be damaged easily. Microprobes are also available that are connected to a source of ultrasound. These can be used for "cutting" metal or polysilicon tracks on the IC for further diagnosis of faulty devices. This "micro-surgery" is very useful for diagnosis and can also be invaluable for carrying out minor modifications to an IC prior to its use for prototype approval when used in the end equipment.

8.8.2 Scanning electron microscopy (SEM)

This technique can be used to look at electrical and metallurgical structures in the integrated circuit. Thus, the presence of diffusions and wells may be verified using SEM as can effective device geometrics. This type of analysis can be invaluable for consistent failures within an IC or across whole wafer batches and would tend to be overseen by a process engineer rather than the designer of the IC.

8.8.3 Voltage contrast SEM

This is a very useful, albeit expensive, analysis tool for the diagnosis of faulty ICs. The potential of a surface conductor (for example, strips of metallization) affects transmission of secondary electrons from the SEM beam. Thus the CRT image contains information on the voltage of the conductor. Many have seen the slow-motion recordings taken of a microprocessor at work for general education or PR release. This technique has been used for more serious applications in the diagnosis of troublesome chips. An extension of this method appeared in the mid-1980s as a fully automated stroboscope electron beam test system for analysis of logic VLSI circuits. In this method the IC design data is read from the CAD system to provide a "design map". Interconnection pattern recognition is then performed by the test system computer by superimposing this map onto an observed stroboscopic SEM image. Once the circuit nodes for voltage waveform measurements have been designated, the corresponding metallization tracks are automatically determined on the superimposed map. Finally, the electron beam is positioned on the actual circuit-under-test conductor tracks and the measured waveforms are displayed. This system can be coupled with a fault diagnostic electron beam tester for a completely unified electron beam test system. Hence interconnection patterns having improper logic states are easily pinpointed on a CRT display and easy (and quick) diagnosis may be made. The system can also be used to check the fault coverage of a test pattern.

8.8.4 Thermal contrast analysis

A much cheaper method for more gross IC fault diagnosis uses liquid crystal technology. Paints containing organic liquid crystals are applied to the surface of an IC under investigation and then pulsed operating voltages are applied. Using microphotography a region of interest can be isolated and lapsed-time exposures taken to record the history of breakdown or current paths in the surface conductors of the IC. This method is often used for tracing the cause of latch-up produced by a parasitic SCR structure near to a pad of the integrated circuit. This phenomena is well known but is still impossible to model accurately and can only be prevented by use of strict layout and design practices in conjunction with epitaxial substrates. Even so, most CMOS circuits are prone to latch-up, and this can happen so quickly that a power supply metal line can be fused before any other observable effect is noted by normal diagnostic methods. However, by using the liquid crystal technique it is often possible to detect where the latch-up process is initiated and hence correct that part of the layout by extra guard-banding, reordering the p^+ and n^+ diffusions or by increasing the separation between current-carrying and "sensitive" areas of the IC. A certain level of skill and experience is required before this method can be usefully exploited but most IC foundries should contain this experience within their process technology areas.

References

1. Williams, T.W., *VLSI Testing*, North-Holland, 1986.
2. Feugate, R.J., McIntyre, J.R. and S.M., *Introduction to VLSI Testing*, Prentice Hall, New Jersey, 1988.
3. Beenker, F.P.M., Eerdewijk, K.J.E., *et al.*, Macro Testing: Unifying IC and Board Test, *Transactions of IEEE Design and Test Conference*, pp.26–32, Dec. 1986.
4. Williams, T.W., Parker, K.P., Testing Logic Networks and Designing for Testability, *Computers*, pp.9–21, October 1979.
5. Mahoney, M., DSP-based testing of analog and mixed-signal circuits, *IEEE Computer Society Press*, New York, 1987.
6. Timoc, C., Buehler, M., *et al.*, Logical models of physical failures, *International Test Conference Proceedings*, IEEE Press, New York, 1983.
7. Prilik, R., Van Horn J., Leet, D., The loophole in logic test: Mixed-signal ASICs, *Proceedings of IEEE 1988 CICC*, **Vol. 16.4**, pp.1–5, Rochester, New York, 1988.
8. Sena, A. De, Design verification systems strive to keep pace with ASIC complexity and speed, *Computer Design*, pp.36–40, June 12 1988.
9. Williams, T.W., Parker, K.P., Design-for-testability – a survey, *Proceedings of IEEE*, **71 No. 1**, pp.98–112, Jan. 1983.
10. Nadig, H.J., Signature analysis – concept, examples and guidelines, *Hewlett Packard Journal*, pp.15–21, May 1977.
11. Fasang, P.P., Circuit module implements practical self-testing, *Electronics*, pp.164–7, May 19 1982.
12. Wharton, D.J., The hitest test generator system – overview, *Proceedings of 1983 International Test Conference*, pp.302–10, New York IEEE Press, New York, 1983.

9. Design example — single chip telephone set ASIC

The effectiveness of the described design method can be demonstrated by the design of the digital and analog functions of a state of the art telephone set in a single CMOS ASIC.

The top-down design procedure starts with the system definition which consists of a set of specifications and a system description in verbal form.

9.1 Functional description of the telephone set ASIC

The telephone set ASIC performs the following functions:

1. It amplifies the incoming signal on the telephone line and feeds it to the earphone (receiver).
2. It amplifies the signal coming from the microphone (transmitter) and feeds it to the telephone line.
3. It processes the dialling information entered from the keyboard and communicates this information to the telephone line either as a pulse dialling signal or as dual tone dialling signal.
4. It performs all functions to operate last number redial and a nine number repertory dialling memory.
5. It provides proper A.C. impedance to the line and proper D.C. termination.

A mixed analog digital ASIC was designed in CMOS technology to fulfil these requirements.[1] Fig.9.1 shows the top level representation of the ASIC. It consists of analog and digital parts. The basic functions of the analog part are to process the received and transmitted voice signals and to interface the telephone line with the earphone and microphone, while the main functions of the digital part are to process the dialling information, to manage the dialling memory, to control the ASIC's status and to interface with the dial/keyboard. A number of interface signals between the analog and the digital parts exist. Fig.9.1 was used as a basis for the functional description of the ASIC. No electrical specifications were added at this point. In the next level of the specification development the modules shown in Fig.9.2 were defined. The specification for each module was developed as part of the design procedure. If the complexity of any module shown in Fig.9.2 was low enough to allow efficient transformation of its specifications into schematics, a design procedure for library level schematic creation was started, followed by

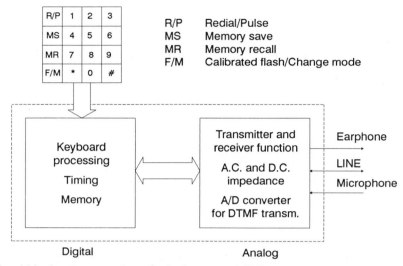

Fig. 9.1 Top level block representation of telephone set ASIC

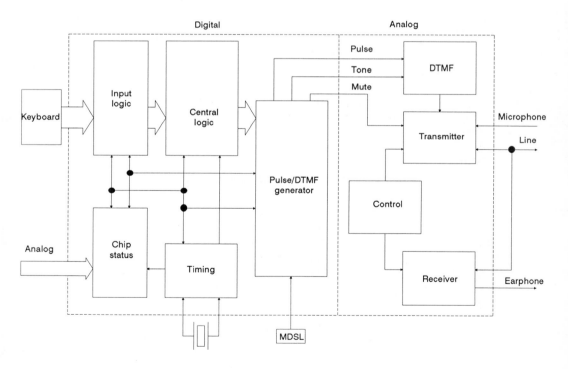

Fig. 9.2 Decomposition of telephone set ASIC into digital and analog part

library cell personalization and module layout generation. If not, a further module decomposition was necessary. Specific modules were chosen to show the detailed design procedure, while for the rest only selected design steps are presented.

9.2 Receiver module

9.2.1 Design level 1: module description and specifications

9.2.1.1 Description

The receiver function is to provide an audible signal to the telephone set earphone and to the speaker amplifier.

Block representation of a receiver module is shown in Fig.9.3.

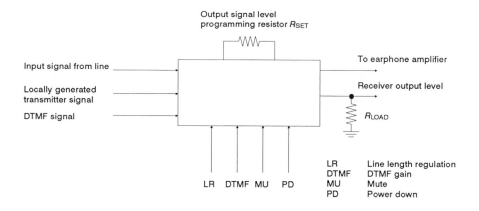

Fig. 9.3 Block representation of receiver module

The output signal level has to be set by an external resistor and to be automatically regulated to compensate the losses introduced by different telephone line lengths. The maximum output sound level must be limited to prevent potential damage to the user's ear. The receiver also performs part of the two to four wire conversion (hybrid function); it amplifies only the incoming signals transmitted from the calling party while suppressing the signals generated by its own (local) microphone amplifier and transmitter. Additional receiver requirements are that it has to be set in a mute mode during pulse dialling, in a low gain mode during dual tone dialling and in a power-down mode when in the on-hook status.

9.2.1.2 Specification

The target specifications shown in Table 9.1 were derived from the listed description from the specifications set by CCITT standards and from selected specifications of external components of the telephone set.

Table 9.1 Receiver specification

V_{DDmin}:	4 V
$V_{DD\ max}$:	7 V
Receive gain:	6 dB max at
	$R_{SET} = 33\ k\Omega, R_{LOAD} = 270\ \Omega$
	$I_{LINE} = 20\ mA$
Side tone attenuation:	14 dB at
	$R_{SET} = 33\ k\Omega, R_{LOAD} = 270\ \Omega$
	$I_{LINE} = 20\ mA$
Gain tolerance:	± 1 dB max
Frequency response:	$f = 300\ Hz - 3600\ Hz \pm 0.5$ dB max
Distortion:	1 per cent max at
	$V_{outp} = 250\ mV$
Nominal output voltage V_{outp}:	250 mV
Maximum clipped voltage V_{clpp}:	1500 mV$_{pp}$
Maximum noise:	-80 dBmp max
Line length regulation:	6 dB at
	$I_{LINE} = 20\ mA \div 45\ mA$
Δ gain mute:	-60 dB
Δ gain DTMF:	-40 dB max
Low line current output level:	$V_{out} = 100\ mV_p$ at
	$I_{LINE} = 6\ mA, V_{DD} > 2\ V$
Power-down current:	$1\ \mu A$ max

At this point the receiver module is represented as a black box defined with its inputs/outputs as specified in Table 9.1.

Additional specifications must be defined at this early design stage. They are:

External pin count:	3
Test strategy:	Frequency domain transfer function measurements
Target test time:	1 second

From the total 28 pin count budget available for the complete chip we can assign only three external pins for the receiver function as seen from the tentative pin assignment in Fig.9.4.

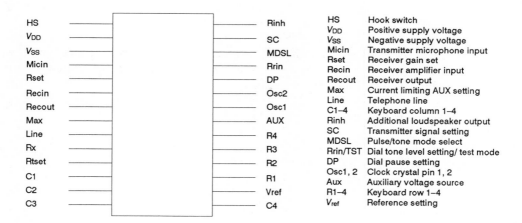

HS	Hook switch	
V$_{DD}$	Positive supply voltage	
V$_{SS}$	Negative supply voltage	
Micin	Transmitter microphone input	
Rset	Receiver gain set	
Recin	Receiver amplifier input	
Recout	Receiver output	
Max	Current limiting AUX setting	
Line	Telephone line	
C1–4	Keyboard column 1–4	
Rinh	Additional loudspeaker output	
SC	Transmitter signal setting	
MDSL	Pulse/tone mode select	
Rrin/TST	Dial tone level setting/ test mode	
DP	Dial pause setting	
Osc1, 2	Clock crystal pin 1, 2	
Aux	Auxiliary voltage source	
R1–4	Keyboard row 1–4	
V$_{ref}$	Reference setting	

Fig. 9.4 Tentative ASIC pin assignment

9.2.1.3 Test considerations and specifications

The precision of the analog specifications preclude the use of a complex digital tester as described in Chapter 8. A complex analog tester must be used. The test strategy heavily depends

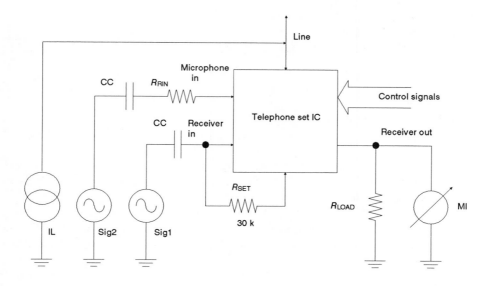

Fig. 9.5 Test set up for receiver section

on the target test time. Since the product is intended for the high volume consumer market the target test time for the complete test of the circuit is a maximum of 5 seconds.

In our first estimation we have assigned 1 second for testing the receiver function. The proposed test set-up for the receiver module is shown in Fig.9.5. This set-up together with the testing procedure will show the module testability.

The test flowchart shown in Table 9.2 is applicable:

Table 9.2 Test flowchart for receiver module

Test activity	Test conditions
SET I_{LINE} = 20 mA	
MEASURE RECEIVER GAIN &	
FREQUENCY RESPONSE	
CHARACTERISTIC (SIG1, M1) :	f_1 = 300 Hz, f_2 = 600 Hz
	f_3 = 1 kHz, f_4 = 2 kHz,
	f_5 = 3.6 kHz,
MEASURE DISTORTION (SIG1, M1)	f = 1 kHz
MEASURE LOCAL GAIN (SIG2, M1)	f = 1 kHz
MEASURE MAX CLIPPED	
VOLTAGE (SIG1, M1)	f = 1 kHz
MEASURE NOISE (M1)	
SET MUTE, MEASURE GAIN (SIG1, M1)	f = 1 kHz
SET DTMF, MEASURE	
OUTPUT LEVEL (SIG1, M1)	
SET I_{LINE} = 45 mA	
MEASURE GAIN (SIG1,M1)	
MEASURE LOCAL GAIN (SIG2, M1)	
SET I_{LINE} = 6 mA	
MEASURE GAIN (SIG1, M1)	

As seen from the test flowchart all the target specifications from Table 9.1 are testable except the power-down current. However, it is specified for the complete ASIC and is measured during the parametric test.

It is important to know that even the complex analog testers described in Chapter 8 do not allow such low noise measurement as specified for the receiver module. Two alternatives have to be considered:

1. Noise characteristics are guaranteed on a sample bench measurements basis.
2. A high gain test mode be provided to increase the output noise level.

Test time estimation: as seen from Table 9.2, fourteen A.C. measurements in the audio frequency range are performed. We can predict 100 mseconds per average A.C. measurement. This includes generator setting, meter reading and ASIC settling time. With the presented test strategy we can expect the test time for the receiver module to be as long as 1.5 seconds, which is 50 per cent more than the target, which at this stage is probably acceptable.

9.2.1.4 Summary of the design level 1 activities

In the first design step the following tasks were accomplished:

1. The receiver module description was summarized.
2. The target specifications were derived to formalize the design goals together with the block representation of the module.
3. The concept of the test strategy was made to prove testability and to give a test time estimation.

We can conclude that the outcome of the first design step is satisfactory so we can proceed to the next design level.

9.2.2   Design level 2: receiver module partitioning and cell definition

In this design level the block representation of the receiver module shown in Fig.9.3. is decomposed down to the level where the synthesis and layout compilation tools can be used to implement the design goal.

Fig.9.6 shows the first attempt to break down the receiver module into three blocks.

The first block is a summing low noise amplifier with externally adjustable gain. The second block is a variable gain stage, where gain is adjustable in the 6 dB range to compensate the loss due to different telephone line lengths. The measure of the line length is line current which varies by a factor of two to one.

The third block is the output stage capable of driving a 270 Ω load at 285 mV peak amplitude and with a signal limiting capability.

Fig.9.6 is further transformed into Fig.9.7 which is composed of basic library cells and primitive library elements.

Creation of the schematic shown in Fig.9.7 is the design step which requires some engineering skills and knowledge, which is not uncommon for system design engineers. In fact this design step represents the most creative part of the design procedure and offers a challenge to the designer's technical imagination.

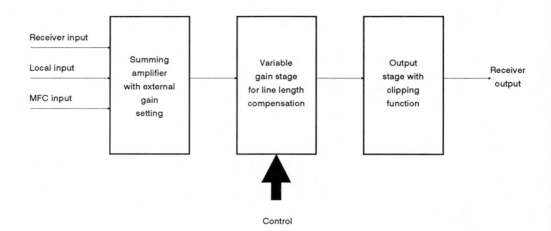

Fig. 9.6 Block diagram of the receiver module after the first decomposition step

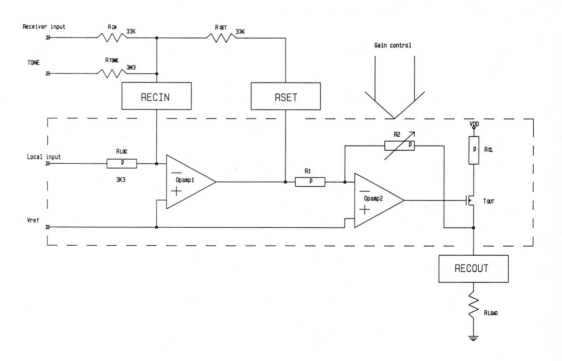

Fig. 9.7 Receiver module represented with library cells and elements

9.2.2.1 Receiver schematic analysis

Equations for different signal paths can be written; gain for receiver signal is given as follows:

$$G_{\text{RECEIVE}} = \frac{R_{\text{SET}}}{R_{\text{RIN}}} \frac{R_2}{R_1} \tag{9.1}$$

Gain for local signal path is similar:

$$G_{\text{LOCAL}} = \frac{R_{\text{SET}}}{R_{\text{LOC}}} \frac{R_2}{R_1} \tag{9.2}$$

as well as for dual tone signal path:

$$G_{\text{TONE}} = \frac{R_{\text{SET}}}{R_{\text{TONE}}} \frac{R_2}{R_1} \tag{9.3}$$

All three equations are valid under the condition that the open-loop gain of the operational amplifiers is much larger than the closed-loop gain which can be assured by proper design of the operational amplifier cell.

From equations (9.1), (9.2) and (9.3) resistor ratios can be derived by choosing the ratio R_2/R_1 equal to 2 for the longest line length at $I_{\text{LINE}} = 20$ mA. For the specified external resistor $R_{\text{SET}} = 33$ kΩ we can calculate other resistor values:

$$
\begin{aligned}
R_{\text{RIN}} &= 33 \text{ k}\Omega \\
R_{\text{L}} &= 3.3 \text{ k}\Omega \\
R_{\text{TONE}} &= 3.3 \text{ M}\Omega
\end{aligned}
$$

As seen from the schematic in Fig.9.7, R_{RIN}, R_{SET} and R_{TONE} are external resistors while R_{LOC}, R_1 and R_2 are internally integrated resistors.

The accuracy of both G_{RECEIVE} and G_{TONE} depends only on the accuracy of resistor ratios of the same type. However, this is not true for the local signal path where the gain depends on the ratio of external resistor R_{SET} and internal integrated resistor R_{LOC}. This situation is completely unacceptable because of the poor absolute resistor value tolerance over the fabrication process and temperature variations. This was described in some detail in Chapter 4. We can correct this situation when designing the local signal generation by providing the opposite cancelling effect. We will return to this point in the transmitter module design.

9.2.2.2 Variable resistor implementation

The next design step is the implementation of variable resistor R_2. A straightforward solution to it is a digitally controlled resistor string as shown in Fig.9.8(a).

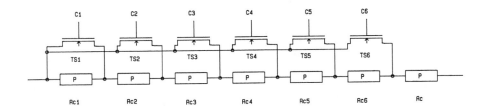

Fig. 9.8(a) Implementation of variable resistor R_2

Digital signals C_1, C_2, ..., C_6 control transistor switches TS1–TS6. The control signals are the outputs of a three bit A/D converter in the control section of the ASIC, measuring the telephone line current. Resistor values can be calculated according to the following equations:

$$\sum_{i=1}^{6} R_{ci} = R_c \tag{9.4}$$

$$20 \log \frac{R_{cx} + R_c + \sum_{i=x}^{6} R_{ci+1}}{R_c + \sum_{i=x}^{6} R_{ci+1}} = 1, \quad x = 1,2,3,4,5 \tag{9.5}$$

Equation (9.4) represents the fact that the total required gain variation is 6 dB while equation (9.5) reflects a 1 dB gain step as is seen from Fig.9.8(b). The receiver gain is approximated by piecewise segments as a function of telephone line length represented by its current and monitored with an A/D converter.

Equations (9.4) and (9.5) give the following resistor values: $R_{C1} = 2.610 \ \text{k}\Omega$, $R_{C2} = 2.332 \ \text{k}\Omega$, $R_{C3} = 2.075 \ \text{k}\Omega$, $R_{C4} = 1.853 \ \text{k}\Omega$, $R_{C5} = 1.651 \ \text{k}\Omega$, $R_{C6} = 1.472 \ \text{k}\Omega$, for $R_C = 12 \ \text{k}\Omega$.

From Fig.9.8(b) we can determine the required gain accuracy. As seen in the figure the worst case is at transitions of control status where gain tolerance is only ±0.5 dB. We can assign some of this tolerance to resistor mismatch and some to A/D inaccuracy, operational amplifier finite gain effect and other possible sources of errors.

9.2.2.3 Completion of the library schematic

The last step in this design level is the completion of the library level schematic with the definition of all library cells and control signals as shown in Fig.9.9. The MUTE and power-down (PD) controls are added at this stage.

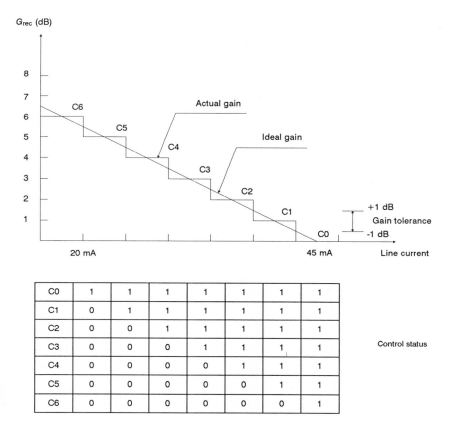

Fig. 9.8(b) Receiver gain characteristics versus line current (line length)

9.2.3 Design level 3: receiver module cell synthesis and layout compilation

At this design level the synthesis of the cells identified at the previous design level is performed and their layout compiled. As shown in Fig.9.9 the following cells need to be created:

1.   Simple resistor cell RCL
2.   Simple resistor cell RLI
3.   Simple transistor cell TOUT
4.   Resistor network cell RIRC
5.   Transistor network cell TS
6.   Operational amplifier cell OPAMP1
7.   Operational amplifier cell OPAMP2

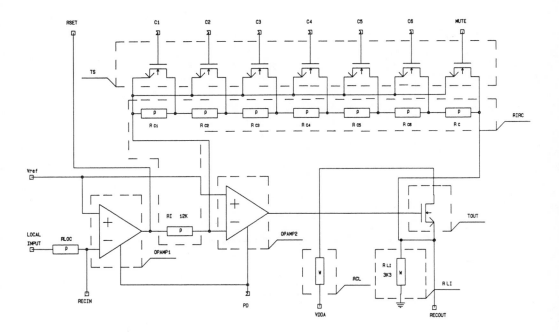

Fig. 9.9 Completed library level schematic of receiver module

9.2.3.1 General cell descriptor identification

The descriptors for the listed cells must be identified in order to use the previously described CAD tools for cell synthesis and layout compilation.

V_{DD} definition

Although the specified power supply voltage for the ASIC varies from 2 V to 7 V under different line conditions, the $V_{DD} = 4V$ is selected for the cell descriptor since this is the worst case V_{DD} voltage, where all ASIC functions must meet the specification. Note that some of the ASIC functions are also specified at lower line voltage or current. They do not, however, represent the highest ASIC performance regarding the analog functions, such as receiver or transmitter gain and its tolerance, e.g. the receiver and transmitter should still function at 2.5 V.

*V*ref definition

The V_{ref} can be calculated simply from the specifications for the maximum peak receiver output voltage:

$$V_{\text{ref}} = V_{\text{outp}} + G_{\text{max}} \cdot V_{\text{off}} = 250 \cdot 10^{-3} + 10.5 \cdot 10^{-3} = 300 \cdot 10^{-3} \text{ V} \tag{9.7}$$

9.2.3.2 Resistor cell RCL descriptor definition

Resistor R_{CL} is the limiting resistor and its value is defined by the signal limiting specifications as follows:

$$V_{\text{DD}} - I_{\text{p}} \; R_{\text{CL}} > V_{\text{outp}} + V_{\text{ds}} \tag{9.8}$$

$$V_{\text{DDmax}} - I_{\text{CL}} \; R_{\text{CL}} < V_{\text{CLP}} \tag{9.9}$$

Where V_{DS} is minimum drain source voltage for transistor TOUT, I_{CL} is maximum limited current, I_{p} is peak signal current and V_{CLP} is maximum positive limited output voltage, i.e. $V_{\text{CLpp}} - V_{\text{ref}}$. Assuming $V_{\text{DS}} = 0.5$ V and using the specified V_{outp} and V_{CLpp} we obtain:

$$R_{\text{CL}} < \frac{V_{\text{DD}} - V_{\text{DS}} - V_{\text{outp}}}{I_{\text{p}}} = \frac{4 - 0.5 - 0.25}{2 \cdot 10^{-3}} = 1625 \; \Omega \tag{9.10}$$

$$R_{\text{CL}} > \frac{V_{\text{DDmax}} - (V_{\text{CLpp}} - V_{\text{ref}})}{I_{\text{CL}}} = \frac{7 - (1.5 - 0.3)}{6 \cdot 10^{-3}} = 967 \; \Omega \tag{9.11}$$

The resistor value R_{CL} is normally between 967 Ω and 1625 Ω, or nominally 1300 Ω ± 325 Ω.

The resulting descriptors for the automated resistor cell layout generation are the following:

Resistor R_{CL}: ratioless
I_{max}: $2 \cdot 10^{-3}$ A
Tolerance: 25 per cent
Resistor nominal value: 1300 Ω
Temperature range: 70 °C $(T_{\text{max}} - T_{\text{min}})$
Parasitic capacitance: N/A
Parasitic leakage current: N/A
Shielding: N/A

The resulting resistor cell dimension is the following:

$x = 72 \, \mu\text{m}$
$y = 168 \, \mu\text{m}$

Resistor R_{LI} serves as output termination when external buffer amplifier is used for earphone and loudspeaker amplifier. Its value is not critical, and is selected to be 3.3 kΩ. The cell descriptors are the following:

Resistor R_{LI}:	ratioless
I_{max}:	$0.2 \cdot 10^{-3}$ A
Tolerance:	50 per cent
Resistor nominal value:	3.3 kΩ
Temperature range:	70 °C
Parasitic capacitance:	N/A
Parasitic leakage current:	N/A
Shielding:	N/A

The selected resistor is of p-well type with the following dimensions:

$$x = 10 \, \mu m$$
$$y = 12 \, \mu m$$

9.2.3.3 Transistor cell TOUT descriptors definition

TOUT transistor scaling factor determining its size is a function of its worst case operating point, which is the following:

$$V_{DS} = V_{ref} + V_{outp} + V_{DS} = 0.3 + 0.25 + 0.5 = 1.05 \tag{9.12}$$

$$V_{SB} = V_{ref} + V_{outp} = 0.3 + 0.25 = 0.55 \text{ V}$$

$$I_d = I_p = \frac{V_{ref} + V_{outp}}{R_{load}} = \frac{0.3 + 0.25}{250} = 2.2 \cdot 10^{-3} \text{ A}$$

$V_B = 0$ V
V_G = (max OPAMP2 output voltage OVRN) = 3.8 V at $V_{DD} = 4$ V
Maximum temperature: 70 °C

The resulting transistor dimensions are $W = 800 \, \mu m$, $L = 4 \, \mu m$. The transistor is located in programmable peripheral cell.

9.2.3.4 Resistor network cell RIRC descriptor definitions

Receiver gain accuracy is a function of matching characteristics of resistors including "on" resistance of transistor switches. The specification of receiver gain accuracy and calculated values of R_{Ci} and assumed "on" resistance of transistor switches (120 Ω) result in the following descriptors for RIRC cell:

Resistor R_I: clustered ratio
I_{max}: $10 \cdot 10^{-6}$ A
Tolerance: 0.1 per cent
Resistor nominal value: 12.000 kΩ
Temperature range: 70 °C
Parasitic capacitance: N/A
Parasitic leakage current: 0.1 nA
Shielding: yes

Resistor R_C: clustered ratio
I_{max}: $10 \cdot 10^{-6}$ A
Tolerance: 0.1 per cent
Resistor nominal value: 11.880 kΩ
Temperature range: 70 °C
Parasitic capacitance: N/A
Parasitic leakage current: 0.1 nA
Shielding: yes

Resistor R_{C1}: clustered ratio
I_{max}: $10 \cdot 10^{-6}$ A
Tolerance: 0.1 per cent
Resistor nominal value: 2.616 kΩ
Temperature range: 70 °C
Parasitic capacitance: N/A
Parasitic leakage current: 0.1 nA
Shielding: yes

Resistor R_{C2}: clustered ratio
I_{max}: $10 \cdot 10^{-6}$ A
Tolerance: 0.1 per cent
Resistor nominal value: 2.332 kΩ
Temperature range: 70 °C
Parasitic capacitance: N/A
Parasitic leakage current: 0.1 nA
Shielding: yes

Resistor R_{C3}: clustered ratio
I_{max}: $10 \cdot 10^{-6}$ A
Tolerance: 0.1 per cent
Resistor nominal value: 2.075 kΩ
Temperature range: 70 °C
Parasitic capacitance: N/A
Parasitic leakage current: 0.1 nA
Shielding: yes

Resistor R_{C4}: clustered ratio
I_{max}: $10 \cdot 10^{-6}$ A
Tolerance: 0.1 per cent
Resistor nominal value: 1.833 kΩ
Temperature range: 70 °C
Parasitic capacitance: N/A
Parasitic leakage current: 0.1 nA
Shielding: yes

Resistor R_{C5}: clustered ratio
I_{max}: $10 \cdot 10^{-6}$ A
Tolerance: 0.1 per cent
Resistor nominal value: 1.651 kΩ
Temperature range: 70 °C
Parasitic capacitance: N/A
Parasitic leakage current: 0.1 nA
Shielding: yes

Resistor R_{C6}: clustered ratio
I_{max}: $10 \cdot 10^{-6}$ A
Tolerance: 0.1 per cent
Resistor nominal value: 1.472 kΩ
Temperature range: 70 °C
Parasitic capacitance: N/A
Parasitic leakage current: 0.1 nA
Shielding: yes

The resulting cell size is $x = 1736\,\mu$m, $y = 168\,\mu$m. The selected resistor type is polysilicon resistor with $10\,\mu$m width.

9.2.3.5 Transistor switch cell TS descriptor definition

Switch on-resistance: 120 Ω
Switch on-resistance tolerance: ± 60 Ω

Switch control voltage: 4 V
D.C. voltage level: 0.3 V

The switch transistor's dimensions are $W = 192 \, \mu\text{m}$, $L = 3 \, \mu\text{m}$, the resulting cell size is $x = 128 \, \mu\text{m}$, $y = 168 \, \mu\text{m}$.

9.2.3.6 Operational amplifier cell OPAMP1 synthesis and layout compilation

General requirements are the following:

1. Power supply voltage range: 2–7 V
2. Common mode input voltage: 0.3 V
3. Low noise
4. Low offset-voltage

The OA13 library cell which is a class A operational amplifier basic cell was selected for personalization.

The following cell descriptors were identified:

$V_{DD} = 4$ V
R_L (parallel combination of R_{SET} and R_{Imin}, where $R_{Imin} = 0.8 \, R_I$ for worst case process parameters)

$$R_L = \frac{R_{SET} \cdot R_{Imin}}{R_{SET} + R_{Imin}} = \frac{33 \cdot 10^3 \cdot 12 \cdot 10^3 \cdot 0.8}{33 \cdot 10^3 + 12 \cdot 10^3 \cdot 0.8} = 7.44 \text{ k}\Omega$$

$C_L = 5$ pF (estimated)
$V_0 = 0.25$ V (max. output voltage)
$I_{DD} = $ N/A
$G = 14$ dB (closed-loop gain)
$GT = 0.1$ per cent (closed-loop gain tolerance)
$V_{n1/f} = 120$ nV/$\sqrt{\text{Hz}}$ at 1 kHz (input $1/f$ noise voltage)
$f_{3dB} = 5$ kHz (3 dB gain band width)
slew rate = N/A

The resulting cell size parameters are the following: $x = 3$, $y = 1$, $z = 1$, $w = 1$, giving the cell dimensions $x = 504 \, \mu\text{m}$, $y = 168 \, \mu\text{m}$.

9.2.3.7 Operational amplifier cell OPAMP2 synthesis and layout compilation

The requirements for the second amplifier stage are less critical than for the first regarding noise and load conditions. The set of descriptors is as follows:

$V_{DD} = 4$ V
$R_L = 10^9$ Ω
$C_L = 10$ pF (estimated)
$V_0 = 0.25$ V (max. output voltage)
$I_{DD} = $ N/A
$G = 6$ dB (closed-loop gain)
$GT = 0.1$ per cent (closed-loop gain tolerance)
$V_{n1/f} = 300$ nV/$\sqrt{\text{Hz}}$ (input 1/f noise voltage)
$f_{3dB} = 5$ kHz (3 dB gain tolerance)
slew rate = N/A

The sizing factors are $x = y = z = w = 1$ which is a minimum cell configuration with the dimensions $x = 408\,\mu$m, $y = 168\,\mu$m.

9.2.3.8 Receiver module layout attribute definition

After completing the cell synthesis for the receiver module the following information is available:

1. Complete schematic including all transistor sizes, resistor and capacitor values
2. Partial layout information (cell sizes)
3. Partial information on characterization (predicted values for noise voltage, offset-voltage, matching characteristics)

Before continuing to the design verification phase and the final layout, the additional and important analog attributes need to be included as described in Chapter 6.

1. Power supply and voltage reference buses attribute definition

Strict noise requirements demand careful design regarding digital crosstalk and digital noise pickup via power supply buses. To avoid digital crosstalk, separate digital (V_{DDD}, V_{SSD}) and analog (V_{DDA}, V_{SSA}) power supply buses are foreseen. At this stage the bus positions cannot be defined, however, we can assign their priorities, i.e.: V_{DDA} and V_{SSA} have the highest priority, say 1000, while V_{DDD} and V_{SSD} have lower priority, say 100. No current flows into the voltage reference node, so we can assign the lowest priority, say 10, to this bus.

2. Grounding buses attribute definition

The grounding scheme is split into two categories. The first is the insensitive common ground bus connected to high impedance nodes where virtually no D.C., A.C. or transient current flows. This bus is generally named GND, however, in this design example its role has V_{REF}.

The second category of ground buses are sensitive ground connections which run separately from the ground pin to a single ground node in the circuit. For the receiver module we can identify one such ground node. This node name has to be specified as a unique node name starting with prefix GNDA. As seen from Fig.9.10 representing the final module schematic it was named GNDA1. Since the maximum current flowing in this node is $8\,\mu A$; this information is entered into the schematic as a current level attribute which defines the associated bus width.

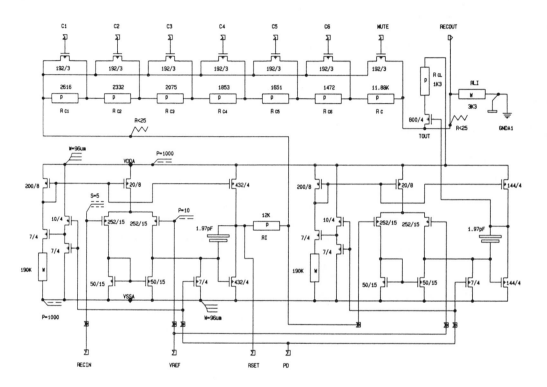

Fig. 9.10 Final schematic diagram of the receiver module with the layout and routing-related attributes

3. Analog requirements for signal interconnection attribute definition

(a) Sensitivity attribute. This attribute allows the designer to specify a shielded interconnection line. For the receiver module this sensitivity requirement is identified for interconnections to the summing input of the operational amplifier OPAMP1.

(b) Interconnection type attribute definition. With this attribute the distinction among less critical digital and more sensitive analog interconnections is provided. The interconnection type is assigned at the cell creation level and has to be specified in the schematic only when an

interconnection between an analog and a digital node occurs. In the receiver module we cannot identify such a case. The signal type definition at the cell level is obvious and is seen in the cell.typ file.

(c) Parasitic resistance and capacitance attribute definition. The interconnection parasitic resistance can affect the accuracy of resistor matching if the layout is not created properly. When automatic layout generation is being considered, the parasitic resistor limits should be entered into the schematic. The necessary attributes can be easily identified and entered into the schematic. For the receiver module this is done for the closed-loop connections determining the amplifier gain.

9.2.3.9 Final module schematic generation

At this stage we are in a position to create the final schematic for the receiver module. This schematic is shown in Fig.9.10. This schematic is used to generate all necessary information to do the design verification phase and the other design steps.

9.2.4 Design level 4: receiver module design verification

The synthesis procedure used to synthesize various cells is reliable and results are trustworthy. However, various synthesis approaches were used to synthesize isolated subcircuits and some of the inputs were based on assumptions.

Consequently, it is possible that the final results are not error free. To check this, a final verification needs to be performed.

Automatic extraction of a SPICE file from the schematic is provided to allow analog simulation.

The SPICE file shown in Table 9.3 was extracted from the schematic in Fig.9.10. One of the receiver transfer function characteristics obtained from simulation is shown in Fig.9.11.

Table 9.3: Print-out of SPICE file for receiver module

```
********** SPICE FILE - RECEIVER **********************
*
*
.MACRO RECEIVER RECIN PD VREF RSET RECOUT C1 C2 C3 C4 C5 C6 MUTE
XR1 EAR1 VDDA RCL
XR2 RECOUT GNDA1 RLI
XTO EAR1 EAR2 RECOUT VSSA TOUT
XR2 RECOUT B C D E F G H RSET RIRC
XTR RECOUT B C D E F G H C1 C2 C3 C4 C5 C6 MUTE TS
XOA1 RECIN VREF RSET PD OPAMP1
XOA2 H VREF EAR2 PD OPAMP2
.EOM RECEIVER
*
*
```

```
.MACRO RCL 1 22
R1 1 2 1.3K
.EOM RCL
*
*
.MACRO RLI 1 2
R1 1 2 3.3K
.EOM RLI
*
*
.MACRO TOUT D G S B
M1 D G S B N W=800U L=4U
.EOM TOUT
*
*
.MACRO RIRC A B C D E F G H I
RC A B 11.88K
RC6 B C 1472
RC5 C D 1651
RC4 D E 1853
RC3 E F 2075
RC2 F G 2332
RC1 G H 2616
RI H I 12K
.EOM RIRC
*
*
.MACRO TS A B C D E F G H C1 C2 C3 C4 C5 C6 MUTE
MS1 G C1 H VSSA N W=192U L=3U
MS2 F C2 H VSSA N W=192U L=3U
MS3 E C3 H VSSA N W=192U L=3U
MS4 D C4 H VSSA N W=192U L=3U
MS5 C C5 H VSSA N W=192U L=3U
MS6 B C6 H VSSA N W=192U L=3U
MS7 A MUTE H VSSA N W=192U L=3U
.EOM TS
*
*
.MACRO OPAMP1 IN- IN+ OUT PD
M1 6 IN- 5 VDDA P W=252U L=15U
M2 7 IN+ 5 VDDA P W=252U L=15U
M3 6 6 VSSA VSSA N W=50U L=15U
M4 7 6 VSSA VSSA N W=50U L=15U
M5 5 4 VDDA VDDA P W=20U L=8U
M6 4 4 VDDA VDDA P W=200U L=8U
M7 4 8 9 VSSA N W=7U L=4U
M8 8 PD VDDA VDDA P W=10U L=4U
M9 8 PD VSSA VSSA N W=7U L=4U
M10 7 PD VSSA VSSA N W=7U L=4U
M11 OUT 4 VDDA VDDA P W=432U L=4U
M12 OUT 7 VSSA VSSA N W=432U L=4U
RZ 9 VSSA 190K
CK OUT 7 1.97PF
.EOM OPAMP1
*
*
```

```
.MACRO OPAMP2 IN- IN+ OUT PD
M1 6 IN- 5 VDDA P W=252U L=15U
M2 7 IN+ 5 VDDA P W=252U L=15U
M3 6 6 VSSA VSSA N W=50U L=15U
M4 7 6 VSSA VSSA N W=50U L=15U
M5 5 4 VDDA VDDA P W=20U L=8U
M6 4 4 VDDA VDDA P W=200U L=8U
M7 4 8 9 VSSA N W=7U L=4U
M8 8 PD VDDA VDDA P W=10U L=4U
M9 8 PD VSSA VSSA N W=7U L=4U
M10 7 PD VSSA VSSA N W=7U L=4U
M11 OUT 4 VDDA VDDA P W=144U L=4U
M12 OUT 7 VSSA VSSA N W=144U L=4U
RZ 9 VSSA 190K
CK OUT 7 1.97PF
.EOM OPAMP2
*
*
*/LIMITS RECEIVER.RIRC.0 RECEIVER.TOUT.2 R=25
*/LIMITS RECEIVER.OPAMP1.0 RECEIVER.RECIN.0 S=5
*/LIMITS RECEIVER.OPAMP1.1 RECEIVER.OPAMP2.1 P=10
*/CELL RLI
*/CELL RCL
*/CELL TOUT
*/CELL RIRC
*/CELL TS
*/CELL OPAMP1
*/CELL OPAMP2
***************
```

As seen from Fig.9.11 the results comply with the predicted values. This was true also for other simulations performed for different temperature and process parameters as recommended in Chapter 7 in the section on design quality.

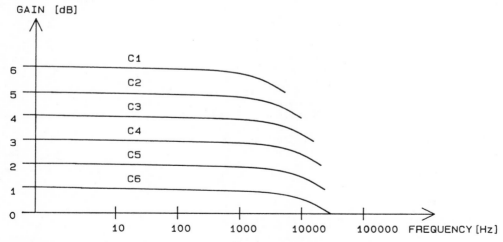

Fig. 9.11 Frequency response of receiver section for various gain settings

9.2.5 Design level 5: macrocell layout preview

This design step could be omitted since it has to be repeated in the final design of the ASIC. Nevertheless it is wise to preview the cell layout provided that a full layout compilation of the subcells was completed in the previous design levels and that very little effort is necessary to provide completed layout. The cell compilation tool was used to create the cell geometry file.This file is called standard.clb and is given in Table 9.4.

Table 9.4: Print-out of receiver cell geometry library file

```
                    STANDARD.CLB - RECEIVER

   TS                  ** cell name
   ANA                 ** cell type
   1280                ** cell X dimension (0.1um)
   0 0                 ** cell origin (0.1um)
   15                  ** cell pin number
   R 135 50 A          ** right analog pin, metal 5um wide
   R 295 50 A          ** right analog pin, metal 5um wide
   R 375 50 A          ** right analog pin, metal 5um wide
   R 615 50 A          ** right analog pin, metal 5um wide
   R 695 50 A          ** right analog pin, metal 5um wide
   R 935 50 A          ** right analog pin, metal 5um wide
   R 1015 50 A         ** right analog pin, metal 5um wide
   R 1255 50 A         ** right analog pin, metal 5um wide
   D 540 40 A          ** down analog pin, poly 4um wide
   D 380 40 A          ** down analog pin, poly 4um wide
   D 220 40 A          ** down analog pin, poly 4um wide
   D 1020 40 A         ** down analog pin, poly 4um wide
   D 1180 40 A         ** down analog pin, poly 4um wide
   D 140 40 A          ** down analog pin, poly 4um wide
   D 60 40 A           ** down analog pin, poly 4um wide

   RIRC                ** cell name
   ANA                 ** cell type
   17360               ** cell X dimension (0.1um)
   0 0                 ** cell origin (0.1um)
   9                   ** cell pin number
   L 135 50 A          ** left analog pin, metal 5um wide
   L 295 50 A          ** left analog pin, metal 5um wide
   L 375 50 A          ** left analog pin, metal 5um wide
   L 615 50 A          ** left analog pin, metal 5um wide
   L 695 50 A          ** left analog pin, metal 5um wide
   L 935 50 A          ** left analog pin, metal 5um wide
   L 1015 50 A         ** left analog pin, metal 5um wide
   L 1255 50 A         ** left analog pin, metal 5um wide
   R 135 50 A          ** right analog pin, metal 5um wide

   OPAMP2              ** cell name
   ANA                 ** cell type
   4080                ** cell X dimension (0.1um)
   0 0                 ** cell origin (0.1um)
   4                   ** cell pin number
```

```
L 1255 50 A        ** left analog pin, metal 5um wide
L 1335 50 A        ** left analog pin, metal 5um wide
U 2700 40 A        ** up analog pin, poly 4um wide
D 2540 40 A        ** down analog pin, poly 4um wide

OPAMP1             ** cell name
ANA                ** cell type
5040               ** cell X dimension (0.1um)
0 0                ** cell origin (0.1um)
4                  ** cell pin number
L 1255 50 A        ** left analog pin, metal 5um wide
L 1335 50 A        ** left analog pin, metal 5um wide
U 2700 40 A        ** up analog pin, poly 4um wide
D 2540 40 A        ** down analog pin, poly 4um wide

TOUT               ** cell name
ANA2               ** cell type
1940               ** cell X dimension (0.1um)
0 0                ** cell origin (0.1um)
3                  ** cell pin number
D 1900 40 A        ** down analog pin, poly 4um wide
U 0 40 A           ** up analog pin, poly 4um wide
U 1900 40 A        ** up analog pin, poly 4um wide
D 1820 40 A        ** down analog pin, poly 4um wide

RCL                ** cell name
ANA3               ** cell type
480                ** cell X dimension (0.1um)
0 0                ** cell origin (0.1um)
2                  ** cell pin number
U 60 40 A          ** up analog pin, poly 4um wide
D 60 40 A          ** down analog pin, poly 4um wide

RLI                ** cell name
ANA3               ** cell type
80                 ** cell X dimension (0.1um)
0 0                ** cell origin (0.1um)
2                  ** cell pin number
U 60 40 A          ** up analog pin, poly 4um wide
D 60 40 A          ** down analog pin, poly 4um wide
```

The standard.clb file and cell.typ file shown in Tables 9.4 and 9.5 create the complete layout information needed for the digital analog router. The cell.typ file contains the information of the cell heights and cell bus positions and widths as is seen from Table 9.5, while the standard.clb file contains the information on the cell x dimension and the cell pin positions, dimensions and type.

The netlist information, buses and other analog requirements are extracted from the schematic and/or SPICE file to create the receiver section layout, as shown in Plate 9.1. It has to be pointed out that the cell position may be rearranged when doing the complete ASIC layout. Although the cells are not necessarily in their final position the designer can get a fair amount of

Table 9.5: Print-out of receiver cell type definition file

```
                    CELL.TYP  -  RECEIVER

ANA                     ** cell type
1680                    ** cell Y dimension (0.1um)
2                       ** bus number
-25  80 VSSA            ** VSSA bus Y location, metal 8um wide
1625 80 VDDA            ** VDDA bus Y location, metal 8um wide

ANA1                    ** cell type
2880                    ** cell Y dimension (0.1um)
3                       ** bus number
1760 480 RXA            ** RXA bus Y location, metal 48um wide
2240 480 VDDA           ** VDDA bus Y location, metal 48um wide
2880  80 VSSA           ** VSSA bus Y location, metal 8um wide

ANA2                    ** cell type
710                     ** cell Y dimension (0.1um)

ANA3                    ** cell type
1850                    ** cell Y dimension (0.1um)
```

information on the receiver block silicon area consumption and functionality. If the macrocell dimensions are unexpectedly large the designer has a good basis for introducing the necessary changes to the specifications.

9.3   Transmitter module

9.3.1   Design level 1: transmitter module description and specifications

The transmitter function is to amplify and to transmit the audio signal from the speaker microphone to the telephone line. A provision for an external resistor is foreseen to set the receiver gain in order to accommodate the ASIC to different types of microphones. The transmitter must also be able to transmit the dual tone dialling signals. The dual tone output level is preset with an external resistor to fulfil different requirements of PABX systems worldwide. For the same reason the telephone line termination impedance has to be set externally to the ASIC. A power-down function is incorporated. In Table 9.6 the specifications for the transmitter module are summarized.

Table 9.6 Transmitter module specifications

Transmitter gain:	$40 \, \text{dB}_{\text{max}}$ at
	$R_{\text{Tset}} = 24 \, \text{k}\Omega$
	$R_{\text{line}} = 600 \, \Omega$
DTMF gain:	$0 \, \text{dB}$ at
	$R_{\text{DTMF}} = 3 \, \text{M}\Omega$
	$R_{\text{line}} = 600 \, \Omega$

Transmitter/DTMF crosstalk:	–30 dB min
Transmitter gain accuracy:	± 1 dB
DTMF gain accuracy:	± 3 dB
Frequency response:	± 0.5 dB
	f = 300–3600 Hz
Line length compensation:	6 dB
Power-down current:	1 A max
Maximum transmitted line signal level:	4.2 V_{pp}
Distortion at maximum signal level:	1 per cent max
Output noise level:	–72 dBm max

The transmitter can be represented as a single block as shown in Fig.9.12.

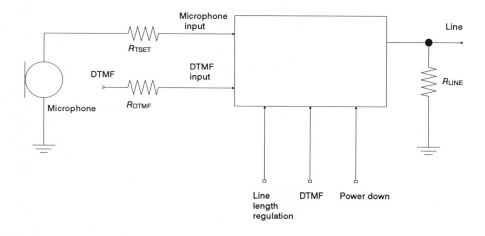

Fig. 9.12 Block representation of the transmitter module

Additional specifications are the following:

External pin count:	2
Target test time:	1 second
Test strategy:	frequency domain transfer function measurement

A very similar test set-up and test procedure is applicable to determine the transmitter characteristics to that used for the receiver module. Since fewer measurements have to be made, the predicted test time is close to 1 second. No provision for noise measurement is foreseen. High performance automatic test and measurement equipment must be provided or bench testing on a sample basis must be accepted for noise measurement. Besides the noise measurements no other testability problems were detected.

9.3.2 Design level 2: transmitter module partitioning and cell definitions

Fig.9.13 shows the decomposition of the receiver module while Fig.9.14 represents a possible implementation at the library cell level.

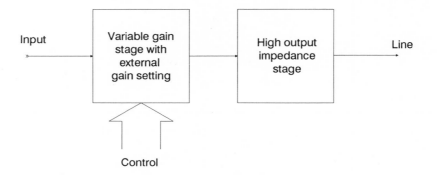

Fig. 9.13 Transmitter module decomposition

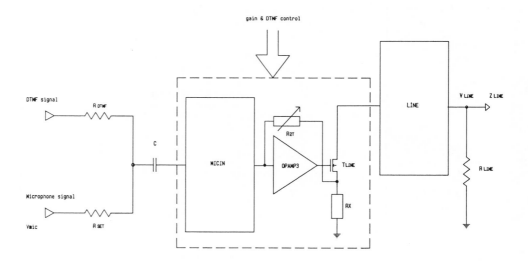

Fig. 9.14 Transmitter module implemented with library cells and elements

The first gain stage is a very similar variable gain stage to the one used in the receiver section. The next stage is the line driver output stage with a high output impedance acting as the transmitter current source. The high output impedance requirement is a consequence of the specification requested for the external line termination impedance.

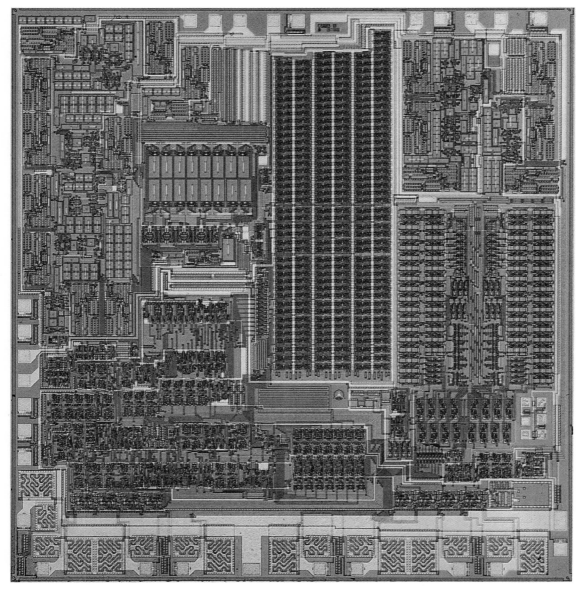

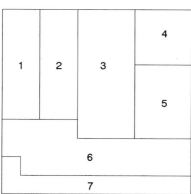

1 Transmit filter
2 PCM coder
3 TSA memory
4 Receive filter and output stage
5 Two PCM decoders
6 Control logic
7 Bidirectional 8-bit parallel PCM bus

Plate 1.1 Photomicrograph of single chip PCM codec

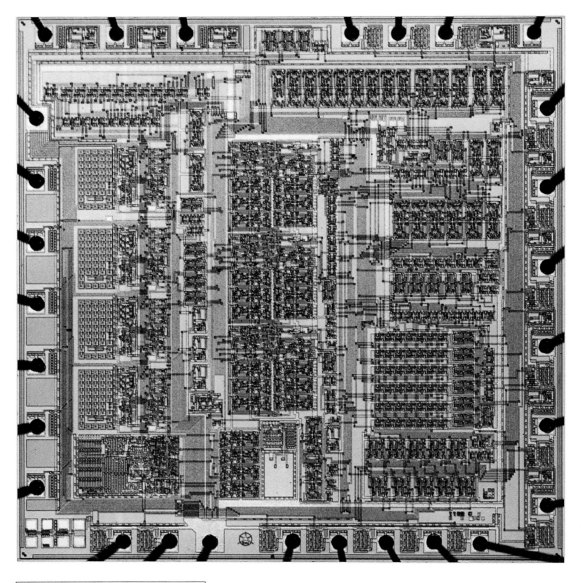

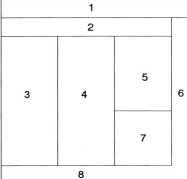

1 Control output stages
2 Timing circuits
3 Line signal analog filters
4 Line signal detection and estimation
5 Control logic
6 Relay drivers
7 Line status and mode control
8 Bidirectional 7-bit parallel signalling bus

Plate 1.2 Photomicrograph of a SLIC design using a personalized cell library

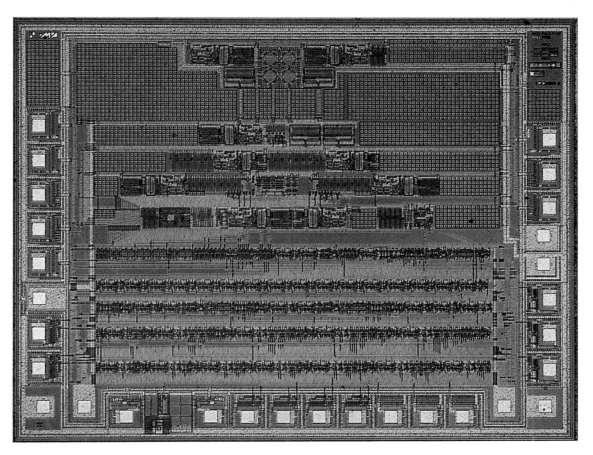

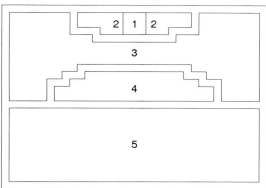

1 Hall sensor structure
2 Analog processing of Hall sensor signals
3 Differential integrator capacitors
4 Analog part of the ASIC
5 Digital part of the ASIC

Plate 1.3 Photomicrograph of a mixed analog digital system containing an integral Hall effect sensor and electrical measurement system

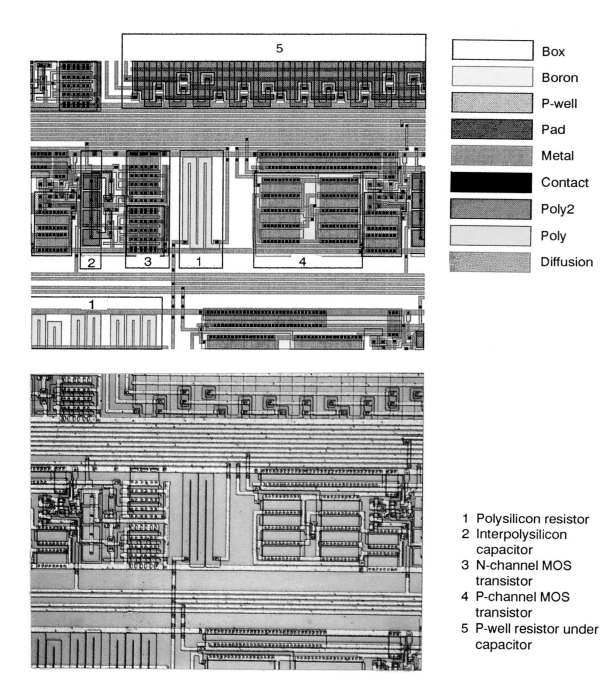

Plate 2.1 Multilevel plot (MLP) in comparison with incident light view of processed silicon at magnification ratio *a*

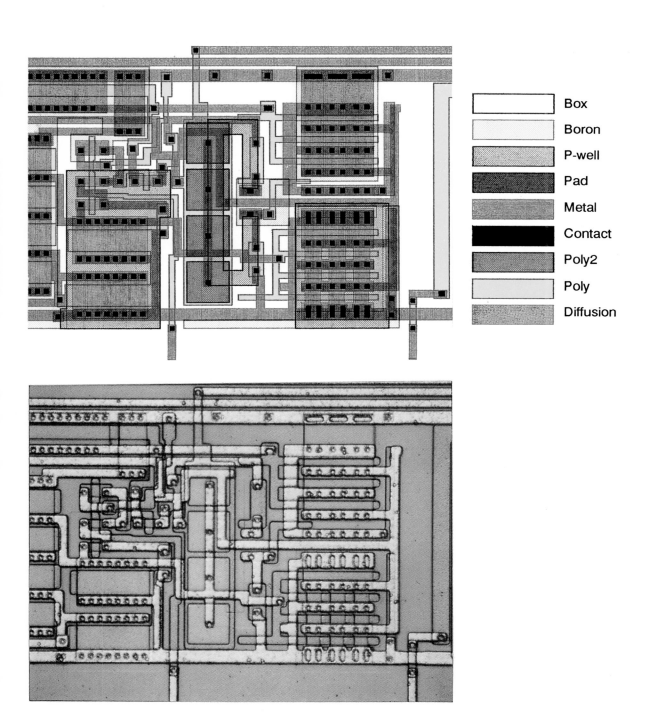

Plate 2.2 Multilevel plot (MLP) in comparison with incident light view of processed silicon at magnification ratio *b*

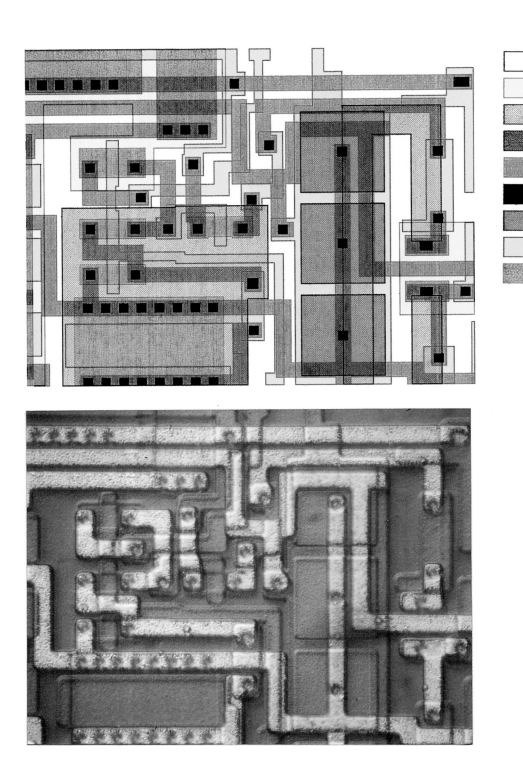

Plate 2.3 Multilevel plot (MLP) in comparison with incident light view of processed silicon at magnification ratio c

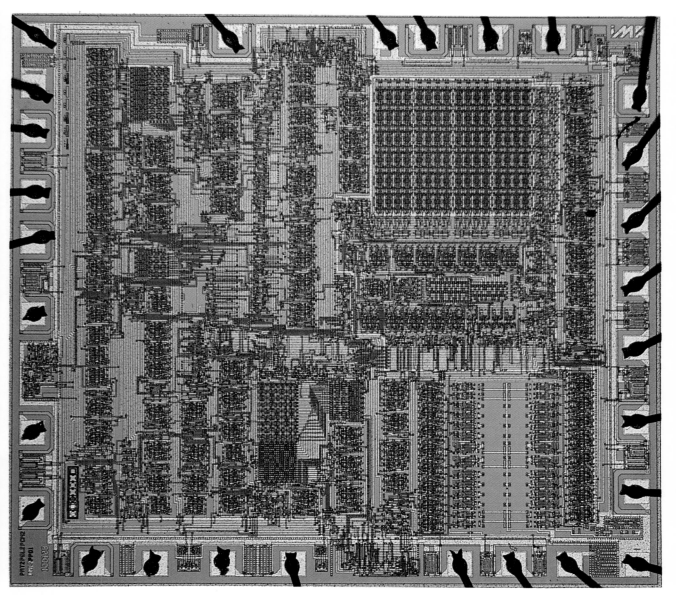

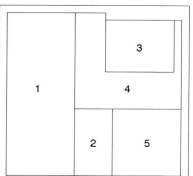

1 Processing logic
2 Filter
3 RAM
4 Interfacing logic
5 D/A converter

Plate 3.1 Photomicrograph of a full custom design

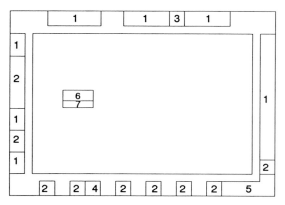

1 Input cells
2 Output cells
3 V_{DD} pad
4 V_{SS} pad
5 Alignment targets
6 Variable height routing channels
7 Fixed height standard cells

Plate 3.2 Photomicrograph of standard cell design

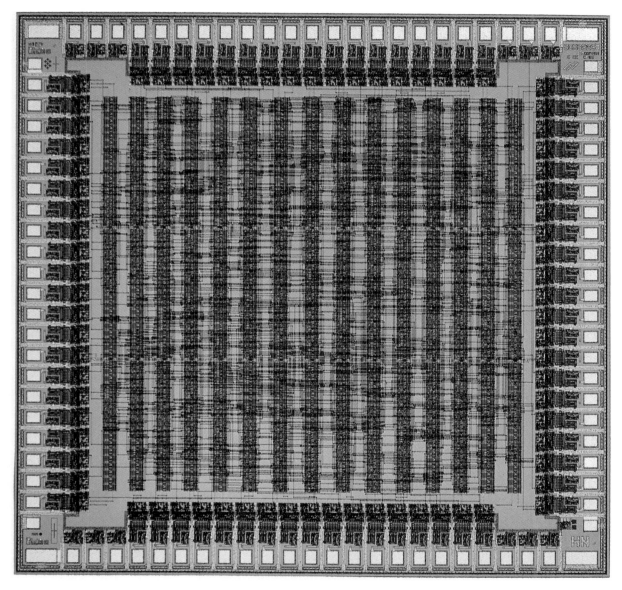

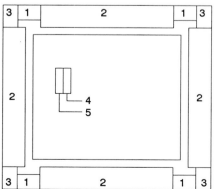

1 Input cells
2 Programmable input or output cells
3 Power pad
4 Fixed height routing channel
5 Fixed height row of transistors

Plate 3.3 Photomicrograph of a gate array

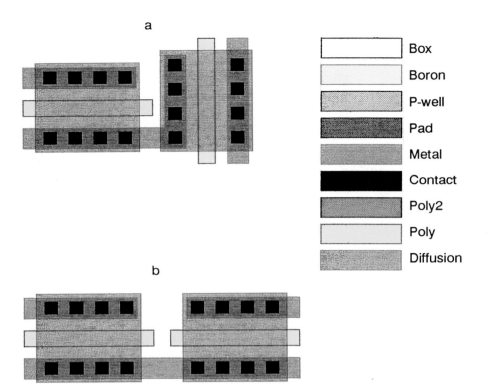

Plate 4.1 Transistor pair (a) in different orientation, (b) in same orientation

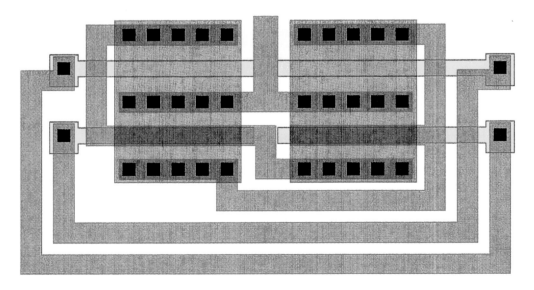

Plate 4.2 Example of centroid placement of transistor pair. This placement is normally used to minimize the input offest-voltage of different stages of the operational amplifier

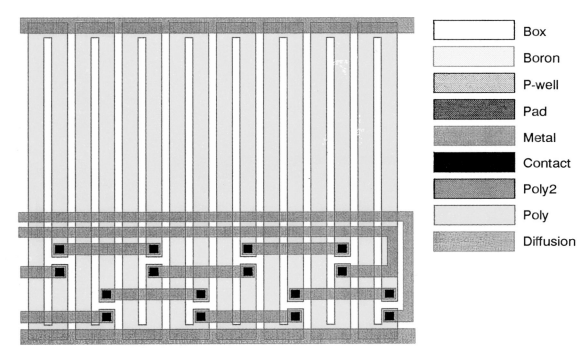

	Box
	Boron
	P-well
	Pad
	Metal
	Contact
	Poly2
	Poly
	Diffusion

Plate 4.3 Automatically generated interleaved structure of polysilicon resistor

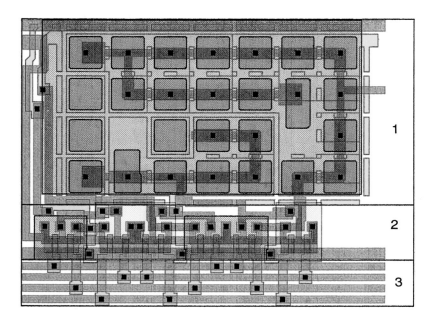

1 Capacitor field
2 Transistor switches
3 Two phase clock bus

Plate 4.4 Precision switched-capacitor structure used for S–C filters

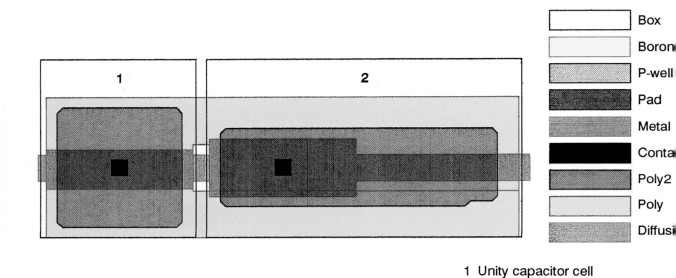

Box

Boron

P-well

Pad

Metal

Conta

Poly2

Poly

Diffusi

1 Unity capacitor cell
2 Non-unity capacitor cell

Plate 4.5 Computer generated unity and non-unity capacitor cell with the value of 1.432 units

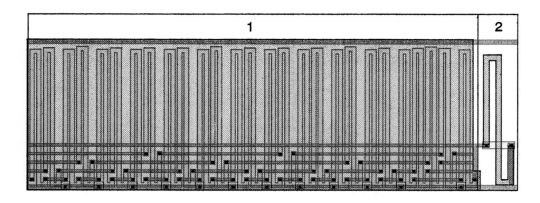

1 Interleaved polysilicon
   resistor network
2 P-well resistor

Plate 4.6 Compiled layout of resistor network cell

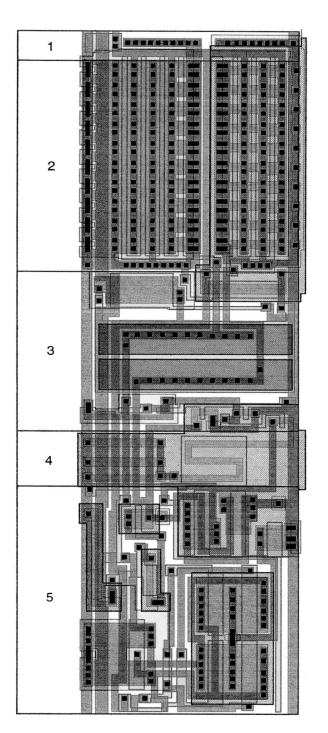
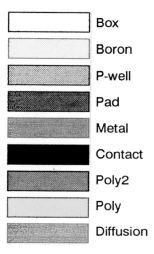

	Box
	Boron
	P-well
	Pad
	Metal
	Contact
	Poly2
	Poly
	Diffusion

1 Output stage termination subcell
2 Programmable output stage
3 Phase compensation
4 Programmable bias generator
5 Differential input stage and
   bias generator

Plate 5.1 Automatically generated layout of general purpose class A–B operational amplifier

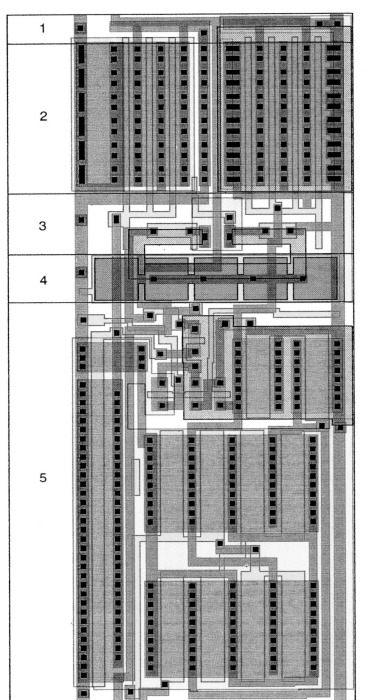

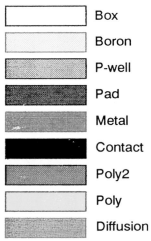

	Box
	Boron
	P-well
	Pad
	Metal
	Contact
	Poly2
	Poly
	Diffusion

1 Output stage termination subcell
2 Programmable output stage
3,4 Programmable phase compensation
5 Programmable differential input stage and bias generator

Plate 5.2 Automatically generated layout of low power, low voltage class A amplifier

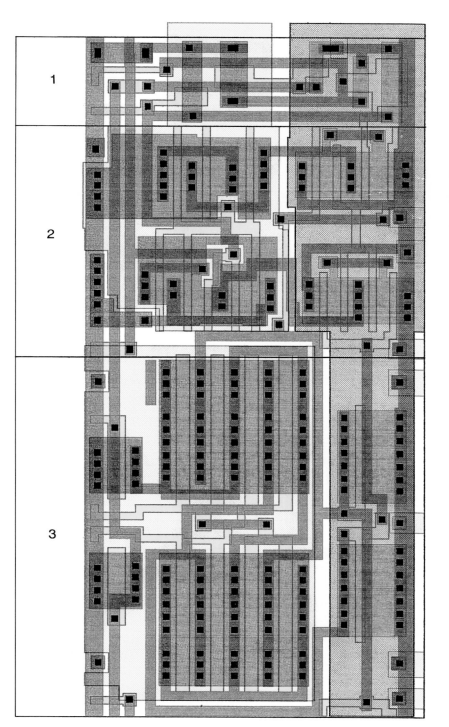
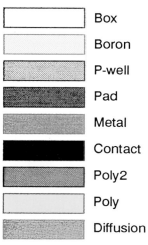

	Box
	Boron
	P-well
	Pad
	Metal
	Contact
	Poly2
	Poly
	Diffusion

1 Cell termination block
2 Cascoded stage
3 Differential input stage

Plate 5.3 Automatically generated layout of cascode operational amplifier

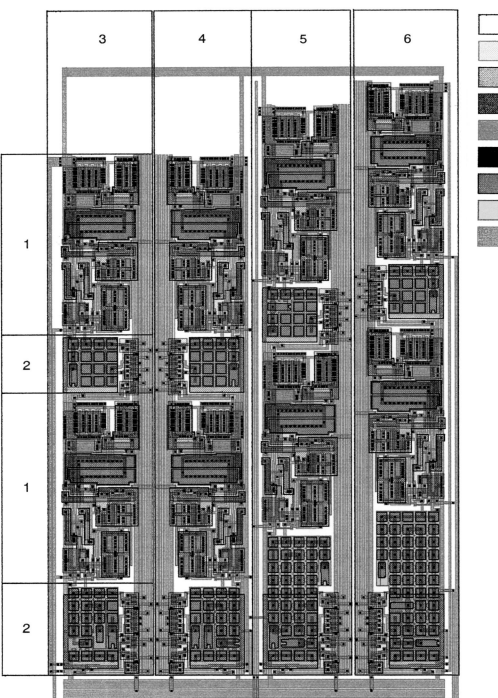

Plate 5.4 Automatically generated and optimized layout of 8th order S–C Chebyshev filter

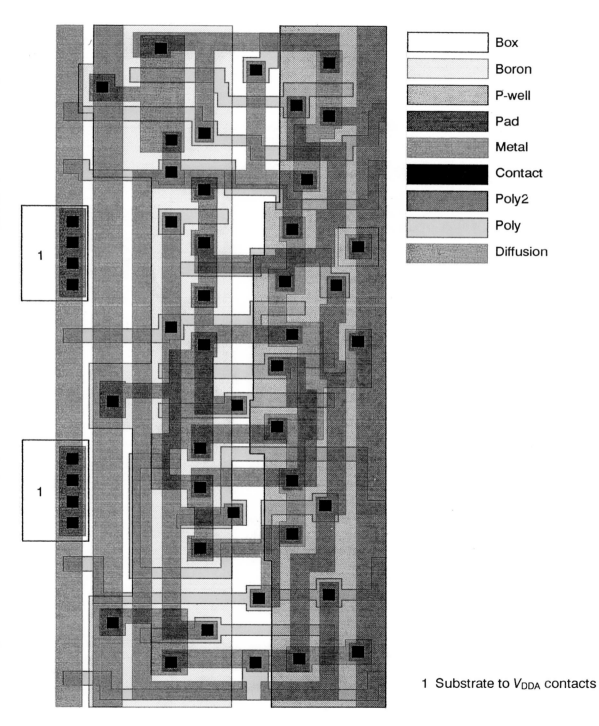

Box

Boron

P-well

Pad

Metal

Contact

Poly2

Poly

Diffusion

1 Substrate to V_{DDA} contacts

Plate 6.1 Digital cell modified for mixed analog digital environment

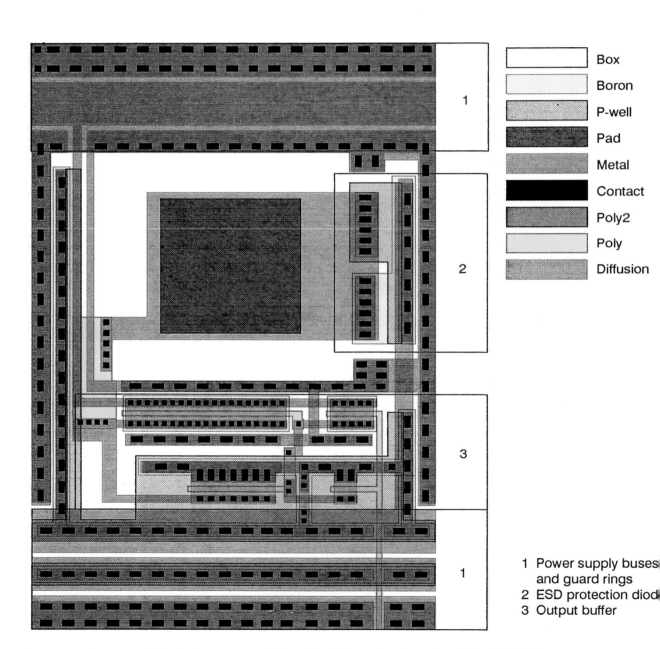

Legend:

- Box
- Boron
- P-well
- Pad
- Metal
- Contact
- Poly2
- Poly
- Diffusion

1 Power supply buses and guard rings
2 ESD protection diode
3 Output buffer

Plate 6.2 Layout of digital output peripheral cell for mixed analog digital ASICs

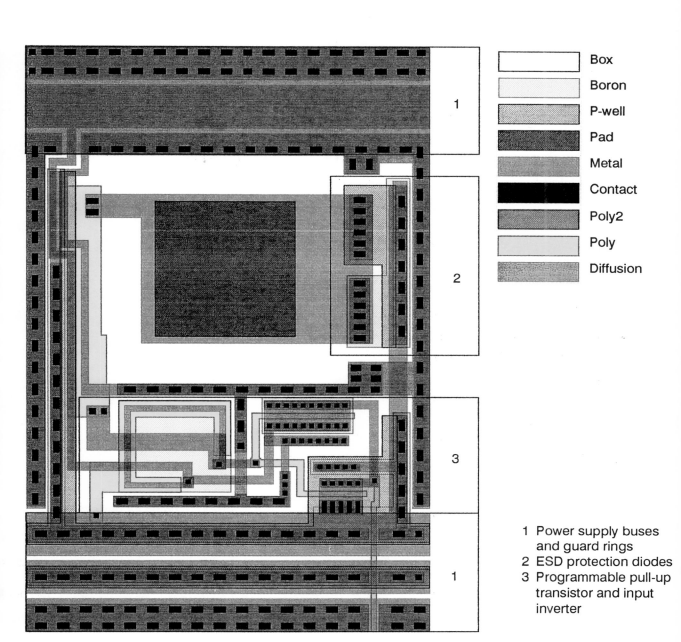

Plate 6.3 Layout of digital input peripheral cell for mixed analog digital ASICs

Legend:
- Box
- Boron
- P-well
- Pad
- Metal
- Contact
- Poly2
- Poly
- Diffusion

1 Power supply buses and guard rings
2 ESD protection diodes
3 Programmable pull-up transistor and input inverter

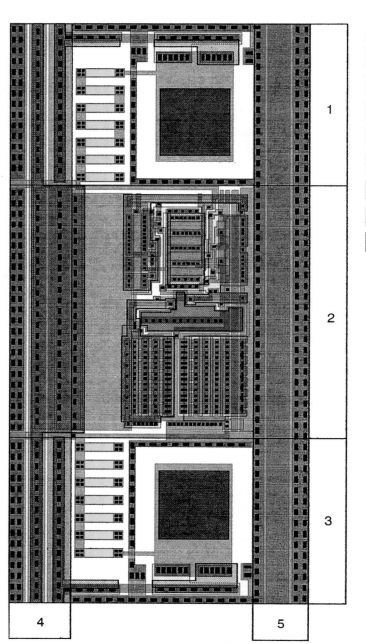
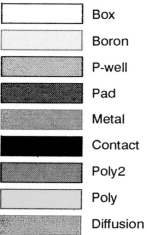

	Box
	Boron
	P-well
	Pad
	Metal
	Contact
	Poly2
	Poly
	Diffusion

1 Input pad with ESD protection and programmable input resistor
2 Buffer amplifier
3 Output pad with ESD protection and programmable output resistor
4 V_{SSA} and V_{SSD} buses and guard ring
5 V_{DDA} and V_{DDD} buses and guard ring

Plate 6.4 Layout of general purpose analog input/output buffer peripheral cell

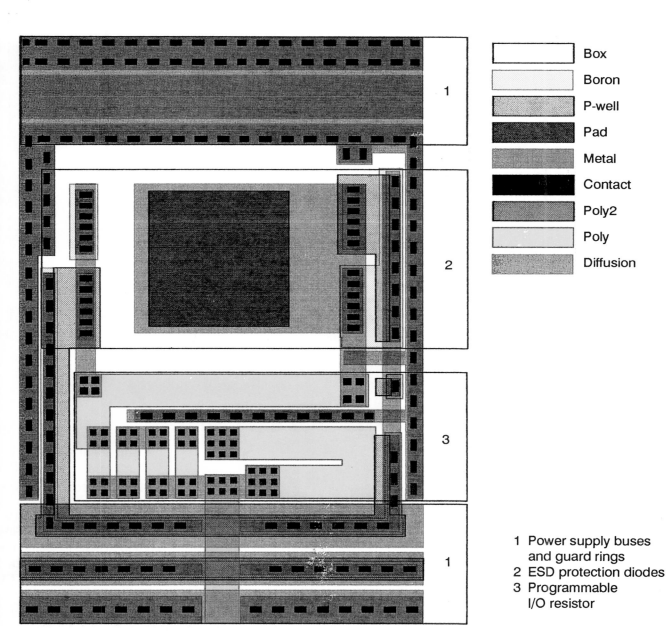

	Box
	Boron
	P-well
	Pad
	Metal
	Contact
	Poly2
	Poly
	Diffusion

1 Power supply buses
and guard rings
2 ESD protection diodes
3 Programmable
I/O resistor

Plate 6.5 Layout of general purpose input/output analog cell

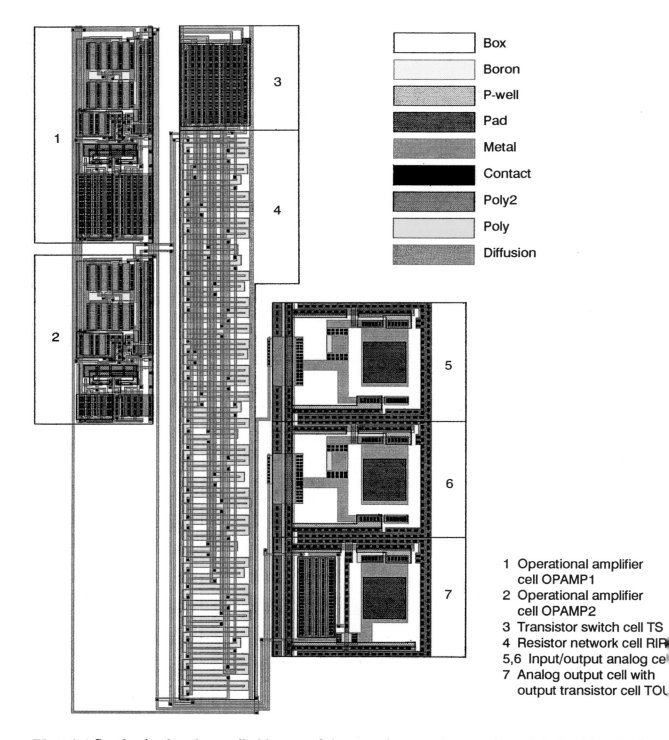

Plate 9.1 Synthesized and compiled layout of the complete receiver section of single chip telephone set ASIC

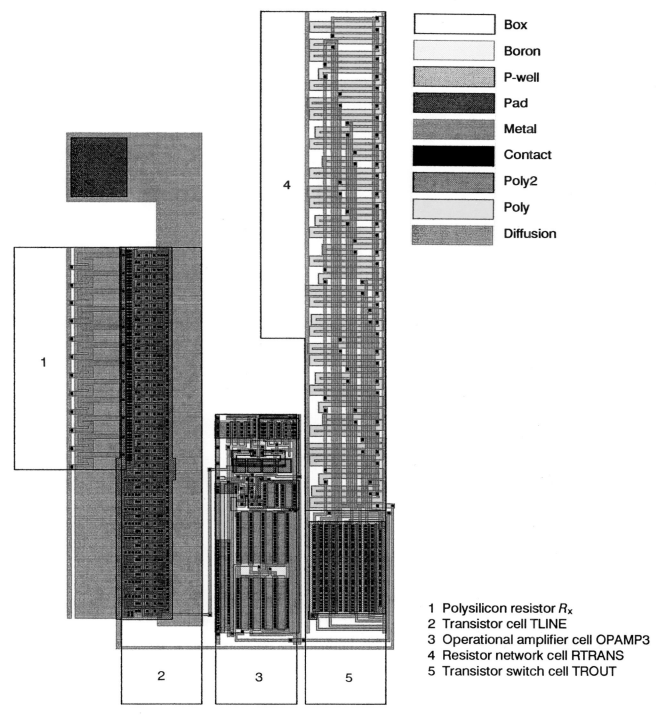

Legend:
- Box
- Boron
- P-well
- Pad
- Metal
- Contact
- Poly2
- Poly
- Diffusion

1 Polysilicon resistor R_x
2 Transistor cell TLINE
3 Operational amplifier cell OPAMP3
4 Resistor network cell RTRANS
5 Transistor switch cell TROUT

Plate 9.2 Automatically generated layout of the transmitter module

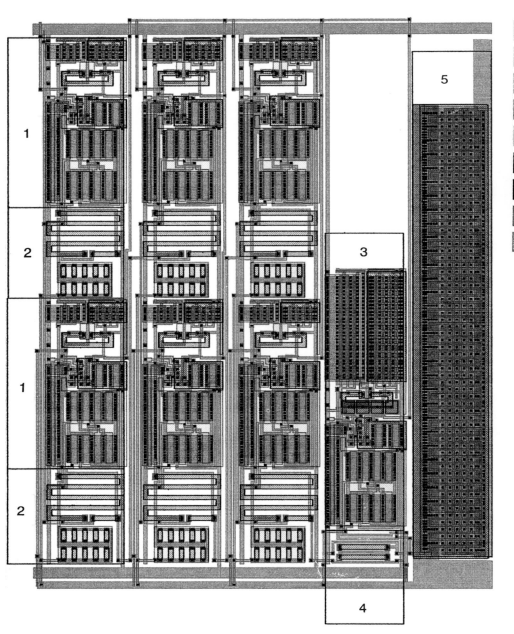

Legend:

- Box
- Boron
- P-well
- Pad
- Metal
- Contac
- Poly2
- Poly
- Diffusi

1 Comparator
  cell COMP
2 P-well resistor
  network cell RCOM
3 Operational amplifi
  cell OPAMP4
4 P-well resistor
  cell RREG
5 Transistor cell TRE

Plate 9.3 Automatically generated layout of the control module

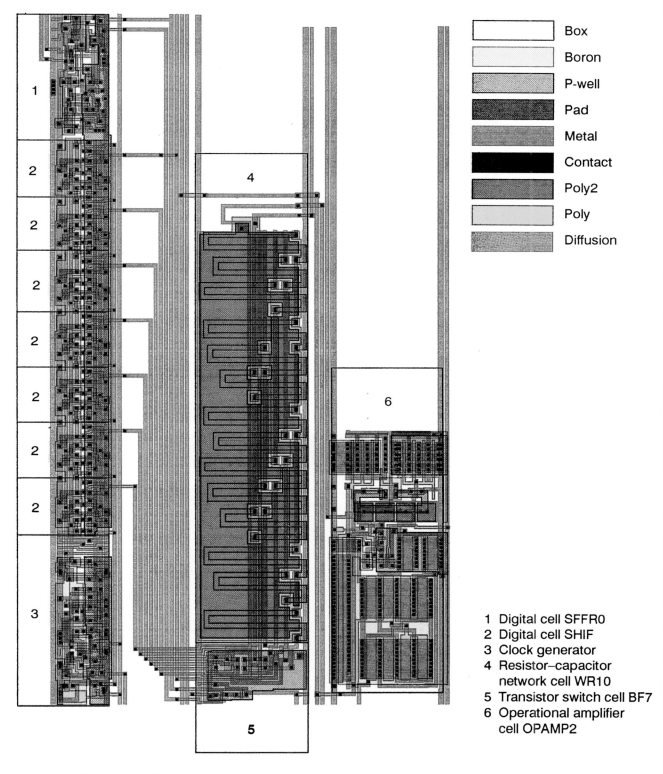

Plate 9.4 Automatically generated layout of the single tone section of DTMF module

Legend:
- Box
- Boron
- P-well
- Pad
- Metal
- Contact
- Poly2
- Poly
- Diffusion

1 Digital cell SFFR0
2 Digital cell SHIF
3 Clock generator
4 Resistor–capacitor network cell WR10
5 Transistor switch cell BF7
6 Operational amplifier cell OPAMP2

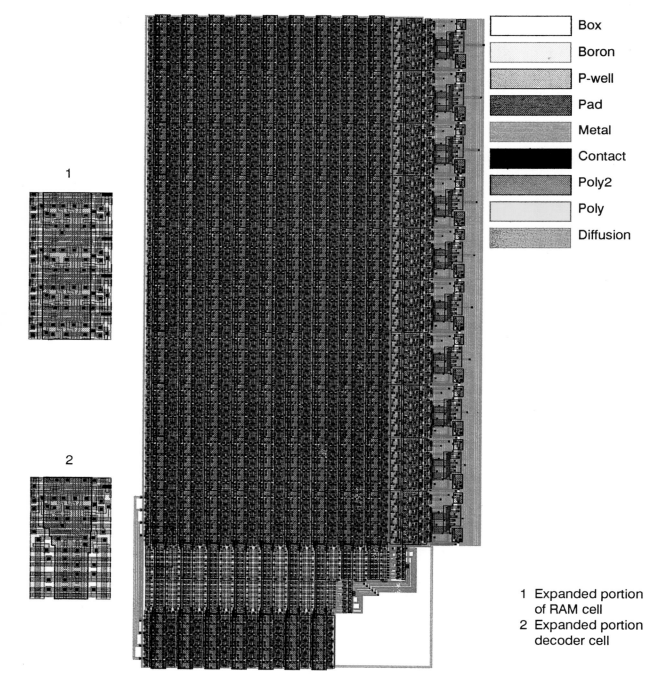

	Box
	Boron
	P-well
	Pad
	Metal
	Contact
	Poly2
	Poly
	Diffusion

1 Expanded portion
   of RAM cell
2 Expanded portion
   decoder cell

Plate 9.5 RAM module layout

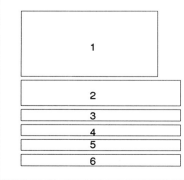

1 RAM module
2 DTMF module
3,4 Receiver, transmitter and AUX module
5 Control module
6 Otput transistor cells TREG, TLINE, TAUX

Plate 9.6 Photomicrograph of test chip for design example of telephone set ASIC

The transmitter gain is defined as:

$$G_{TR} = \frac{V_{LINE}}{V_{mic}} = \frac{I_{LINE}(R_{LINE} \mid\mid Z_{LINE})}{V_{mic}} \qquad (9.13)$$

Transmitter gain is specified for the case when R_{LINE} is equal to the telephone line characteristic impedance, hence we can write:

$$G_{TR} = \frac{1}{2} \frac{R_{LINE}}{R_x} \frac{R_{2T}}{R_{TSET}} \qquad (9.14)$$

As we can see a good matching resistor ratio can be achieved since resistors R_{2T} and R_x are internally integrated resistors of the same type, while R_{LINE} and R_{TSET} are external and accurate resistors.

Similar equation can be written for DTMF gain:

$$G_{DTMF} = \frac{1}{2} \frac{R_{LINE}}{R_x} \frac{R_{2DT}}{R_{TSET}} \qquad (9.15)$$

Variable resistors R_{2T} and R_{2DT} are implemented in a very similar way to that used in the receiver module. The specifications for transmitter gain control as a function of telephone line length are exactly the same so we can simply use the same R_2 implementation. The R_{2DT} implementation is given with the transmitter/DTMF crosstalk specification. For transmitter/DTMF rejection ratio (*TDRR*):

$$TDRR = \frac{R_{2DT}}{R_{2Tmin}} < -30 \text{ dB} \qquad (9.16)$$

The complete library level schematic for the transmitter module is presented in Fig.9.15.

In the schematic we have also incorporated resistor R_{LOC} which was not determined in the receiver module design because no same type resistor ratio was identified. If we rewrite the complete local signal gain path we obtain:

$$G_{LOCAL} = \frac{R_{2T}}{R_{TSET}} \frac{R_{SET}}{R_{LOC}} \frac{R_2}{R_1} \qquad (9.17)$$

As seen from equation (9.17) the same type resistor ratio condition is fulfilled if R_{LOC} is made part of the transmitter matched resistor network.

9.3.3 Design level 3: transmitter module cell synthesis and layout compilation

According to Fig.9.14 the following cells need to be created:

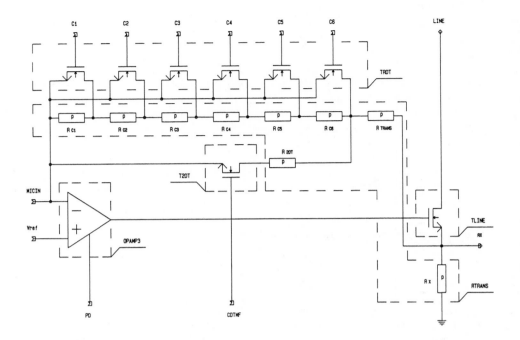

Fig. 9.15 Final library level schematic of transmitter module

1. Simple transistor cell TRDT
2. Simple transistor cell TLINE
3. Resistor network cell RTrans
4. Operational amplifier cell OPAMP3

Transistor network cell TS has the same function and descriptors as the one used in the receiver section so it will be used also in the transmitter module.

We can proceed to the descriptor definitions for each cell.

9.3.3.1 TRDT descriptor definition

Transistor TRDT is used for switching the R_{2DT} resistor which determines the crosstalk between transmitted microphone signal and DTMF signal. The calculated value for R_{2DT} from equation (9.16) is 600 Ω. If we allow 1 dB gain variation due to the transistor on-resistance we obtain the following descriptors:

Switch on-resistance: 60 Ω
Switch on-resistance tolerance: ± 30 Ω

Switch control voltage: 4 V

D.C. voltage level: 0.3 V

9.3.3.2 TLINE descriptors definition

$V_{ds} = 4$ V

$V_{sb} = 0.3$ V

$$I_d = \frac{I_p}{2} = \frac{V_{LINEp}}{2\,R_{LINE}} = 7 \cdot 10^{-3} \text{ A}$$

$V_g = OVRN = 3.8$ V

$T_{max} = 70\ °C$

9.3.3.3 RTRANS descriptor definition

For resistors R_C, R_{C1}, R_{C2}, R_{C3}, R_{C4}, R_{C5} and R_{C6} the same descriptors apply as in the receiver module cell RIRC.

The resistors R_x and R_{LOC} are added with the following descriptors:

Resistor R_x: clustered ratio

I_{max}: $7 \cdot 10^{-3}$

Tolerance: 0.1 per cent

Resistor nominal value: 42 Ω

Temperature range: 70 °C

Parasitic capacitance: N/A

Parasitic leakage current: 10^{-10} A

Shielding: yes

Resistor R_{LOC}: clustered ratio

$I_{max} = 10 \cdot 10^{-6}$ A

Tolerance: 0.1 per cent

Resistor nominal value: 300 Ω

Temperature range: 70 °C

Parasitic capacitance: N/A

Parasitic leakage current: 10^{-10} A

Shielding: yes

9.3.3.4 Operational amplifier OPAMP3 synthesis and layout compilation

The following descriptors are identified:

$V_{DD} = 4$ V

$R_L = 10^9\ \Omega$

$C_L = 10$ pF

$V_o = 0.3$ V (max. output voltage)

$I_{DD} = $ N/A

$G_{max} = 10$ dB (closed-loop gain)

$G_t = 0.1$ per cent (closed-loop gain tolerance)

$V_{n1/f} = 60$ nV/$\sqrt{\text{Hz}}$ at 1 kHz (input $1/f$ noise voltage)

$f_{3dB} = 5$ kHz (3 dB gain tolerance)

slew rate $= $ N/A

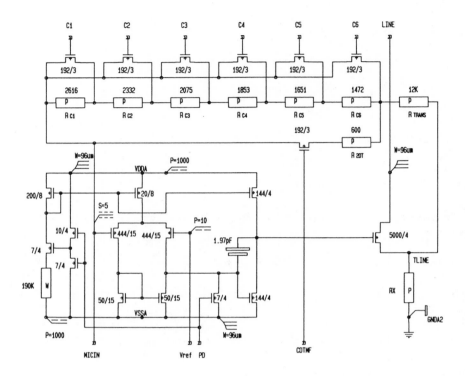

Fig. 9.16 Final schematic diagram of the transmitter module with layout attributes

The final schematic diagram of the module is shown in Fig.9.16 where the layout attributes can also be seen.

9.3.4 Design level 4: transmitter module design verification

The synthesis tools and design procedure have proved to be correct in this case also since no discrepancy between specifications and simulation results were found when using the simulation file generated from Fig.9.16.

9.3.5 Design level 5: transmitter macrocell layout preview

Plate 9.2 shows the preliminary layout of the transmitter module. The resulting module silicon area consumption is 0.64 mm^2.

9.4   Control module and DTMF module

For the remaining two analog modules—control module and DTMF module—the design procedure is very similar so it is not necessary to repeat all details of the design discipline. For the sake of completeness we show only the results of design level 3 and design level 5.

Fig.9.17 presents the library level schematic diagram of the control module and Plate 9.3 shows the resulting layout.

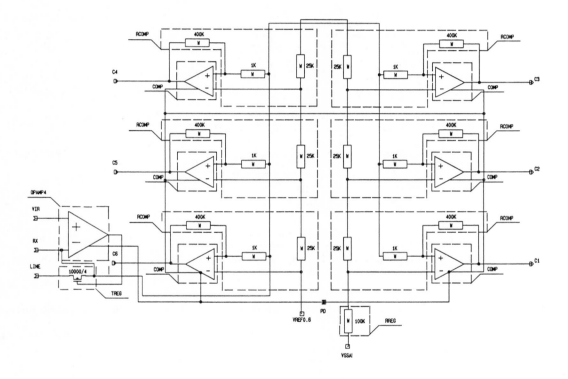

Fig. 9.17 Library level schematic diagram of the control module

Fig.9.18 shows the library level schematic diagram of single tone generator of DTMF module and Plate 9.4 displays its layout. The complete DTMF module is combination of two single tone generators and summing amplifier.

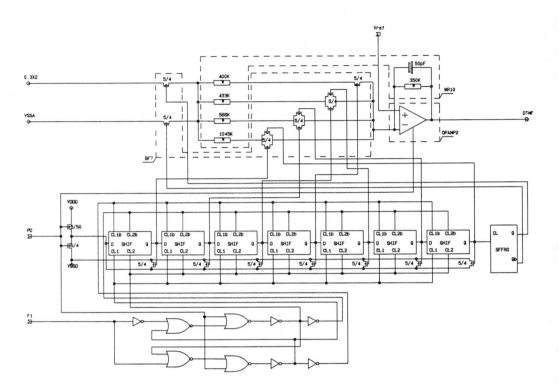

Fig. 9.18 Library level schematic diagram of the single tone generator of the DTMF module

9.5   Digital modules

As it was shown in Fig.9.2 (the level of decomposition of the digital section of the ASIC) the following functional blocks can be identified:

1.   Central logic
2.   Pulse/DTMF generator
3.   Timing
4.   Input logic
5.   Chip status

It is not our intention to show the detailed design procedure for the digital part of the ASIC. However, we would like to present its complexity and to highlight a structured hierarchical design approach. The application of the personalized standard cell approach to the digital section of the ASIC is well demonstrated by the personalization of the RAM module where an optimization of electrical characteristics and layout density was achieved.

9.5.1 Central logic decomposition

Fig.9.19 shows the decomposition of the central logic. It consists of a functional unit, memory activity unit, read counter, write counter, input decoder, output decoder, communication unit and static RAM.

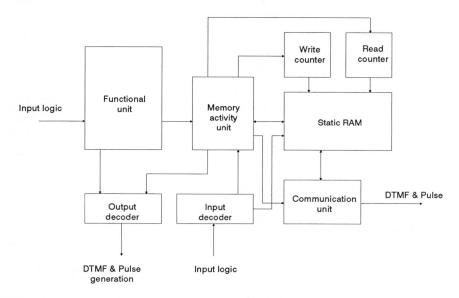

Fig. 9.19 Central logic decomposition block diagram

The most interesting module of the central logic block is the static RAM. Its specifications are the following:

1. Operating voltage range: 2.5 V – 8 V
2. Minimum memory retention voltage: 1.5V
3. Memory bank size: 18 × 4 bits
4. Memory bank size: 14 × 4 bits
5. Memory organization: 9+1 memory banks of size 1
                                         1 memory bank of size 2

The combination of one bank of size 1 and one bank of size 2 forms the 32 digit last number redial capability. The rest of the nine banks provide for nine 18-digit dialling numbers stored in memory. The organization of the RAM modules is shown in Fig.9.20. The RAM library cell

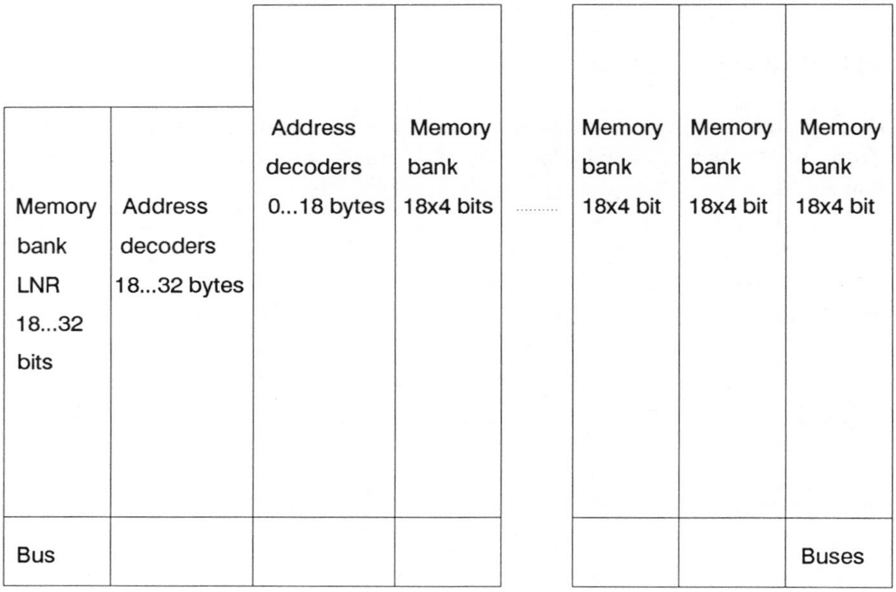

Memory bank LNR 18...32 bits	Address decoders 18...32 bytes	Address decoders 0...18 bytes	Memory bank 18x4 bits		Memory bank 18x4 bit	Memory bank 18x4 bit	Memory bank 18x4 bit
Bus							Buses

Fig. 9.20 RAM module organization

was personalized to meet the low voltage requirements. The memory module layout was optimized for the specific RAM organization. Plate 9.5 shows the resulting layout of the RAM module. The resulting silicon area is 3.73 mm^2.

9.5.2 Pulse/DTMF generator decomposition

Fig.9.21 shows the decomposition of the pulse/DTMF generator. It is decomposed into the following modules: signal generator, pulse dialling generator, communication unit, low group counter, high group counter.

The low group counter and the pulse dialling generator are shown in greater detail.

9.5.2.1 Low group counter module

The following specifications are valid for the low group counter module:

1.   Input clock frequency: 27.880 Hz
2.   Output frequency at pin OUT defined with input conditions:

$R_1 = \text{``1''(active)}$ $f_{OUT} = 697\ \text{Hz}$
$R_2 = \text{``1''(active)}$ $f_{OUT} = 710\ \text{Hz}$
$R_3 = \text{``1''(active)}$ $f_{OUT} = 852\ \text{Hz}$
$R_4 = \text{``1''(active)}$ $f_{OUT} = 941\ \text{Hz}$

The solution for the low group counter using the library cell level schematic is shown in Fig.9.22.

The following library cells were used to create low group counter module:

DDR: trailing edge triggered static D flip-flop with reset
RSS: set–reset latch with synchronous set
DDSSR: static D flip-flop with set and reset
MUX: 2 to 1 multiplex
SRNOR: asynchronous set–reset latch

The module consists of a 6 bit polynomial counter with a preset combination to determine division ratio. The division ratio is set according to the required low dialling tone frequencies and is 40 for R_1 active, 36.5 for R_2 active, 33 for R_3 active and 29.5 for R_4 active. The division

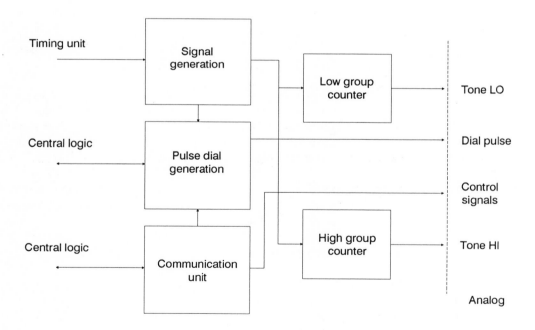

Fig. 9.21 Pulse/DTMF generator decomposition block diagram

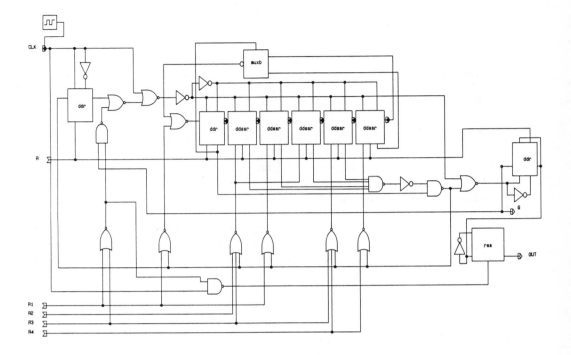

Fig. 9.22 Low counter module library level schematic diagram

of 0.5 clock period is achieved by a one half clock cycle stealing technique. Fig.9.23 shows the results of the logic simulation when R_2 is active and a division ratio of 36.5 is achieved. Very similar schematic was used to create the high group counter module.

9.5.2.2 Pulse dialling generator module

The library cell level schematic of the pulse dialling generator module is shown in Fig.9.24.

It uses the following complex library cells:

MLFF:	D flip-flop with preset
RCDEC:	4 to 8 decoder cell
VHDEC:	8 to 16 decoder cell
SRNOR:	asynchronous set−reset latch

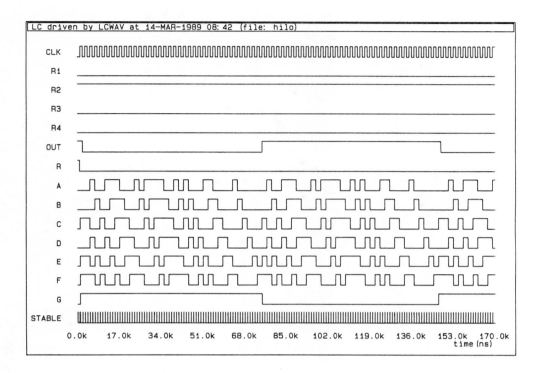

Fig. 9.23 Logic simulation results of low counter module

9.6   Results

In this section some of the measured results are presented to show a comparison between the final performance and the target specifications.

Fig.9.25 shows the measured results of transmitter and control modules. As can be seen from the figure, the predicted gain step which was designed to be 1 dB is actually 0.95 dB, which is well within the allowed tolerances.

The same is true for the receiver gain as shown in Fig.9.26. Fig.9.27 shows a representative oscillogram of high and low tones generated in the DTMF generator. The harmonic distortion is very well filtered out as seen from Fig.9.28, which shows the spectral analysis of the single (high) tone DTMF signal.

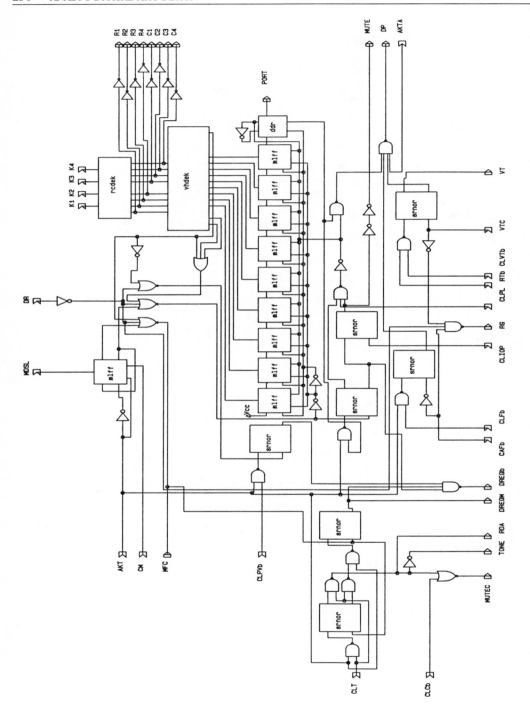

Fig. 9.24 Library level schematic diagram of pulse generator module

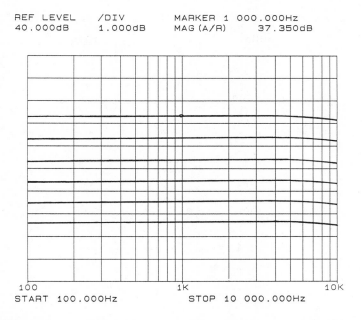

Fig. 9.25 Plot of transmitter gain versus frequency for various line lengths

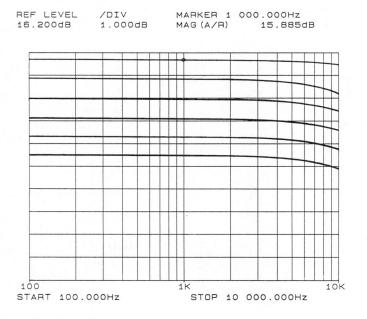

Fig. 9.26 Plot of receiver gain versus frequency for various line lengths

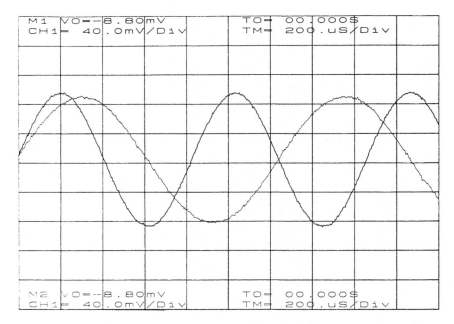

Fig. 9.27 Oscillogram of low and high group of tones of DTMF and filter module

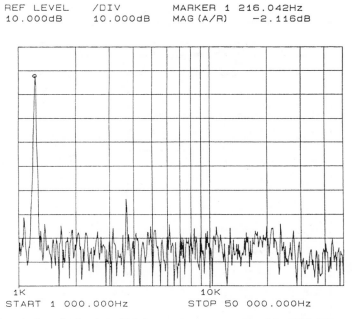

Fig. 9.28 Spectral analysis plot of high group tone generated by DTMF module

9.7 Conclusions

A test ASIC was fabricated to demonstrate the effectiveness of the design method presented for mixed analog digital design. A photomicrograph of the chip is shown in Plate 9.6. Although this is a complex chip, a group of three designers finished the complete design task from specifications to geometrical data base in six weeks. The ASIC was fully functional at first silicon and has met all of the analog specifications within the allowed limits.

Reference

1. Trontelj, J., Trontelj, L., CMOS speech network with the tone ringer for telephone set, *Proceedings of Integrated Circuits Conference*, pp.373–5, Rochester, May 1983.

Index